WITHDRAWN

METHODS in
MICROBIOLOGY

METHODS in MICROBIOLOGY

Edited by

J. R. NORRIS
Borden Microbiological Laboratory,
Shell Research Limited,
Sittingbourne, Kent, England

D. W. RIBBONS
Department of Biochemistry,
University of Miami School of Medicine,
and Howard Hughes Medical Institute,
Miami, Florida, U.S.A.

Volume 6 B

 1972

ACADEMIC PRESS
London and New York

ACADEMIC PRESS INC. (LONDON) LTD
24–28 Oval Road,
London NW1 7DX

U.S. Edition published by
ACADEMIC PRESS INC.
111 Fifth Avenue
New York, New York 10003

Library of Congress Catalog Card Number: 68–57745
ISBN: 0–12–521546–0

PRINTED IN GREAT BRITAIN BY
ADLARD AND SON LIMITED
DORKING, SURREY

LIST OF CONTRIBUTORS

M. J. ALLEN, *Shell Research Ltd, Borden Microbiological Laboratory, Sittingbourne, Kent, England*

R. B. BEECHEY, *Shell Research Ltd, Woodstock Agricultural Research Centre, Sittingbourne, Kent, England*

G. W. CROSBIE, *Department of Biochemistry, The University, Hull, England*

N. R. EATON, *Department of Biology, Brooklyn College of the City University of New York, Brooklyn, New York, U.S.A.*

A. FERRARI, *Division of Biomedical Sciences, Damon Corporation, Needham, Mass., U.S.A.*

W. W. FORREST, *The Australian Wine Research Institute, Glen Osmond, South Australia*

P. B. GARLAND, *Department of Biochemistry, University of Dundee, Dundee, Scotland*

J. H. HASH, *Department of Microbiology, Vanderbilt University School of Medicine, Nashville, Tennessee, U.S.A.*

J. MARTEN, *Division of Biomedical Sciences, Damon Corporation, Needham, Mass., U.S.A.*

D. G. NICHOLLS, *Department of Medicine, University of Nottingham, Nottingham, England*

J. L. PEEL, *Agricultural Research Council Food Research Institute, Colney Lane, Norwich NOR 70F, England*

J. R. POSTGATE, *S.R.C. Unit of Nitrogen Fixation, University of Sussex, Falmer, Sussex*

J. R. QUAYLE, *Department of Microbiology, University of Sheffield, Sheffield, England*

D. W. RIBBONS, *Department of Biochemistry, University of Miami School of Medicine, and Howard Hughes Medical Institute, Miami, Florida, U.S.A.*

C. H. WANG, *Radiation Center and Department of Chemistry, Oregon State University, Corvallis, Oregon, U.S.A.*

ACKNOWLEDGMENTS

For permission to reproduce, in whole or in part, certain figures and diagrams we are grateful to the following—

Ekco Electronics Limited, Southend-on-Sea, England; G.E.C. Limited, Kingsway, London; Master Instruments, Sidney, Australia; The Nuclear-Chicago Corporation, Des Plaines, Illinois, U.S.A.; The Packard Instrument Company; Pergamon Press, London; 20th Century Electronics Limited, Croydon, Surrey, England.

Detailed acknowledgments are given in the legends to figures.

PREFACE

The main theme in Volume 6 of "Methods in Microbiology" is the application of biochemical techniques to the study of micro-organisms. The topics covered include the use of biochemical and enzymic tests to characterize microbial types, the quantitative separation and analysis of fermentation products produced by micro-organisms, a critical appraisal of methods available to elucidate metabolic pathways and the control of enzyme synthesis, the assay of selected enzymes in crude extracts of cells as indicators of metabolic pathways, the use of antimetabolites to study biosynthesis and electron transport. The applications of radiotracer techniques are described in detail in five chapters: respiratory measurements with dyes and with electrodes for oxygen and carbon dioxide are included while manometric methods, which are so well described elsewhere (Umbreit, Burris and Stauffer, 1964) have been excluded from this series; articles on nitrogen fixation, calorimetry, electrochemical measurements and methods for studying sporulation and germination are also provided.

The detailed choice of the contents of the various contributions has been left largely to the individual authors. We have, as in the past, edited only to conserve consistency, bridge the gaps and avoid, where possible, overlaps between the articles.

Volume 6, like Volumes 3 and 5, has been divided into two parts. The division of the contributions, although somewhat arbitrary, was made by grouping the more chemical and enzymological topics into Volume 6A and allocating the more physical techniques of isotopes, electrodes, electrometry and calorimetry to Volume 6B.

We are grateful for the pleasant way in which our contributors have co-operated with us during the last three or four years. We must particularly thank those authors who have had the patience to wait for this publication. Some completed manuscripts were received three years ago, and many were subsequently revised by their authors.

J. R. NORRIS

D. W. RIBBONS

September, 1971

CONTENTS

CONTENTS OF PUBLISHED VOLUMES

CHAPTER I

The Use of Electron Acceptors, Donors and Carriers

J. L. Peel

Agricultural Research Council Food Research Institute, Colney Lane,
Norwich NOR 70F, England

I. INTRODUCTION

In the investigation of electron (hydrogen) transfer chains, it is common practice to introduce an artificial electron donor or acceptor into the experimental system. Usually, this is a substance whose oxidation or reduction is easily measured and it is added to the system in place of one of the natural substrates. It may react at either end of the catalytic chain or at an intermediate point. Substances which react at more than one point may also be used catalytically to by-pass portions of the chain. By a suitable choice of such reagents, different assays may be devised for the functional separation of the chain into its component parts. A few natural electron carriers, notably NAD, are also readily available for use in such studies.

This section deals with the use of natural or artificial reagents as donors, acceptors or carriers of electrons. When necessary, the term "electron carrier" will be used collectively to include all such substances; it will be obvious from the context when the more limited reference to substances acting catalytically is intended. With micro-organisms, the use of these reagents has not been limited to the study of aerobic species and the scope of this contribution will be taken to include fermentative as well as respiratory systems. Published information on the use of electron carriers is both widely scattered and deeply buried, so that important practical details are easily overlooked. In consequence, the topics given detailed treatment in this contribution reflect the writer's interests and experiences and some topics have been treated in review form.

II. TECHNIQUES

A. Measurement of the reaction

1. *Spectral methods*

At the present time, the vast majority of oxidation–reduction reactions are followed by making use of changes in the absorption spectrum of the electron donor or acceptor. These methods have the advantage that observations can usually be made without disturbing the reaction mixture or consuming portions of it. Tests of this kind were first made by visual observations of colour changes and were put on a quantitative basis by measuring the time taken for complete decolorization of dyes. This gives only a crude indication of the reaction rate since the progress of the reaction is rarely, if ever, linear over the full period of the reaction. The successive introduction of colorimeters and spectrophotometers and subsequent improvements in their performance and availability have enabled more refined measurements to be made with ease, so that the precise and rapid or continuous measurement of optical density over a narrow waveband is now a common place laboratory operation. Provided that the Beer–Lambert Law is obeyed by the chromophore being monitored, such measurements are proportional to concentration and give a direct indication of the progress of the reaction. The spectrophotometer has thus become the apparatus of choice for following oxidation–reduction reactions. Measurement of decolorization time however, is still useful as a simple means of dealing with turbid preparations that avoids the need for more sophisticated instruments.

Details of the construction and operation of individual colorimeters and spectrophotometers are obtainable from manufacturers' literature and will not be given here. Remarks will be confined to two practical matters concerning the reaction vessels. First, when making kinetic experiments it is desirable to start the reaction by adding the final component and to mix quickly and at a precise time. A convenient method applicable to standard cuvettes is to use a thin glass or plastic rod, the lower end of which is flanged or shaped into a cup. The required component, in a small volume, is pipetted onto this end of the rod to form a drop. The addition and mixing are then accomplished rapidly by lowering the end of the rod into the cuvette and agitating.

Second, the standard optical cuvette of 1 cm light path and 3 ml operating volume is designed primarily for the precise measurement of optical density. As a reaction vessel it is inferior to the test tube in cost, robustness and ease of handling and cleaning. In some instances, and especially where high precision is not called for, or large numbers of tests have to be made, it is often more convenient to use tubes. These may be used down to about 300 nm where glass ceases to be transparent. Suitable adaptors for this purpose are available with some instruments, or can be readily made. Tubes with similar optical properties may be made from selected lengths of glass tubing or from precision bore tubing. Alternatively, batches of ordinary tubes may be screened to select those with similar optical properties within certain limits of tolerance; this may be done by determining the extinctions of each tube empty and when filled with a standard solution of a suitably coloured substance. As the optical paths of such tubes usually differ across different diameters, the tubes should be marked so that the same face may always be presented to the light path.

2. *Other methods*

Because spectral measurements conveniently satisfy the majority of experimental requirements and especially those for routine enzymic assays, other methods of following the reaction of electron carriers have received comparatively little attention. Further, many artificial carriers in common use have been selected with a view to spectrophotometric use. The useful range of concentration over which they can be employed is determined by their extinction coefficients and other methods of following reactions are mainly used when it is necessary to work outside this concentration range. This may arise for example, when Michaelis constants are being determined, when high concentrations are required to permit the determination of other reactants or products, or when concentration influences the specificity of action of the electron carrier.

As instruments suitable for the continuous measurement at biological temperatures of other physical properties such as optical rotation become more readily available it may be expected that they will be applied to the measurement of electron carriers and that future electron carriers will be selected with the appropriate properties in mind. At present, it seems unlikely that newer physical methods will oust spectrophotometry for general use because of the resources of practical knowledge and equipment which have accumulated in relation to the latter. Moreover, spectral methods utilizing electron carriers which give a visible colour change have the advantage that qualitative preliminary experiments are easily done visually.

Mention will be made here of three alternative modes of following oxidation–reduction reactions which have been used to follow the reactions of electron carriers and which appear capable of wider application.

(a) *Fluorescence measurements.* Fluorescence methods have been used for the measurement of NAD and NADP and are described by Udenfriend (1962). The method is much more sensitive than absorption spectrophotometry but is more susceptible to interference and requires more careful use. To date, the method has been mainly used for measuring the NAD and NADP contents of tissues and following changes in their intracellular concentration.

(b) *Potentiometric measurements.* Measurements of electrode potential may be used to follow the reaction of some electron carriers. Whittaker and Redfearn (1967) have used this method to investigate the reduction of ferricyanide by succinate in presence of heart muscle preparations. The potential difference between a platinum electrode and a standard calomel electrode inserted into the reaction vessel was recorded against time. Potential differences were converted to ferricyanide concentrations using a calibration curve obtained by measuring the potential difference with known ferricyanide–ferrocyanide mixtures in buffer containing the heart muscle preparation. With this method it was possible to study the enzyme system over a wider range of ferricyanide concentration than was possible by either spectrophotometric or manometric means. The apparatus is described in more detail by Spikes *et al.* (1954).

The potentiometric method was used as early as 1929 to follow the reduction of dichlorophenolindophenol (Lehmann, 1929) and would appear to be capable of wider application, especially with electron carriers whose spectral properties are unsuited to spectrophotometry.

(c) *Measurements of gas exchange.* Many reactions involving artificial electron carriers can be made to produce an output or uptake of gas. This may be followed manometrically using the standard Warburg techniques (e.g. Umbreit *et al.*, 1964), or in the case of oxygen and carbon dioxide, by electrode methods. Suitable apparatus and procedure for the polarographic measurement of oxygen has been described by Bellamy and Bartley (1960), Stickland (1960), Peel (1963) and by Beechey and Ribbons (this Series). The use of carbon dioxide electrodes is described by Nicholls *et al.* (1967) and by Garland and Nicholls (this Series).

For convenient measurement, the manometric method requires gas exchanges of several μmoles and these changes are frequently 10–100 greater than those suitable for spectrophotometric observations. Because the manometric method measures exchanges rather than the amount of gas present at any one time, rates may be measured with large concentrations of reactants. The electrode methods, especially those for oxygen, are much more sensitive and typical ranges of concentration are up to 0·25 mM. The electrode methods also lend themselves readily to continuous automatic recording, a further advantage over the manometric methods. The manometric and electrode methods are unaffected by turbidity and so can be easily used with cell suspensions and insoluble enzyme preparations, reactants or products.

Measurements of oxygen uptake may be used to assay many dehydrogenases by adding autoxidizable electron carriers, singly or in combination, to substitute for natural carriers transferring electrons to oxygen. One much used example is the assay of succinic dehydrogenase with phenazine methosulphate (Singer and Kearney, 1957). The suitability of particular carriers depends upon the specificity of their action with natural electron carriers and dehydrogenases. Thus methylene blue reacts directly with several dehydrogenases but not with NAD. The method may be extended to NAD-linked dehydrogenases by adding a diaphorase (e.g. lipoic dehydrogenase) to bridge the electron transfer gap between NAD and methylene blue.

Oxygen may also be used in the absence of added electron carriers as an "unphysiological" oxidant with preparations from strictly anaerobic bacteria. This method was used by Stadtman and Barker (1949) to study the oxidation of ethanol and butyrate by dried cells of *Clostridium kluyveri* and by Nisman (1954) to study the oxidation of amino acids by washed cells of *Clostridium sporogenes*.

Measurements of carbon dioxide exchange in bicarbonate buffer may be used to follow reactions which are accompanied by the gain or loss of protons. The ferricyanide–bicarbonate system was first introduced by Quastel and Wheatley (1938) for succinic dehydrogenase. When ferricyanide is reduced by succinate, the transfer of each electron results in the release of one molecule of carbon dioxide and the system is thus four times as sensitive as when oxygen is the terminal oxidant. Hochster and Quastel (1952) later used manganese dioxide as the oxidant with a bicarbonate buffer. In that case, the transfer of a pair of electrons to the manganese dioxide results in the uptake of one molecule of carbon dioxide. These bicarbonate buffer systems are used with carbon dioxide/nitrogen mixtures as the gas phase and are thus particularly useful with enzyme preparations which are sensitive to oxygen.

Measurements of hydrogen exchange have been used in conjunction with substrate amounts of artificial electron carriers for the manometric assay of hydrogenase in either direction in several bacterial species (Peck and Gest, 1956). Dithionite was used as the reductant when assaying hydrogenase by release of hydrogen and methylene blue was used as the oxidant when measuring the enzyme by hydrogen uptake.

B. Anaerobic techniques

1. *Introduction*

For various reasons it is frequently necessary to make measurements under anaerobic conditions. First, the electron acceptor may be autoxidized at a sufficient rate to interfere unduly with measurements of its reduction. Second, the reduced form of the electron acceptor may be subject to enzymic, as opposed to non-enzymic, oxidation when oxygen is present. This occurs commonly with NADH and NADPH and, perhaps unexpectedly, crude extracts of many strictly anaerobic bacteria possess powerful NADH oxidase activity. With *Peptostreptococcus elsdenii* for example, a typical activity for a crude extract is 10 μmoles NADH oxidized/h/mg protein at 37°, and this completely prevents the spectrophotometric detection of several dehydrogenases reducing NAD, unless strictly anaerobic conditions are used (Somerville, 1965). Third, the enzyme preparations or their substrates may be sensitive to oxygen. Fourth, the substrate of the reaction under investigation may be a gas, as in the case of hydrogenase. To meet these requirements special reaction vessels and methods of purifying gases are used.

2. *Anaerobic reaction vessels*

Manometric apparatus may be used anaerobically without modification. For spectral measurements, the use of evacuated reaction tubes was first introduced by Thunberg (1918). A single evacuation with a water pump is often adequate; if not, the tube is refilled with oxygen-free gas and evacuated again, repeating the process until a sufficiently low oxygen tension is reached. The original pattern of tube used by Thunberg had no second compartment for separating the substrate (or other component) from the reaction mixture until the evacuation was complete. Quastel and Whetham (1924) met this requirement by using an evacuated U-tube; Keilin (1929) introduced tubes with a curved hollow stopper which have come to be regarded as the standard form of the Thunberg tube. With tubes made to fit colorimeters, or those spectrophotometers suitable for round tubes, the progress of the reaction may be followed quantitatively. With many spectrophotometers, however, and for precision work, measurements must be made in an optical cuvette of square cross section and this has resulted in modified Thunberg tubes terminating in a cuvette (Fig. 1a). A variation which abandons the hollow stopper and uses a side arm is illustrated in Fig. 1b. Although this pattern is longer it occupies less room laterally and is particularly useful when a version with two side arms is needed.

A disadvantage of the evacuated tube is that, because of the unavoidable boiling which occurs on evacuation, a minimum length of free tube is required between the surface of the liquid and the side arm or hollow stopper. This results in tubes which cannot be accommodated within the confines of the cell compartment of most spectrophotometers, although the difficulty may often be overcome by substituting an inverted box for the normal lid of the compartment. The pattern of cuvette illustrated in Fig. 1c is much more compact. The side arm and the main tube are sealed with rubber caps and anaerobic conditions are established by flushing both liquid and gas phases with oxygen-free gas. For this purpose a syringe needle or a Pasteur pipette is inserted into the main compartment through a fine slit cut into the centre of the rubber cap with a scalpel. A similar slit in the

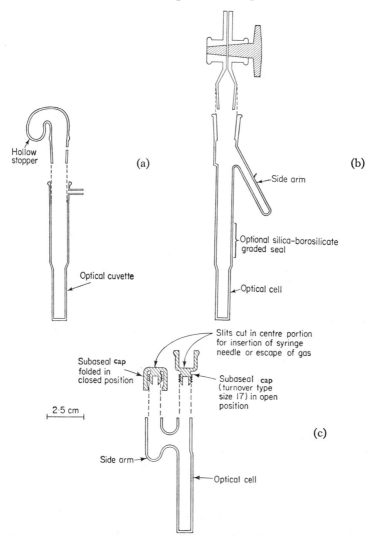

FIG. 1. Anaerobic cuvettes for spectrophotometric use. (a) Modified Thunberg tube with hollow stopper and with tube terminating in optical cuvette. (b) Evacuated tube with side arm. (c) Smaller cuvette suitable for flushing with gas. (Subaseal caps—Freeman & Co.)

other cap serves as a Bunsen valve for the escape of surplus gas. Flushing for 2–5 min is usually sufficient. A further advantage of this type of cuvette is that any reactants which are sensitive to oxygen need not be added until the cuvette has been well flushed with gas. The rubber cap can be left off the side arm until such additions are complete, or alternatively the reactants may be added from a syringe inserted through either cap.

A more complex apparatus for taking spectrophotometric measurements at successive stages during anaerobic titrations is described by Foust et al. (1969).

These various specialized optical cells are often best obtained from a local glassworker to suit individual requirements. The common forms of optical cuvette, made by fusing, sintering or cementing plates of material together, are unsuitable for modification as they crack too readily at the seams. Cells made from square-drawn borosilicate tubing are suitable (obtainable from Pyrocell Manufacturing Co., 91, Carver Ave., Westwood, N.J., U.S.A.). For work in the ultraviolet below about 300 nm, silica cells are obligatory and complex designs may be obtained from specialists in silica-ware (e.g. The Thermal Syndicate, Wallsend, Northumberland, England). It is sometimes convenient to obtain a silica cuvette with either a ground joint or a graded seal from silica to borosilicate fitted immediately above the cuvette. The upper parts may then be added locally.

3. *Removal of oxygen from gases*

Commercial cylinders of gases, including some designated as "oxygen-free", frequently contain sufficient oxygen to interfere with measurements when used as the gas phase in anaerobic experiments. Several treatments have been used to remove this impurity; the first two treatments mentioned below have been used by the writer and his colleagues and found highly satisfactory in experiments where it was necessary to eliminate the oxidation of NADH due to the NADH oxidase in extracts of strictly anaerobic bacteria.

(a) *Removal by copper*. The gas is passed through a combustion tube (approx. 30 cm × 24 cm diam.) containing copper turnings and heated to 400–700°. A suitable apparatus is described by Moore (1966). The precise temperature is not critical as far as the removal of oxygen is concerned, but the lower temperature is desirable when nitrogen is the bulk gas since Keilin and Hartree (1943) found that traces of oxides of nitrogen, sufficient to inhibit catalase were formed at temperatures above 400°. As an alternative to copper turnings, cupric oxide in wire form may be used to pack the column; it is reduced before use by passing hydrogen and heating. Both types of column are regenerated by the same means.

(b) *Removal by chromous sulphate.* The gas is passed through two successive towers (approx. 30 cm × 2·5 cm diam.) filled to two-thirds capacity with glass beads which are just covered by a solution of chromous sulphate. The latter is prepared by passing a saturated solution of chrome alum in 2N-H_2SO_4 through a Jones reductor dispersed in a column (15 cm × 2·5 cm diam.) of glass beads to facilitate flow. The Jones reductor (zinc amalgam) is prepared according to Vogel (1962). The effluent from the column is fed into the scrubbing towers which are gently flushed with nitrogen during the filling operation. The chromous solution is a clear colour when freshly prepared; it acquires a grey tinge as the column becomes exhausted and the spent solution may be regenerated by the same treatment as the original chrome alum.

An alternative chromous reagent, chromous chloride-acetic acid, is described by Stone and Skavinski (1945) who point out that chromous reagents may produce small amounts of hydrogen on standing.

(c) *Other methods.* Other reagents which have been used to absorb oxygen include vanadous sulphate–zinc amalgam (Meites and Meites, 1948), and alkaline dithionite with anthroquinone-β-sulphonate as catalyst (Fieser's solution; Vogel, 1956). Alkaline pyrogallol is not recommended; it reacts much less readily than the other reagents mentioned here, it often gives deposits which impede the gas flow and it may give rise to carbon monoxide on standing (Stone and Skavinski, 1945).

When hydrogen is the bulk gas, oxygen may be removed by catalytic combustion, e.g. by passing through a heated column of platinized asbestos. A convenient alternative is a tube of catalyst operative at room temperature and suitable for attachment to gas cylinder valves. Such tubes are available under the trade name of "Deoxo" (obtainable from Engelhard Industries Ltd., St. Nicholas House, St. Nicholas Rd., Sutton, Surrey, England, or 113 Astor St., Newark, N.J., U.S.A.).

Further details of some of these methods and others are given by Umbreit *et al.* (1964).

4. *Preparation of autoxidizable electron donors*

It is occasionally necessary to start with the reduced form of an electron carrier and measure its oxidation instead of the reverse reaction. As the reduced forms of most of these carriers are not available commercially this usually involves their preparation by reduction of the oxidized forms. If the reduced form is autoxidizable this must be done under anaerobic conditions.

(a) *Chemical reduction.* In general, chemical methods of reduction are preferable. The following method, employing catalytic hydrogenation has been used by Paynter (1964) to prepare reduced methyl viologen for the assay of fumaric reductase in preparations from *Selenomonas ruminantium*. The method is of general application and has the merit that the product is uncontaminated with excess reducing agent or substances derived from it.

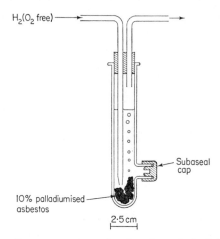

FIG. 2. Apparatus for preparation of reduced methyl viologen (after Paynter 1964). (Subaseal cap—Freeman & Co).

The apparatus shown in Fig. 2 is used. The viologen solution is placed in the tube with a little 10% palladiumized asbestos and flushed with oxygen-free hydrogen. The palladiumized asbestos, as supplied, is alkaline and is washed exhaustively with water before use. Samples of the solution are removed for use by means of a syringe inserted through the rubber cap at the side, the first samples being used to wash out the syringe and expel air from it. With 5 mM-methyl viologen in 0·1M-phosphate buffer pH 7·8, the reaction ceases in about 40 min at room temperature, when approximately 70% of the dye is reduced. This presumably reflects the low redox potential of methyl viologen and complete reduction would be expected with most carriers of biological importance. The degree of reduction is estimated by removing a sample and titrating with 0·1M-ferricyanide from a micro-titrating pipette under anaerobic conditions.

Another method of wide application is by titration with dithionite under anaerobic conditions. This is described in detail by Singer and Kearney (1957) in connection with the assay of succinic dehydrogenase. They advise the use of a slight excess of dithionite followed by the controlled admission of oxygen until a small portion of the reduced carrier is oxidized.

Care may be needed with chemical methods to avoid the formation of unwanted derivatives by over-reduction. This is especially so with benzyl viologen. When this is reduced by dithionite the colourless viologen is first converted to a violet free-radical form with the addition of a single electron. On further treatment a second electron is taken up and the product is colourless.

(b) *Enzymic reduction.* In some cases it is possible to reduce carriers by enzymic means; this method has so far been used mainly where the necessary enzymes were already present in the preparations being used to study the subsequent reoxidation. The main experimental problem is to ensure that the system used to bring about the reduction of the carrier does not interfere with subsequent observations of its reoxidation. If the reduction process is quantitative this requirement may be met by adding only an equivalent amount of the reducing substrate. Two alternative ways of overcoming this problem have been used. Quastel and Whetham (1924) and later Stickland (1934), working with washed suspensions of bacteria in evacuated tubes, used the endogenous metabolism to effect the reduction of dyes, including methylene blue, phenosafranine and the viologens. These reductions were relatively slow and hence did not interfere appreciably with observations on the reoxidation. Second, by using a photoreductive system, the reaction may be stopped by removing the light. Thus Whatley *et al.* (1963) using green plant chloroplasts and taking precautions to eliminate interference by evolved oxygen, were able to reduce spinach ferredoxin in the light with ascorbate as the electron donor. The oxidation of the reduced ferredoxin by added NADP was then followed in the dark. The use of a similar system for the preparation of reduced bacterial ferredoxin has been described by Sobel and Lovenberg (1966).

III. PROPERTIES OF ELECTRON CARRIERS

A. Selection of a suitable carrier

1. *Redox potentials*

In choosing an electron carrier for a particular purpose first consideration is usually given to the redox (oxidation-reduction) potential since this can be used to ascertain whether the equilibrium of the proposed oxidation-reduction reaction will be favourable. Oxidation-reduction reactions may be regarded as the resultant of two reversible half-reactions, each of the form

$$\text{reduced form} \rightleftharpoons \text{oxidized form} + \text{electrons.}$$

Each redox couple (i.e. mixture of the oxidized and reduced forms of one of the reactants) is able to accept or donate electrons and the redox potential gives a quantitative measure of the affinity of each couple for electrons and hence its tendency to oxidize other couples. The couple of higher potential therefore oxidizes the one of lower potential and the difference between the two potentials is proportional to the free-energy change and determines the final equilibrium reached. By comparing the potential of the redox couple of an electron carrier with that of the redox couple of a substrate it is possible to predict whether the reaction between the two will proceed in the required direction when, for example, the reduced form of the substrate is allowed to react with the oxidized form of the carrier.

Redox potentials are expressed on a scale based on the "normal hydrogen electrode" as zero and the values usually quoted are for E'_0, the redox potential under standard conditions, i.e. at pH 7, at 25° and with the oxidized and reduced forms of the reactant present at the same concentration (ideally 1·0M). In practical situations the operative redox potential differs from E'_0 by an amount which depends upon temperature, the relative proportions of the oxidized and reduced forms, the number of electrons involved in the half-reaction, and in those cases where the half-reaction involves protons as well as electrons, the pH. The effect of temperature over the common biological range is small. The effects of pH may be considerable, e.g. with methylene blue $E'_0 = 0·01$ V at pH 7 whereas the corresponding potentials at pH 5 and pH 9 are 0·10 V and $-0·05$ V respectively. The relative proportions of the oxidized and reduced form affect the equilibrium in accordance with the Law of Mass Action. Because of these effects, an unfavourable potential gradient between couples as indicated by the E'_0 values can often be counteracted by increasing the concentration of the appropriate reactants, by manipulating the pH or by removal of one of the products. The latter is liable to occur spontaneously if a product has low solubility (as with the formazans); alternatively it can be brought about by coupling to a secondary reaction which need not involve electron-transfer.

An illustration is provided by the oxidation of ethanol to acetaldehyde at the expense of NAD, catalysed by alcohol dehydrogenase. The E'_0 value for the ethanol/acetaldehyde couple is $-0·20$ V, considerably higher than that for the NAD/NADH couple ($-0·32$ V). If equimolar amounts of ethanol and NAD were allowed to react at pH 7, the reaction would only proceed to about 1% completion. However, by using a pH of 9 and adding semicarbazide to trap the acetaldehyde, the oxidation of ethanol becomes quantitative and is used for its enzymic estimation (Bonnichsen, 1963).

Relatively small changes in the structure of molecules may influence redox potentials. Thus the 3-acetylpyridine analogue of NAD has a redox potential E'_0 of $-0·25$ V as opposed to $-0·32$ V for NAD (Kaplan *et al.*, 1956). This analogue is still active with dehydrogenases and the increase in redox potential facilitates the estimation of alcohol, lactate and glutamate with the appropriate dehydrogenases.

For further details of the theory and use of redox potentials the reader is referred to biochemical texts (e.g. Morris, 1968). The recent compilation by Loach (1968) is a useful source of data on redox potentials of electron carriers and biological substrates; earlier sources are Burton (1961), Clark (1960) and Andersen and Plaut (1949) (see also Jacob in Volume 2 this Series).

2. *Rate of reaction and specificity*

Assuming that the redox potential of a particular carrier is suitable, its usefulness may hinge on the rate and specificity of its reaction with the biological system in question. Few general rules are available for guidance but it is useful to note that dyes usually react readily with flavoproteins but not with NAD or NADP and that manganese dioxide reacts with the cytochromes. Ferricyanide is less specific and reacts directly with a variety of enzymes and natural electron carriers, including NAD and NADP. One aspect of specificity of particular practical importance is whether the carrier reacts directly with oxygen. This property is desirable when the carrier is required to act catalytically and oxygen is the terminal oxidant. On the other hand, autoxidizable substances are less convenient as terminal acceptors since they may make it necessary to work under anaerobic conditions. In this context, ferricyanide and the nicotinamide nucleotides have the advantage that they are not autoxidizable. The autoxidation of dichlorophenolindophenol at neutral pH is slow and does not interfere unduly; the same is true of methylene blue at pH 5 or below (Bach *et al.*, 1946).

3. *Other considerations*

The importance of other factors such as solubility, chemical stability, spectral characteristics, permeability and freedom from the difficulties mentioned in the next section, depends very much upon the particular experimental circumstances. Comment will be restricted to one aspect of spectral characteristics. When spectrophotometry is used to follow the early stages of a reaction it is advantageous to choose an electron carrier which gives an increase in extinction rather than a small decrease in an already large extinction. The majority of electron carriers absorb more strongly in the oxidized form at the wavelengths commonly employed. The most common exceptions are the nicotinamide nucleotides, the tetrazoliums and the viologen dyes. In the case of ferricyanide, reduction is usually followed by the decrease in the absorption peak at 420 nm where the extinction coefficient is $1 \cdot 01 \times 10^3$ cm^{-1} litre mole^{-1}. It is not widely appreciated that ferrocyanide has a much larger absorption peak at 218 nm with an extinction coefficient of 230×10^3 cm^{-1} litre mole^{-1}. In consequence, ferrocyanide absorbs more strongly than ferricyanide below 370 nm and the extinction

TABLE I

Properties of some commonly used artificial electron carriers in ascending order of reduction potential

Name, structure and reduction reaction	Molecular wt. (oxidized form)	E'_0 (volts)	Extinction[b] coefficients (cm^{-1} litre mole^{-1})	Autoxidizability of reduced form	Other properties[c]
Methyl viologen (R = CH$_3$)	257·2 (Chloride)	−0·45	ε_{600} very approximately 10^4 (reduced form)	Rapidly autoxidized	Reduced form is a free radical. Further reduction to a colourless form may occur with strongly reducing systems. Ref. Homer *et al.* (1960); Michaelis and Hill (1933*a, b*).
Benzyl viologen (as methyl viologen but (R = C$_6$H$_5$.CH$_2$−)	409·3 (Chloride)	−0·36	As for methyl viologen	Rapidly autoxidized	As for methyl viologen. Dithionite reduces to colourless product.

| | 663·5 | −0·32 | $\varepsilon_{340} = 6·2 \times 10^3$ $\varepsilon_{366} = 3·3 \times 10^3$ (reduced form) | Not autoxidized. | Oxidized and reduced form stable when stored cold and dry. Sensitive to U.V. light. NAD rapidly destroyed in alkali. NADH relatively stable. Ref. Boehringer[a], Pabst[a]. |

Nicotinamide adenine dinucleotide
(NAD, DPN, Coenzyme I,
R = Adenosine-5′-diphosphoriboside)

(small absorption at 338 - 340 nm)

$2e + H^+$

(absorption peak at 338 - 340 nm)

TABLE I (continued)

Name, structure and reduction reaction	Molecular wt. (oxidized form)	E'_0 (volts)	Extinction[b] coefficients (cm^{-1} litre mole^{-1})	Autoxidizability of reduced form	Other properties[c]
Nicotinamide adenine dinucleotide phosphate (NADP, TPN, Coenzyme II, cf. NAD. R = Adenosine-2'-monophospho-5'-diphosphoriboside) Reduction reaction as for NAD.	743·4	−0·32	$\varepsilon_{340} = 6·2 \times 10^3$ $\varepsilon_{366} = 3·3 \times 10^3$ (reduced form)	Not autoxidized	As for NAD. Ref. Boehringer[a], Pabst[a].
Triphenyltetrazolium (TTC, 2:3:5-triphenyltetrazolium chloride, tetrazolium salt; ($R_1 = R_2 = C_6H_5$). (pale yellow). (red formazan, insoluble in water)	334·8 (Chloride)	−0·08	$\varepsilon_{485} = 12 \times 10^3$ (formazan)	Autoxidation not important if occurs	Readily soluble in water. Sensitive to light. Formazan may be extracted from aq. soln. with ethyl acetate or butanol. Reduction beyond formazan may proceed biologically under certain conditions at pH 6 or below (Jambor, 1954). Ref. B.D.H.[a] (general information on tetrazoliums). For Neotetrazolium see Glock and Jensen (1953).

Iodonitrotetrazolium (INT, 2-(*p*-iodophenyl)-3-(*p*-nitrophenyl)-5-phenyltetrazolium). cf. Triphenyltetrazolium and derived formazan (R₁=*p*-introphenyl, R₂=*p*-iodophenyl)	505·7 (Chloride)	$\varepsilon_{490} = 20{\cdot}1 \times 10^3$ (formazan)	Autoxidation not important if occurs	Similar to TTC but only 0·5% soluble in water at 25° and less sensitive to light. Ref. Pennington (1961).
Methylene blue (methylthionine chloride) 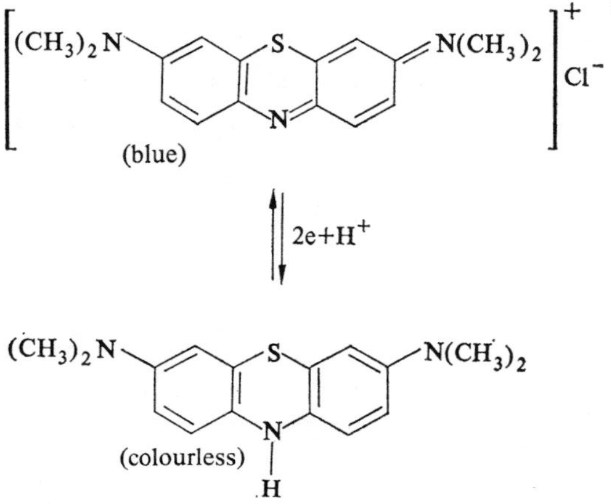	373·9 (Chloride) 0·01	$\varepsilon_{668} = 63 \times 10^3$ (oxidized form)	Autoxidized fairly rapidly at pH 7, only slowly at pH 5	"Anhydrous" dye contains approx. 15% water. May crystallize with 4 or 5 moles of H_2O. Soluble in chloroform, insoluble in ether. 4% soluble in water.

$(CH_3)_2N$ —— $N(CH_3)_2$]⁺ Cl⁻

(blue)

$\rightleftharpoons$ 2e+H⁺

$(\dot{C}H_3)_2N$ —— $N(CH_3)_2$

(colourless)

TABLE I (continued)

Name, structure and reduction reaction	Molecular wt. (oxidized form)	E'_0 (volts)	Extinction[b] coefficients (cm^{-1} litre mole^{-1})	Autoxidizability of reduced form	Other properties[c]
Phenazine methosulphate (PMS, N-methylphenazinium methosulphate)	306·3 (methosulphate)	0·08	Maximum difference is at 387 nm	Readily autoxidized	Sensitive to light. Interacts directly with NAD(P). Reduction product is a free radical. Mainly used catalytically. Ref. Singer and Kearney (1957); Dickens and McIlwain (1938).

2:6-Dichlorophenolindophenol (DCPIP, Sodium 2:6-dichlorophenolindophenol)	290·1 (Na salt)	0·21	$\varepsilon_{600} = 21 \times 10^3$ at pH 8 (oxidized form)	Autoxidized slowly at neutral pH	Spectrum dependent on pH (Fig. 2). Slowly deteriorates in solution. Solid may contain 1–2 moles H_2O per mole. Does not react directly with NAD(P). Acid form extracted from aq. solution by ether. Ref. Savage (1957); Armstrong (1964).

(blue or red according to pH.)

$2e + H^+$

(colourless)

Cytochrome C. Ferricytochrome $\overset{e}{\rightleftharpoons}$ ferrocytochrome (pink)	13,000	0·26	$\varepsilon_{550} = 19\cdot7 \times 10^3$ (Difference: reduced form-oxidized)	Not autoxidized	
Potassium ferricyanide $Fe(CN)_6^{3-} \overset{e}{\rightleftharpoons} Fe(CN)_6^{4-}$	329·2	0·36	$\varepsilon_{420} = 1\cdot01 \times 10^3$ (oxidized)	Not autoxidized	Reacts directly with NAD(P). Can be removed as insoluble Zn salt.

---

a These references refer to information booklets about the substances in question, obtainable respectively from the following manufacturers: B.D.H.—The British Drug Houses Ltd., Poole, Dorset, England; Boehringer—Biochemische Abteilung, C. F. Boehringer & Soehne, GmbH, Mannheim, Germany; Pabst—P-L. Biochemicals Inc., Milwaukee, Wis., U.S.A.

b Extinction coefficients are given for the coloured form. The coefficient for the other form may be assumed to be negligible except where otherwise indicated.

c References given at the end of each entry are to general sources of information.

below that wavelength could be used to give a very sensitive measure of ferrocyanide formation.

Properties of a selection of the more important electron carriers are given in Table I and references to the use of some other electron carriers in Table II. In addition, many useful practical details are to be found in the article by Quastel (1957) and in the review by Singer and Kearney (1957) of the methods which have been used to assay succinic dehydrogenase.

TABLE II

Some other useful electron carriers

Compound	E_0' (volts)	References
Dithionite	$-0\cdot50^*$	Peck and Gest (1956)
Bacterial ferredoxin	$-0\cdot43$	Lovenberg et al. (1963); Mortenson et al. (1963)
Phenosafranine	$-0\cdot25$	Singer and Kearney (1957)
Flavin mononucleotide	$-0\cdot22$	Singer and Kearney ((1957); Peel (1960)
Rubredoxin	$-0\cdot06$	Lovenberg and Sobel (1965)
Menadione	$-0\cdot01$	Kashket and Brodie (1963)
Ferri-oxalate	0	Hill and Scarisbrick (1940)
Coenzyme Q	$0\cdot09$	Doeg et al. (1960); Lester et al. (1959)
Metmyoglobin	$0\cdot13^*$	Davenport and Hill (1960)
Methaemoglobin	$0\cdot13^*$	Hill and Scarisbrick (1940)
Manganese dioxide	$1\cdot23$	Hochster and Quastel (1952)

* Approximate values only.

B. Some complications and pitfalls

1. *Insolubility*

The insolubility of the oxidized or reduced forms of some electron carriers restricts their usefulness. For example manganese dioxide has probably received little use because it is insoluble and in consequence has to be used as a suspension and is not suitable for spectrophotometric work. Coenzyme Q is not readily soluble in water and special steps are needed to disperse it before use (e.g. Doeg et al., 1960). The formazans produced by the reduction of tetrazolium salts are only slightly soluble and for measurement are usually extracted with butanol or some other organic solvent; this prevents continuous measurement but gives a more specific estimation of the formazan. Dithionite in all but the lowest concentrations gives rise to a turbidity, as does the reduced form of phenazine methosulphate.

2. Inhibitions

Several artificial electron carriers are known to inhibit enzymes. For example, 0·3 mM methylene blue inhibits the hydrogenase of *Micrococcus aerogenes* (Curtis and Ordal, 1954); only the oxidized form of the dye is inhibitory. At concentrations suitable for manometric assays, phenazine methosulphate and ferricyanide both inhibit succinic dehydrogenase, especially in the absence of the substrate (Singer and Kearney, 1957). This action appears to be due to the oxidation of –SH groups in the enzyme and is prevented by the addition of serum albumen to the reaction mixture. The autoxidation of several electron carriers, including methylene blue, phenazine methosulphate and flavins leads to the formation of hydrogen peroxide which may contribute to some of the observed inhibitions. Catalase has been used to protect enzymes against hydrogen peroxide but this is not possible with phenazine methosulphate which strongly inhibits catalase. Undue inhibitions may sometimes be avoided by using a catalytic concentration of an electron carrier in conjunction with some less toxic substance as the ultimate electron donor or acceptor.

The pyruvate dehydrogenase system of the strict anaerobe, *Peptostreptococcus elsdenii* is subject to various kinds of interference by artificial electron carriers (Peel, 1960 and unpublished observations). Iodonitrotetrazolium is unsatisfactory as an electron acceptor because it produces rapid inhibitions. Dichlorophenolindophenol is satisfactory at the concentrations (up to 0·04 mM) used for routine spectrophotometry but at 0·4 mM there is 40% inhibition. Ferricyanide has a more subtle effect. At 0·7 mM, this oxidant is readily utilized, the immediate product of pyruvate oxidation is acetyl CoA, and the reaction requires an acetyl-accepting system (oxaloacetate plus citrate synthase). Ferricyanide is still reduced rapidly at 10 mM but the reaction is modified since the oxidation product is now free acetate. Oxygen will also act as oxidant, but under these conditions no acetyl-accepting system is required, suggesting that free acetate is again the product. Oxygen also inactivates the enzyme rapidly in presence of pyruvate (Peel and Watkinson, 1965). Finally, dichlorophenolindophenol at 0·04 mM oxidizes CoA non-enzymically to the inactive disulphide form and this inactivates the system if these two components are brought together in the absence of enzyme plus substrate. The effect is not easily counteracted by adding reducing agents since these may react directly with the dye, but can be avoided by adding the coenzyme as acetyl CoA. Similar difficulties are a potential hazard with other thiol coenzymes.

3. Interference with other estimations

Some electron carriers interfere with the estimation of other reactants or products by virtue of their spectra or chemical properties. Interfering

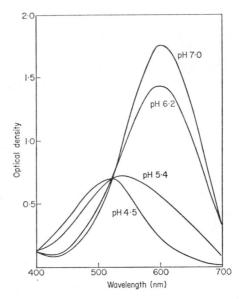

FIG. 3. Effect of pH on the absorption spectrum of 2:6-dichlorophenolindophenol. Data for the same arbitrary concentration (approximately 0·08 mM) calculated from measurements in 0·05M-sodium acetate buffer (pH 4·5 and 5·4) or in 0·05M-potassium phosphate buffer (pH 6·2 and 7·0) with suitable dye concentrations.

dyes may often be removed from reaction mixtures by extraction with organic solvents. The removal of formazans with butanol has already been referred to; methylene blue may be removed in the same way and dichlorophenolindophenol by extraction with ether from acid solution. Ferricyanide may be removed by treating mixtures with zinc sulphate to precipitate the zinc salt.

4. pH effects

The effects of pH on redox potentials and on the autoxidizability of methylene blue have already been mentioned. In addition, many dyes behave as indicators, i.e. their absorption spectra change with pH. The most important case is probably dichlorophenolindophenol which is blue at pH 7 or above but red at pH 4·5 or below; the marked change of spectrum over the intervening pH range is indicated in Fig. 3.

Changes of pH may also modify the reaction of the electron carrier. With the tetrazolium dyes, reduction above pH 6·0 results in the formation of a red formazan. Below pH 6·0, on the other hand, the formazan is not formed quantitatively and the main product is colourless (Jambor, 1954).

5. *Trace metals*

The reaction of some electron carriers is catalysed by trace amounts of metals, especially copper, and adequate amounts are often present in enzyme preparations and chemical reagents. For example, both the enzymic and non-enzymic oxidations of ascorbic acid require copper (Meiklejohn and Stewart, 1941) and Haas (1955) states that commercial preparations of methylene blue usually contain sufficient copper salts to catalyse the oxidation of the leuco form by molecular oxygen. The case of Straub's diaphorase is particularly interesting (Veeger and Massey, 1960). Treatment of this enzyme with copper (approximately 1 g ion Cu^{++}/mole of enzyme) led to almost complete loss of the ability to catalyse the oxidation of NADH by lipoic acid; this was attributed to catalytic oxidation of essential –SH groups of the enzyme. The same treatment however gave a 20-fold increase in activity when dichlorophenolindophenol replaced lipoic acid as the oxidant.

REFERENCES

Andersen, L., and Plaut, G. W. E. (1949). *In* "Respiratory Enzymes", (Ed. H. A. Lardy). p. 71. Burgess Publishing Co., Minneapolis.

Armstrong, J. McD. (1964). *Biochim. biophys. Acta*, **86**, 194.

Bach, S. J., Dixon, M., and Zerfas, L. G. (1946). *Biochem. J.*, **40**, 229.

Bellamy, D., and Bartley, W. (1960). *Biochem. J.*, **76**, 78.

Bonnichsen, R. (1963). *In* "Methods of Enzymatic Analysis" (Ed. H. U. Bergmeyer), p. 285. Academic Press, London.

Burton, K. (1961). *In* "Biochemist's Handbook" (Ed. C. Long), p. 90. Spon, London.

Clark, W. M. (1960). "Oxidation-reduction Potentials of Organic Systems". Williams and Wilkins, Baltimore.

Curtis, W., and Ordal, E. J. (1954). *J. Bact.*, **68**, 351.

Davenport, H. E., and Hill, R. (1960). *Biochem. J.*, **74**, 493.

Dickens, F., and McIlwain, H. (1938). *Biochem. J.*, **32**, 1615.

Doeg, K. A., Krueger, S., and Ziegler, D. M. (1960). *Biochim. Biophys. Acta*, **41**, 491.

Foust, G. P., Burleigh, B. D., Mayhew, S. G., Williams, C. H., and Massey, V. (1969). *Analyt. Biochem.*, **27**, 530.

Glock, E., and Jensen, C. O. (1953). *J. biol. Chem.*, **201**, 271.

Haas, E. (1955). *In* "Methods in Enzymology" (Eds S. P. Colowick and N. O. Kaplan), Vol. II p. 712. Academic Press, London.

Hill, R., and Scarisbrick, R. (1940). *Proc. Roy. Soc.*, B **129**, 238.

Hochster, R. M., and Quastel, J. H. (1952). *Arch. Biochem.*, **36**, 132.

Homer, R. F., Mees, G. C., and Tomlinson, T. E. (1960). *J. Sci. Food. Agric.*, **11**, 309.

Jambor, B. (1954). *Nature, London*, **173**, 774.

Kaplan, N. O., Ciotti, M. M., and Stolzenbach, F. E. (1956). *J. biol. Chem.*, **221**, 833.

Kashket, E. R., and Brodie, A. F. (1963). *J. biol. Chem.*, **238**, 2564.

Keilin, D. (1929). *Proc. Roy. Soc.*, B **104**, 206.

Keilin, D., and Hartree, E. F. (1943). *Nature, Lond.*, **152**, 626.

Lehman, J. (1929). *Skand. Arch. Physiol.*, **58**, 173.

Lester, R. L., Hatefi, Y., Widmer, C., and Crane, F. L. (1959). *Biochim. biophys. Acta*, **33**, 169.

Loach, P. A. (1968). *In* "Handbook of Biochemistry" (Ed. H. A. Sober), p. J 27. The Chemical Rubber Co., Cleveland.

Lovenberg, W., Buchanan, B. B., and Rabinowitz, J. C. (1963). *J. biol. Chem.*, **238**, 3899.

Lovenberg, W., and Sobel, B. E. (1965). *Proc. Natl. Acad. Sci. U.S.*, **54**, 193.

Meiklejohn, G. T., and Stewart, C. P. (1941). *Biochem. J.*, **35**, 755.

Meites, L., and Meites, T. (1948). *Anal. Chem.*, **20**, 984.

Michaelis, L., and Hill, E. S. (1933a). *J. gen. Physiol.*, **16**, 859.

Michaelis, L., and Hill, E. S. (1933b). *J. Amer. Chem. Soc.*, **55**, 1491.

Moore, W. E. C. (1966). *International Journal of Systematic Bacteriology*, **16**, 173.

Morris, J. G. (1968). "A Biologist's Physical Chemistry", p. 300. Arnold, London.

Mortenson, L. E., Valentine, R. C., and Carnahan, J. E. (1963). *J. biol. Chem.*, **238**, 794.

Nicholls, D. G., Shepherd, D., and Garland, P. B. (1967). *Biochem. J.*, **103**, 677.

Nisman, B. (1954). *Bact. Rev.*, **18**, 16.

Paynter, M. J. B. (1964). Ph.D. thesis, University of Sheffield.

Peck, H. D., and Gest, H. (1956). *J. Bact.*, **71**, 70.

Peel, J. L. (1960). *Biochem. J.*, **74**, 525.

Peel, J. L. (1963). *Biochem. J.*, **88**, 296.

Peel, J. L., and Watkinson, R. J. (1965). *Biochem. J.*, **94**, 21C.

Pennington, R. J. (1961). *Biochem. J.*, **80**, 649.

Quastel, J. H. (1957). *In* "Methods in Enzymology" (Eds S. P. Colowick and N. O. Kaplan), Vol. IV, p. 329. Academic Press, London.

Quastel, J. H., and Wheatley, A. H. M. (1938). *Biochem. J.*, **32**, 936.

Quastel, J. H., and Whetham, M. D. (1924). *Biochem. J.*, **18**, 519.

Savage, N. (1957). *Biochem. J.*, **67**, 146.

Singer, T. P., and Kearney, E. B. (1957). *In* "Methods of Biochemical Analysis" (Ed. D. Glick), Vol. IV, p. 307. Interscience, New York and London.

Sobel, B. E., and Lovenberg, W. (1966). *Biochemistry*, **5**, 6.

Somerville, H. J. (1965). Ph.D. thesis University of Sheffield.

Spikes, J. D., Lumry, R., Rieske, J. S., and Marcus, R. J. (1954). *Plant Physiol.*, **29**, 161.

Stadtman, E. R., and Barker, H. A. (1949). *J. biol. Chem.*, **180**, 1095.

Stickland, L. H. (1934). *Biochem. J.*, **28**, 1746.

Stickland, R. G. (1960). *Biochem. J.*, **77**, 636.

Stone, H. W., and Skavinski, E. H. (1945). *Ind. Eng. Chem. Anal. Ed.*, **17**, 495.

Thunberg, T. (1918). *Skand. Arch. Physiol.*, **35**, 163.

Undenfriend, S. (1962). "Fluorescence Analysis in Biology and Medicine", p. 249. Academic Press, London.

Umbreit, W. W., Burris, R. H., and Stauffer, J. F. (1964). "Manometric Methods", 4th ed. Burgess Publishing Co., Minneapolis.

Veeger, C., and Massey, B. (1960). *Biochim. biophys. Acta*, **37**, 181.

Vogel, A. I. (1962). "A Textbook of Quantitative Inorganic Analysis", 3rd ed., p. 288. Longmans, London.

Vogel, A. I. (1956). "A Textbook of Practical Organic Chemistry", 3rd ed., p. 186. Longmans, London.

Whatley, R. F., Tagawa, K., and Arnon, D. I. (1963). *Proc. Natl. Acad. Sci. U.S.*, **49**, 266.

Whittaker, P. A., and Redfearn, E. R. (1967). *Biochem. biophys. Acta*, **131**, 234.

CHAPTER II

Oxygen Electrode Measurements

R. B. BEECHEY

Woodstock Agricultural Research Centre, Shell Research Limited, Sittingbourne, Kent, England

AND D. W. RIBBONS

Department of Biochemistry, University of Miami School of Medicine, and Howard Hughes Medical Institute, Miami, Florida, U.S.A.

I. INTRODUCTION

An oxygen electrode can be operationally defined as a device that produces an electric current which is proportional to the concentration of oxygen in the medium in which the electrode is placed. Microbiologists have two main uses for the oxygen electrode:

(i) To replace the manometric assay of oxygen consumption or evolution; in practice these experiments are of short duration, usually less than 30 min, and often less than 2 min.

(ii) To measure continuously the oxygen levels, (either dissolved oxygen or that in the effluent air) during the growth of micro-organisms; here the time may extend to weeks or months.

These two experimental situations require different apparatus. Thus in terms of size, manometric style experiments are performed with relatively small amounts of biological materials. This imposes a requirement for an oxygen micro-electrode which in turn requires electronic apparatus to detect the very small electric current (usually less than 1 μamp) produced in response to the oxygen concentration. However, growth experiments can usually be performed in vessels whose volume can be measured in litres, thus, enabling a much larger device to be used. These produce a large current, approximately 10–50 μamps and hence require less sophisticated electronic apparatus to be used. The difference in time scale of the experiment also imposes different requirements for the response time of electrodes used in these types of experiments. In a short-term, manometric type experiment, the rate of respiration may be modified many times in a single short duration experiment, thus a relatively rapid response time is required of an oxygen electrode used in these experiments. In a growth experiment the time scale is such that a response time of even 1 min is often quite acceptable. Again the different time scale imposes different demands on the stability of electrodes (i.e., the ability to produce the same electric current in response to a set oxygen concentration). The manometric type experiment requires a short term stability, whereas long term stability is of paramount importance in growth experiments. The response of the electrode to components of the reaction medium is also important. In manometric type experiments the composition of the reaction mixture is known and the effects of the individual components on the response of the electrode can be easily assessed in simple control experiments. In contrast, it is not always possible to control the composition of the growth medium and hence in such experiments it is essential to have a device which responds only to oxygen concentration under a wide variety of conditions. These electrodes must also be able to resist sterilization processes.

The scope of this article is limited to devices used in short-term experiments. Information regarding oxygen electrodes used in long-term experiments will be found in Volume 2 of this Series (Brown, D. E., 1970).

II. DESCRIPTION OF OXYGEN ELECTRODES

Basically, these consist of a small area of platinum or gold which is made the cathode of a circuit and polarized to approximately 0·6 V with respect to the anode. The oxygen electrode is placed in an electrical circuit which has two functions:

(i) To impose a potential difference between the oxygen electrode and some reference anode; this is usually a calomel half cell or a silver–silver chloride half cell.

(ii) To measure the current passing through the cathode.

The cathodic current has two components, that due to the reduction of oxygen at the electrode, and that due to the discharge of cations which are present in the medium. The nature of the reaction of oxygen electrodes is in some doubt. Laitinen and Kolthoff (1941) initially suggested a two electron reaction:

$$2H^+ + O_2 + 2e^- \rightarrow H_2O_2$$

whereas Davis and Brink (1942) and subsequently Kolthoff and Lingane (1952) suggested a two step reduction:

$$2H_2O + O_2 + 2e^- \rightarrow H_2O_2 + 2OH^-$$
$$H_2O_2 + 2e^- \rightarrow 2OH^-$$

The precise stoicheiometry of the electrode reaction probably depends on the nature of the electrode, applied voltage and precise conditions under which the electrode is exposed. Operationally the electrode reaction is not important, but it is vital for constant sensitivity that the electrode reaction is consistent throughout any one experiment (see Lessler and Brierley, (1969) for discussion).

On the application of a potential difference to the oxygen electrode circuit, the concentration of oxygen in the volume immediately surrounding the electrode becomes much lower than that in the bulk of the medium. This is due to the fact that the rate of reaction of oxygen at the electrode is faster than the rate of diffusion of oxygen through the medium. Once this diffusion layer has been created, the rate at which oxygen can react at the electrode is controlled by the rate of diffusion of oxygen across the diffusion layer.

For this particular situation Fick's law of diffusion may be expressed thus:

$$\frac{dO_2}{dt} = -D\frac{dc}{dx}$$

where $\frac{dO_2}{dt}$ = the quantity of oxygen passing through the diffusion layer in unit time

D = the diffusion coefficient of oxygen in the aqueous solution.

$\frac{dc}{dx}$ = the concentration gradient in the diffusion layer.

Since the amount of oxygen per unit time reaching the electrode, and which is reduced there (dO_2/dt) is the source of the electrical current (i) being measured, we have:

$$i = kD \frac{dc}{dx}$$

since the magnitude of dc/dx is obviously dependent on the oxygen concentration in the reaction medium we can generalize,

$$i = kD[O_2]$$

i.e., the electrode produces a current the magnitude of which is directly proportional to the oxygen concentration. This implies that D must also be constant.

Current–voltage relationships

The plot of current passing through an oxygen electrode against the applied voltage may assume shapes as different as curves (a) and (b) in Fig. 1. In curve (a) the long plateau indicates that the limiting of current by diffusion has been reached at low applied voltages. The rapid increase in current at higher applied voltages is due to the deposition of protons at the cathode. However, the extreme case of little or no plateau is frequently seen with the open type oxygen electrodes (see later). The absence of a well-defined plateau does not imply that the response of the electrode to oxygen is in any way unreliable. A normal working applied voltage is the voltage giving least variation in current with variation in voltage, region x–y in curves (a) and (b).

III. THE DESIGN OF ELECTRODES

A. The open electrode

All the early designs of oxygen electrodes consisted of an inert metal, usually platinum but sometimes gold, sealed in glass. With few exceptions the tip of the electrode was ground and polished so that the surface of the metal was flush with the glass.

1. *Stationary open electrodes*

As discussed by Davis (1962), the diffusion calculations for spherical electrodes approximately apply to stationary open electrodes in a static medium. In the steady state the concentration, c of oxygen around a spherical electrode of radius r at a point distance, a from the electrode assuming a zero oxygen concentration at the surface of the electrode is:

$$c(a) = C(1 - r/a)$$

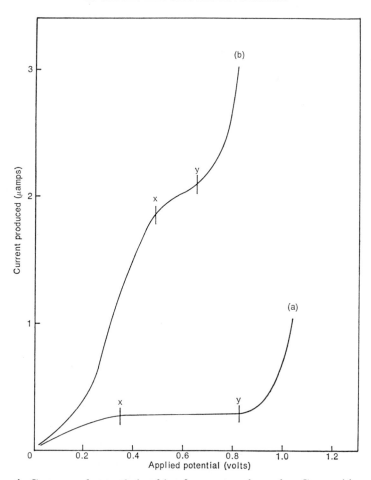

FIG. 1. Current-voltage relationships for oxygen electrodes. Curves (a) and (b) exemplify extremes of relationship.

where C is the initial uniform oxygen concentration. Thus at $a = 10r$ the oxygen concentration is 90% of C and at $r = 100a$ the oxygen concentration is 99% of C (see Fig. 2). Therefore, the electrode is affected by oxygen concentration some distance from the electrode and hence the volume of the fluid in which the oxygen concentration is to be measured should be much larger than that of the electrode.

The electrode current (i) is given by:

$$i = KCDr \left(1 + \frac{r}{\sqrt{\pi Dt}}\right)$$

where t is the time after applying the electrical potential.

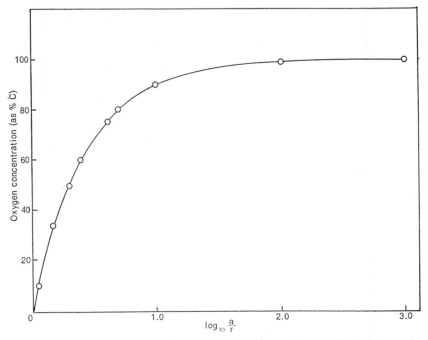

Fig. 2. Variation of oxygen concentration around a stationary spherical electrode. The point at which the oxygen concentration is measured is expressed as the logarithm of the ratio of the distance of the point from the electrode (a) to the radius of the electrode (r). C is the oxygen concentration in the bulk of the solution surrounding the electrode.

Again it can be seen that the steady state electrode current is proportional to the diffusion constant in the medium, also that the electrode current is the sum of two factors. One ($KCDr$) is constant and the other, $KCD^{\frac{1}{2}}r^2\pi^{-\frac{1}{2}}t^{-\frac{1}{2}}$ is time dependent. As r decreases the time dependent factor decreases as the square of r and becomes a smaller proportion of the constant factor; i.e., that the time taken to achieve the steady state decreases. Davis (1962) states that if the relaxation time is defined as the time required for the transient factors to decline to 10% of the steady state current, then a spherical electrode with a diameter of 1 mm in a medium where $D = 2 \times 10^{-5}$ cm^2 sec^{-1} (approximately the value for the diffusion coefficient of oxygen in an aqueous salt solution) has a relaxation time of approximately 4000 sec. For a diameter of 10 μ the relaxation time is 0·4 sec. and for a diameter of 1 μ it is 4 msec.

The magnitude of the electric currents given by open electrodes made with 200 μ diameter wire when immersed in air-saturated water or saline solutions is usually greater than 10 μamp. When the wire is 0·2 μ in diameter the currents produced are 0·1 μamp (Davis and Brink, 1942).

2. *Moving electrodes*

Stationary electrodes, whilst requiring little ancillary apparatus, do have some limitations; e.g., the relatively slow response time, this is less than ideal in a situation where the oxygen concentration is constantly changing. Secondly, external concentration and temperature changes also act as sources of variation. The sensitivity to vibration is not helpful in an experiment where it is wished to make several additions during the course of a short-term experiment, each addition requiring stirring of the reaction medium. Laitinen and Kolthoff (1941) eliminated these problems by rapidly rotating the electrode. The main effect of rotating the electrode is to produce a much thinner diffusion layer than is the case for the stationary electrode. As a result the diffusion current is much larger and attains a constant value much sooner; i.e., the speed of response is increased, also the sensitivity towards external vibration is greatly decreased, and the effects due to convectional currents are eliminated.

(a) *Vibrating electrodes.* Harris and Lindsey (1948) and Lindsey (1952) demonstrated that reproducible polarograms could be obtained with platinum micro-electrodes vibrating at a constant frequency. They showed that above a certain frequency, the frequency and the amplitude of vibration of the electrode had little effect on the diffusion current. Thus one can afford to neglect variations in applied amplitude in frequency of vibration providing they were well in excess of the minimum required to give maximum diffusion currents. It is the authors' experience that the optimum rates in amplitude and frequency of vibration tend to be unique for individual systems and hence should be ascertained for each vibrating electrode assembly.

Electrode design. A design of open vibrating electrode* which gave excellent service to the authors, is shown in Fig. 3. It consisted of a platinum wire (diameter approximately 0·1 mm) which was sealed into one end of a soft lead glass capilliary tube (3–4 cm long and approximately 2 mm in diameter) some 2 mm of the platinum wire protruded from the seal. A piece of polyethylene tube with a hole sufflciently large to allow the platinum wire to pass through it was placed over the open end of the glass tube. A wider diameter of firm plastic tubing was then pushed down over the first narrower plastic tube and passed the exit port for the wire, so

---

* This was based on the then available brief description of a vibrating electrode by Chance and Williams (1955).

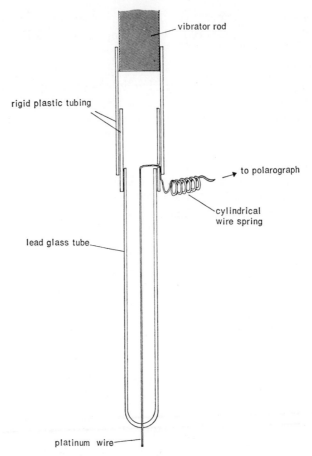

vibrator rod

rigid plastic tubing

to polarograph

cylindrical
wire spring

lead glass tube

platinum wire

FIG. 3. Diagram of home made open platinum electrode. The drawing is not to scale, see text for approximate dimensions.

trapping the wire between the plastic tubing for some 5mm. This end of the wire was then coiled into a cylindrical spring and attached to the cathode terminals of the polarizing and recording circuit. The firm plastic tubing was used to attach the electrode to the vibrator. The anode used in conjunction with this electrode was a calomel half cell taken from a pH meter. Electrical connection between the reaction vessel and the calomel half cell was made *via* an agar bridge (4% agar in saturated KCl solution) contained in a pliable plastic tube, 2 mm internal diameter. This electrode had a sensitivity of 4 namp per μM oxygen; i.e., approximately 2 μamp for air saturated oxygen solutions at 25°C.

The electrode could be cleaned with strong detergent or nitric acid. In

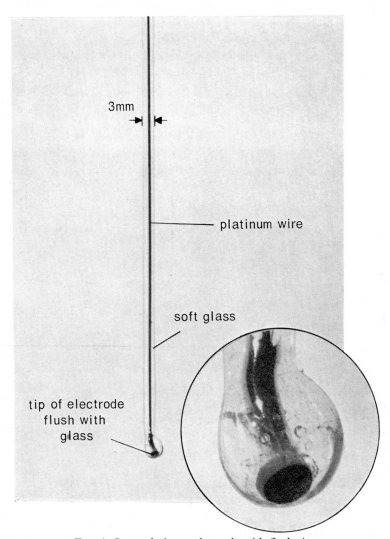

3mm

platinum wire

soft glass

tip of electrode
flush with
glass

FIG. 4. Open platinum electrode with flush tip.

practice it was noticed that a very clean electrode gave erratic results. However, contact for a period of minutes with protein containing solutions usually damped this noise and a steady signal was obtained. Poisoning of the electrode was indicated by an obvious change in response time and also by a decrease in sensitivity; i.e., the current per unit oxygen concentration began to decrease rapidly. This situation was simply remedied by cleaning. The response time of this electrode was less than one second.

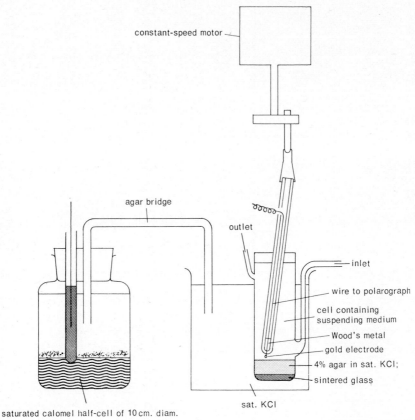

FIG. 5. Diagram of the apparatus designed by Longmuir. See the text for further details.

The open electrodes with flush tips (see Fig. 4) as supplied by Gilson Medical Electronics (Middleton, Wisconsin) and Aminco-Bowman (American Instrument Co., Silver Spring, Maryland) give much smaller electrical current per unit oxygen concentration.

(b) *Rotating open electrodes.* Two highly successful rotating open electrodes have been described—Longmuir (1954) and Hagihara (1961). The apparatus of Longmuir (1954) is limited in scope, having been designed for the specific purpose of measuring the affinity constant of bacterial oxidases for oxygen. However, for this type of use it is excellent. The high sensitivity of the electrode enables an accurate assay of very low oxygen concentrations. A design of the apparatus is reproduced in Fig. 5. The electrode is a gold sphere 1·5 mm in diameter. This is sealed into a soft glass tube. The electrode gives an electrical current of 150 μamp when the oxygen concentration is that of air saturated water. The following description of the apparatus is taken from Longmuir's (1954) paper.

"Electrical connection between the electrode and the wire to the polarograph is made with Wood's metal. The electrode is inserted into the cell through a hole in a rubber disc. The fit of the electrode into the disc, and of the disc into the cell, is so tight that leakage of air cannot occur even when the pressure difference between the cell and the atmosphere is 760 mm of mercury. The other end of the electrode is connected by a piece of rubber tubing to an iron rod which engages through a journal bearing concentrically situated in a brass disc rotated at 1300 rev/min by a constant-speed motor. The lower end of the cell is closed by a sintered glass disc, on top of which is a layer of 4% agar in saturated KCl. This end is immersed in a solution of saturated KCl which is connected with a saturated calomel electrode by means of an agar bridge. This electrode and the bridge must be large enough not to polarize with the passage of 150 μamp. In practice a 3 lb bottle of 10 cm diameter and tubing of 1 cm bore satisfied this requirement. The cell is filled with the suspending medium, all air bubbles being removed. The volume of liquid in the cell is about 20 ml.

"The gold electrode is made the cathode, and the calomel cell the anode in their connexions with a Cambridge pen-recording polarograph."

The design of a rotating electrode described by Hagihara (1961) is reproduced in Fig. 6. The electrode is made of platinum wire (28–32 gauge) the tip of which is melted to form a sphere approximately 1 mm in diameter. This sphere is sealed into a soft glass capilliary tube and the tip is then gently ground at an angle to expose a flat platinum surface. The surface is polished with very fine carborundum powder. The electrode is then joined to a toughened glass tube by a relatively unpliable piece of plastic tubing, so the platinum wire enters the lumen of the toughened glass tube. The lumen is then filled with mercury, so that the negative lead from the cathode can dip into the mercury and make continuous electrical connection whilst the electrode is rotated at greater than 500 rev/min. If necessary the electrode may be used in closed reaction vessels with the aid of a Teflon (PTFE) sleeve between the electrode and walls of the reaction vessel. This sleeve acts as a self-lubricating bearing and also as a barrier to oxygen diffusion into the reaction medium from the atmosphere. The lead to the reference anode can either be via a potassium chloride agar bridge or potassium chloride solution bridge. The junction of the bridge and the electrode vessel is a frit of alundum through which the potassium chloride solution passes at the rate of approximately 10 μl/h. Under these conditions a current of 2–3 μamp is given by such an electrode apparatus

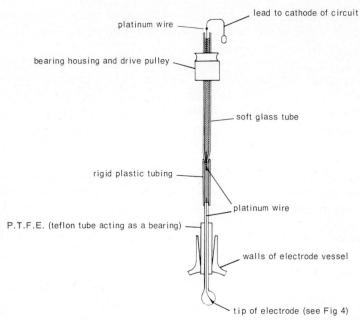

FIG. 6. Rotating glass electrodes designed by Hagihara.

when operating in an air saturated saline solution. The 95% response time is approximately 1 sec. In addition to describing this apparatus, Hagihara discusses in some detail the basic properties of this electrode system. A commercially available model based on this design is available from the Yanagimoto Manufacturing Co. Ltd, Kiyamachi, Sanjo Sagaru 181, Nakagyoku, Kyoto, Japan.

B. Coated electrodes

The problems caused by the reactions of constituents of the experimental reaction mixture with the electrode may become unacceptable. Thus the response time of the electrode can become so sluggish as to cause very large errors in the measurement of slow respiration rates (Hagihara, 1961). To avoid such complications the electrode may be protected by a thin layer of collodian. The electrode should be first thoroughly cleaned with nitric acid, then water washed and finally rinsed in methanol followed by a diethyl ether wash. The cleaned electrode should then be dipped deeply into an ethereal solution of collodian clarified by the addition of methanol. The electrode is then removed from the collodian solution and hung vertically for the solvents to evaporate. The electrode should then be placed in water for 30–60 min to enable the plastic coating to become thoroughly

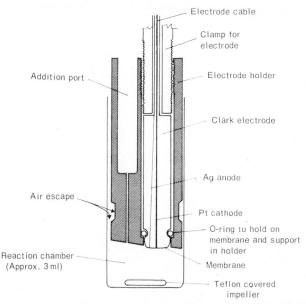

FIG. 7. A Clark electrode and reaction vessel—this design is similar to that provided by Yellow Springs Instrument Company, Yellow Springs, Ohio.

wetted. If this process results in a greater than 40% decrease in the electrode sensitivity the electrode coating is too thick and it is advisable to recoat the electrode. This coating procedure not only lowers the sensitivity of the electrode but also increases the response time by 50–100%.

1. *Membrane electrodes*

The commercial availability and robustness of the Clark type membrane covered electrode makes this the electrode of choice for most laboratories. It differs from those previously described only by the separation of the anode and cathode from the reaction medium by a thin semi-permeable membrane through which oxygen readily diffuses into the electrolyte that immerses the anode and cathode (Fig. 7). The membrane material is usually Teflon or polyethylene and the electrolyte used is half-saturated KCl solution or a similar paste formulation. As with most mass transfers across membranes, diffusion gradients are set up and these must be removed by continuous replenishment of fluid across the surface. This is easily achieved with a magnetic stirrer and a flea impeller (Fig. 7).

Membrane electrodes are not poisoned so readily as open electrodes, unless left in contact for extended periods with cells or proteins. Usually a change of membranes, which takes 1–2 min, is sufficient to restore the

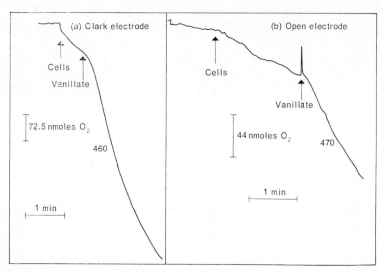

FIG. 8. Comparison of recorder traces obtained from measurements made with (a) a Clark electrode and (b) a vibrating open electrode (Gilson Medical Electronics). Washed suspensions of *Ps. aeruginosa* are oxidizing vanillic acid. Reaction mixtures contained: 50 mM Tris/HCl, pH 7·6 (2·9 ml); cell suspension (13 mg/ml) (0·1 ml) and 25 mM vanillate as indicated (6 μl); and (b) 50 mM tris/HCl, pH 7·6 (1·4 ml); cell suspension (25 μl) and 25 mM vanillate (3 μl). Temperature, 30°C. Figures appearing under the traces represent Q_{O_2} values (μl O_2 consumed, h^{-1} (mg dry weight of cells)$^{-1}$). In similar experiments, but with necessarily higher substrate concentration (1 mM), in a constant pressure respirometer, Q_{O_2} values of 468 and 483 were recorded.

efficiency of the electrode. The use of a membrane to isolate the anode and cathode, and their electrolyte, from the solution being measured also allows measurements to be made in gaseous phases and in non-conducting fluids. Another big advantage of the membrane electrode is that some of the classical inhibitors of respiration; e.g., cyanide or sulphide, are unable to interact with the cathode, since they cannot traverse the membrane.

Commercially available Clark micro-electrodes (Yellow Springs Instrument Company, Ohio; Beckman Instrument Company, California; Rank Bros., Bottisham, Cambridge, England) give a current of approximately 200 namps in air saturated buffers. With 1 mil Teflon membranes the manufacturers quote response times of 90% of final value in 5–10 sec. Our own experience suggests that the response time is a little faster than this, but that the ammeter needle readout is limiting; i.e., direct potentiometric recording of the output signal reduces this lag. Table I and Fig. 8 provide a comparison of measurements made with a Clark electrode and a vibrating open type electrode.

TABLE I

**Comparison of results of oxygen measurements by polarography
and manometry**

Washed suspensions of *Ps. testosteroni* oxidizing vanillate, in 50 mM phosphate, pH 7·1. Reaction volume, 3 ml; vanillate saturating (1·7 mM) temperature, 30°C.

	Q_{O_2} μl. O_2, h^{-1} (mg dry wt. cells)$^{-1}$	Period to maximum respiration rate (sec)
Constant pressure manometry	468, 495	measuring intervals too long (e.g. 2 min)
Clark O_2 electrode	460, 440, 450	9–12
Bare vibrating electrode	470, 468, 510	< 1

2. *Micro-oxygen sensors*

This is a recent advance in electrode design which is available commercially (Transidyne General Corporation, Ann Arbor, Michigan). The electrode tips are between 1–10 μ. They are supplied in glass capillary micropipettes or on glass or metal rods (1–2 mm). They may be used with their own internal reference electrode or with an external electrode. The platinum cathode may also be covered by a hydrophilic membrane resin which protects the electrode surface from macromolecular or cellular species. Because the electrode surface is so small, the current produced in response to different oxygen tensions is also small; e.g., air saturated buffer solutions give currents of about 20 namps. Representations of these currents require special electronic apparatus, which however is only a little more expensive than that required for a Clark electrode.

The small electrode surface provided by these "microtrodes", and consequently the small consumption of oxygen at the electrode surface has the advantage that it now falls within the critical diffusion range; i.e., oxygen deficits at the electrode surface and the immediate surrounding phases are so small that the rates of diffusion of oxygen from external regions ensures that oxygen depletion around the electrode does not occur. Thus stirring or vibrating mechanisms are not required with these electrodes. As a consequence and with this advantage of small size they are ideally suitable for use in small spectrophotometric cuvettes without designing stirring or vibrating mechanisms for use within spectrophotometer housings. Indeed such is their size that they may be easily inserted directly into a standard 1 or 4 ml (10 mm light path) cuvette without interference with the optical path.

Details of their application and for their operation are available from the manufacturers (Transidyne General Corporation). The various designs offered suggest that exploration of the oxygen tensions within and around colonies on agar surfaces is now a possibility.

IV. SOURCES OF ERROR IN MEASUREMENTS

With the design of the smaller electrodes the oxygen consumption by the electrode itself can usually be considered as a negligible contribution to the total. There are three other practical points to be aware of: (a) depths of diffusion of oxygen into the reaction medium; (b) the effect of temperature on oxygen concentration and electrode response; (c) the adequacy of mixing in the reaction vessel.

A. Depths of diffusion of oxygen into reaction medium

If the surface of an aqueous suspension of respiring micro-organisms is exposed to an atmosphere which contains oxygen, then as the concentration of the dissolved oxygen is lowered due to the respiratory activity of the micro-organisms, oxygen will tend to dissolve at the surface and diffuse into the bulk of the suspension. This diffusion of oxygen from the atmosphere could obviously interfere with the measurement of respiration rates by oxygen electrodes leading to an under estimation of the rate. Thus provided that the tip of the oxygen electrode is placed below the deepest level to which the oxygen diffuses then no complications or errors from this source will arise. The requisite minimum depths below which the tip of the electrode should be are listed in Table 2. These data (calculated from the equation described by Hill (1928)) refer to diffusion in a stationary medium, great care should be taken to control the possible continuous electrode error due to the enhanced oxygen concentrations which might be caused by either stirring the reaction medium directly or with rotating and vibrating electrodes. It therefore becomes essential with stirred (but not usually vibrating) systems that enclosed systems are used and that air bubbles are not trapped (see Fig. 7).

B. Temperature and agitation

Electrode measurements are very sensitive to temperature and agitation variations. Thus Clark electrodes have temperature coefficients of 2–8% of the reading per °C change in temperature. Agitation conditions can only be assessed by showing that increased agitation produces no further increase in the response of the electrode system. This is easily done in stirred or rotating systems; fortunately, vibrating electrodes usually operate at frequencies beyond those that limit the oxygen measurements.

TABLE II

Depths of diffusion of oxygen in suspensions of micro-organisms respiring at different rates

Respiration rate of oxygen (nmoles/min/ml of suspension)	Depth to which diffusing oxygen penetrates at 25°C, pH 7·0 (cm)
700	0·09
600	0·1
500	0·11
400	0·12
300	0·13
200	0·18
100	0·25
50	0·35
25	0·59
10	0·78

Data obtained using $D = 2·12 \times 10^{-5}$ cm^2 sec^{-1} for oxygen dissolved in 0·1M KCl–0·01M K-phosphate, pH 7·0 at 25°C (Jordan, Ackerman and Berger, 1956) and oxygen solubility = 237 μM at 25°C (Chappell, J. B., 9164).

$$b = \sqrt{D\frac{[O_2]}{a}}$$

(Hill, 1928)

Where b is the greatest depth of suspension to which oxygen may diffuse.

D—diffusion constant of oxygen in the medium which contains the micro-organisms.

[O$_2$]—concentration of oxygen in solution at the surface of the suspension of micro-organisms.

a—rate of disappearance of oxygen per unit volume of reaction mixture.

V. ELECTRODE MEASUREMENTS

The most popular electrodes currently used for the respiratory measurements in microbial systems are the membrane covered Clark type microelectrodes. Several excellent versions are available commercially with their associated amplification electronics and reaction vessels. The examples presented here were taken from experiments using either the Yellow Springs Instrument Company or the Beckman apparatus, attached to suitable potentiometric recorders.

A. Calibration of oxygen electrodes

As indicated earlier, the current produced when the electrode is exposed to oxygen is a function of the individual electrodes (and its functional state) and the exact conditions of measurement such as temperature, ionic strength etc. Consequently, it is essential to calibrate the ammeter or recorder

4

response by exposure to known concentrations of dissolved oxygen. Fortunately, this is very easily done by selection of two convenient reference concentrations of oxygen since the current output by these electrodes is usually linear with oxygen concentration. The most convenient oxygen concentrations to use are those of air-saturated solutions, and those of zero oxygen content. The former are easily prepared by the continuous gentle bubbling of air through the buffer in use at the desired working temperature. Solutions with a zero oxygen content are prepared by a variety of methods as outlined in the following paragraphs.

Oxygen electrodes measure the activity of oxygen and not its concentration hence it is also important to make direct calibrations to ascertain readily oxygen concentration, particularly if it is suspected that there is a large variation in activity such as that produced by changes in ionic strength (see later).

1. Indirect methods of calibration

(a) *Use of sodium dithionite.* Sodium dithionite (hydrosulphite) is a convenient reagent that reacts rapidly with dissolved oxygen to provide anaerobic situations. Thus injection of 0·1 ml of a saturated solution of dithionite (prepared immediately previous to the addition) to a reaction vessel containing 3 ml, will deplete the dissolved oxygen in less than 5–10 sec and this may be followed on the recorder. A suitable procedure is to adjust the span control of the amplifier and/or recorder to 95–100% of full scale deflection for the electrode immersed in an air saturated solution. Then add the sodium dithionite solution (e.g., 0·1 ml for a 3 ml reaction mixture), and note the new value obtained, usually 0–1% of the full scale deflection, which is due to a residual current output of the electrode in the absence of oxygen. Additions of more dithionite should produce no further change. Many workers remove the electrode and add solid sodium dithionite (1–2 mg) to the reaction vessel. In either case the electrode should be removed from contact with the dithionite solutions as soon as possible as prolonged exposure causes a poisoning of the electrode. This is particularly so with the open electrodes. Dithionite solutions are fairly stable at pH 7·5–8·0, in the absence of O_2.

(b) *Use of nitrogen-saturated buffer.* Nitrogen-saturated buffer is frequently used as an alternative zero buffer. The authors find it an unnecessary burden to have to equilibrate a second solution by discharging nitrogen gas through it. On the other hand the availability of air equilibrated and nitrogen equilibrated buffers provides the opportunity for easily testing the linearity of the electrode response to oxygen concentration. Thus mixtures of these two solutions in known proportions provide solutions of desired and known oxygen concentration.

After prolonged use of electrodes (particularly at higher oxygen concentrations) non-linear responses are exhibited. Such a phenomenon is usually readily detected by the appearance of non-linear traces on the recorder of reactions known to give zero-order kinetics. This is easily checked by careful preparation of mixtures of nitrogen-equilibrated and air-saturated buffers; mixtures are most easily prepared with hypodermic syringes. The reason for the non-linearity of response to oxygen concentration is usually due to silver chloride deposition on the anode. Fortunately, this is easily removed by swirling the bare electrode tip in 8–10N NH_4OH solution for a minute or two.

2. Direct method of calibration

As indicated earlier, oxygen electrodes measure activities of oxygen and not concentrations. This was amply demonstrated by Chappell (1964) for the Clark electrode by measurement of the current obtained when immersed in air-saturated water and air-saturated 1M KCl solutions. Thus values within 1% of the other were obtained although it had been firmly established by direct analysis that the oxygen concentration in 1M KCl was only 73% of that in pure water. Since it is laborious to calculate the ionic strengths of several incubation mixtures and thus estimate the effect on the activity coefficient for oxygen, rapid and direct determinations of oxygen concentrations are more convenient. There are further uncertainties of activity coefficient calculations introduced by the unknown effects of non-electrolytes and suspensions of biological materials. Hence exposure of electrodes to solutions equilibrated with known oxygen tensions cannot give accurate calibrations unless the solubility of oxygen is known for the particular medium. Published solubility determinations are available for a limited range of aqueous solutions; e.g., pure water, NaCl, concentrated acids or Ringer's solution (Umbreit, Burris and Stauffer, 1964). (Fig. 9).

(a) *Mitochondrial oxidation of NADH.* NADH is quantitatively oxidized by partially disrupted mitochondrial preparations from either liver or heart (Chappell, 1964). Since NADH is readily determined spectrophotometrically (molar absorbance coefficent at 340 nm ≡ 6.2×10^3) oxygen concentrations are readily determined. Thus, Chappell (1964) determined the variation of oxygen concentration at different temperatures in his incubation mixtures (Fig. 9).

The conditions used for these determinations were solution of 80 mM KCl, 15 mM phosphate, 20 mM triethanolamine-HCl buffer, pH 7.2 and 1 μM cytochrome c (3.9 ml); phosphate treated, saline washed liver mitochondria (Eastabrook, 1957) (100 μl) and successive additions of 20 mM NADH (20 μl). Anaerobiosis was reached after five additions of

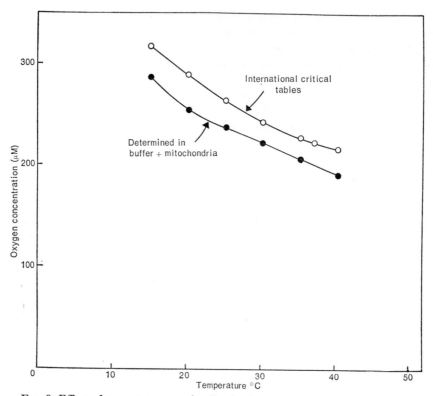

F<small>IG</small>. 9. Effect of temperature on the dissolved oxygen concentration in (a) water and (b) buffer plus mitochondria (Chappell, 1964).

NADH. The recorder responses for the first four additions of NADH should be identical, and may be directly related to the NADH concentration determined independently, according to the equivalence of NADH to $\frac{1}{2}O_2$.

Since liver mitochondria are not always readily available in microbiological laboratories similar measurements of NADH oxidation may be made with NADH oxidase preparations from micro-organisms. It is important, however, to establish that H_2O_2 is NOT a product of these reactons as this will alter the stoicheiometric relations of the reaction. This is easily determined by the addition of catalase. Other side reactions such as the reduction of some endogenous substrate are usually avoided by dialysis or passage of the extract through a short Sephadex G-25 column.

(b) *Non-enzymic oxidation of NADH.* Robinson and Cooper (1970) have provided a more convenient direct calibration method based on NADH oxidation, particularly for those laboratories which would find it tedious to prepare mitochondria. It is based on the non-enzymic oxidation of NADH by N-methylphenazonium methosulphate (PMS) and the subsequent reaction of oxygen with the reduced PMS:

$$NADH + H^+ + PMS \rightarrow NAD^+ + PMSH_2$$

$$PMSH_2 + O_2 \rightarrow PMS + H_2O_2$$

Since H_2O_2 spontaneously decomposes to varying extents to water and O_2, commercially available catalase is also added so that the net reaction of NADH oxidation becomes

$$NADH + H^+ + \tfrac{1}{2}O_2 \rightarrow NAD^+ + H_2O$$

The composition of the calibration reaction mixture used by Robinson and Cooper (1970) is as follows: 100 mM phosphate buffer, pH 7·4, containing 20 μg PMS and 400 μg catalase (200 IU, obtained from Sigma Chemical Company); NADH solution was added as desired in μl quantities and the electrode responses recorded for each addition. Values obtained were in close agreement with those obtained for mitochondrial oxidations, but reaction rates were slower at lower oxygen tensions. Low concentrations of PMS (as indicated above) are recommended to avoid NADH–PMS interactions. Among the advantages offered by this chemical method is the range of solution composition for testing which is not a feature of the mitochondrial determinations.

(c) *Other direct methods.* Provided the stoicheiometric relationships for any oxygen consuming reaction are well established then these may be used to determine the relationship of electrode response to oxygen concentration. Thus the dioxygenase reactions that cleave benzenoid compounds are ideally suitable for these determinations, even when crude extracts of the bacteria are used. Examples of the use of these are given in the next section.

B. Examples of electrode measurements

The use of oxygen electrodes to measure respiration has had a relatively late introduction in microbiology, particularly in research areas outside electron transport and oxidative phosphorylation. This is surprising since one of the earliest and most significant papers on the use of electrodes was entitled "Respiration rate of bacteria as a function of oxygen concentration" (Longmuir, 1954). Even today, manometric techniques are preferred by many laboratories, though the answers to many experiments could be obtained in a fraction of the time and with a fraction of the substrate materials by electrode measurements.

Several examples of the use of oxygen electrode measurements are given below; these measurements encompass the determination of respiratory rates and stoicheiometric relationships for whole cells and purified enzymes. The values obtained mainly with a Clark electrode are compared directly with similar measurements made with a vibrating bare electrode and those obtained manometrically (Table 1, Fig. 8).

1. *Respiratory activities of washed suspensions of cells*

Oxygen electrode measurements can be used to obtain data about oxidation rates and the stoicheiometric relationships of substrate oxidation. However, it is rarely possible to do both in one experiment since the substrate concentrations required for measurement of stoicheiometries with cell suspensions are rarely high enough for the maximum respiratory rates to be exhibited. Figure 10 provides an example of this. When the larger amount of vanillate (250 nmoles/3·2 ml) is supplied, which allows maximum oxygen consumption rates, all of the dissolved oxygen of the reaction mixture is utilized and the oxidation ceases due to anaerobiosis (not shown). The use of lower concentrations of vanillate in which oxidation ceases due to vanillate utilization, does not support the maximum rates of oxidation. It is not always known if this is a problem of substrate permeation into the cell or of a low K_m, affinity constant of the substrate for the enzyme concerned. In the particular case given, however, it is clear that the low substrate concentration offered to the whole cells is insufficient to allow maximal rates of permeation into the cell (see Fig. 13b for comparison). Extracts of the cells rapidly oxidize low concentrations of these substrates.

Whole cell experiments are subject to at least two other experimental parameters that are not seen in manometric experiments. Since pre-incubation times of the cell suspensions in the absence of substrate are short in electrode experiments (i.e., 1–2 min or about 10% of those periods in manometric experiments) it is important to see that the suspensions used are properly washed and possibly pre-incubated to deplete the residual exogenous (or endogenous) substrates. Otherwise the apparent endogenous respiration may mask that which occurs on addition of a substrate.

The second feature shown by electrode measurements is the speed of response of cell suspensions to the oxidation of a substrate. Thus manometric experiments cannot usually provide meaningful results until at least 3 min have elapsed after the cells have been exposed to the substrate. On the other hand, many electrode experiments are complete within this time and measurements are usually significant after 5–10 sec.

Thus, it is possible to measure lag periods of short duration which may be due to permeation of the substrate or the metabolic state of the cells (Fig. 11). Such a phenomenon has also been observed for ammonia oxida-

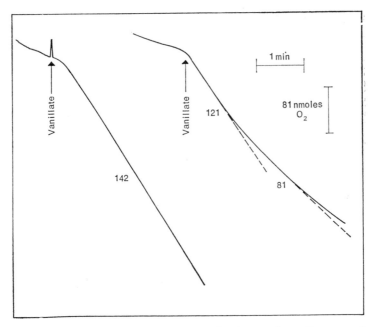

FIG. 10. Oxidation of limiting amounts of substrate by cell suspensions of *Ps. aeruginosa*. Reaction mixtures contained: 50 mM Tris/HCl, pH 7·2 (3·2 ml); washed cell suspension (100 μl) and volumes (2·5 or 5 μl) of 50 mM vanillate as indicated. Temperature, 30°C. Figures appearing under the recorder traces are the oxidation rates (nmoles of O_2 consumed/min).

tion by *Nitrosomonas* (Hooper, 1969). Even with the extracts of cells, lag periods occur which are indicative of enzyme or cofactor modification (Ribbons, 1970).

2. Oxygen consumption by extracts of cells and purified enzymes

Respiratory activities catalysed by extracts of cells are usually less complicated than those with whole cells. Thus the respiration which occurs in the absence of added substrates may usually be removed by dialysis or passage through a low number permeation gel. The NADH oxidase activity of many microbial cells may be sedimented by centrifugation for $6 \times 10^6 \, g$ min. Thus the values of rates obtained for "soluble" oxygenases acting on their substrates become more meaningful. It is also easier to provide quantitative values for oxygen consumption when extracts of cells are used.

Most of the text has been concerned with the measurement of respiration. However, electrode measurements are also ideally suited for the measurement of oxygen evolution reactions; e.g., oxygen evolution by catalase or

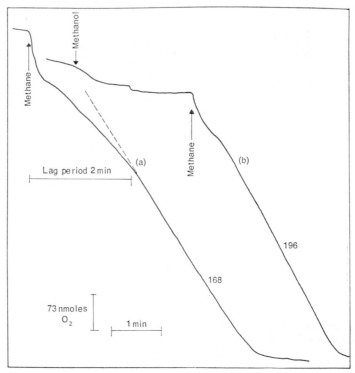

Fig. 11. Oxidation of methane by aerated cell suspensions of *Methylococcus capsulatus*. A lag period of 2 min occurs before maximum oxidation rates are exhibited (trace a). This lag can be relieved by the previous addition of minute amounts of methanol which itself does not contribute to the respiration rate (trace b). Figures appearing by the recorder traces are the oxidation rates (nmoles O_2 consumed/min). Each reaction mixture contained: air-saturated 50 mM-KH_2PO_4–NaOH, pH 7·1 (2·0 ml); washed suspension of *M. capsulatus* (0·5 ml). 10 mM-Methanol (4 μl.) and methane-saturated 20 mM-KH_2PO_4–NaOH, pH 7·1 (0·5 ml) were added as indicated. Temperature, 30°C.

oxygen evolution during photosynthesis. Examples of the ease of these measurements are given in Fig. 12 (Taylor, 1970 unpublished).

C. Calculation of results

Polarographic traces of oxygen consumption can provide information about respiratory rates and the stoicheiometric relationships of the reactions, and often within a single experiment. The way in which results are presented thus assumes some importance. Thus, we do not advocate the direct comparison of reaction rates by units of recorder or galvanometer deflection. This kind of presentation has appeared too frequently in mano-

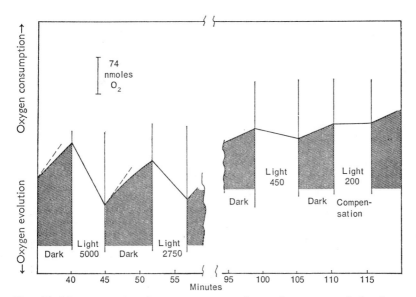

FIG. 12. Measurements of oxygen consumption and oxygen evolution by suspensions of the symbiotic micro-alga *Platymonas convolutae* in the dark and at varying light intensities. The reaction mixture contained sterile sea water with a 2% mineral enrichment and *Platymonas convolutae* (2·28 μg of chlorophyll a). Total volume, 3 ml. The figures appearing in the light periods represent the light intensities in μwatts cm⁻². At compensation, net exchange of oxygen is zero; i.e., the light intensity applied allowed photosynthetic oxygen evolution rates equivalent to the respiratory rates. Note also the variation in respiratory rate after exposure to varying light intensities—the post illumination gulp of respiration is most obvious after exposure to high light intensities. Two-hour experiment with a Clark micro-electrode at 20°C. (Courtesy of Dr. Dennis Taylor, Department of Functional Biology, Rosentiel School of Marine and Atmospheric Sciences, Miami, Florida.)

metric experiments (e.g., as mm pressure change). Such values are quantitatively meaningless unless full details are provided and the onus is on the experimenter to provide results in suitable values; e.g., mole, g atoms, μl of oxygen, the former two values are preferable for stoicheiometric relationships with other reactants and products.

The dissolved oxygen concentration is readily determined from recorder traces if two reference points have been noted. If $R_1 = \%$ recorder reading with air saturated buffer and $R_2 = \%$ recorder scale reading of buffer of zero oxygen concentration, then each division of the recorder is equivalent to

$$\frac{\text{reaction volume} \times \text{solubility at } R_1}{R_1 - R_2} \text{ units of oxygen.}$$

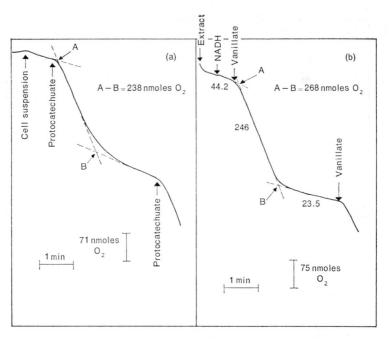

FIG. 13. Stoicheiometry of oxidation of (a) protocatechuate by suspensions of *Ps. testosteroni* and (b) vanillate by extracts of *Pa. testosteroni* supplemented with NADH. See text for further details.

Example. For a 3 ml air-saturated reaction mixture at 30°C $R_1 = 96$ recorder divisions, the oxygen concentration is 225 μM. At zero oxygen concentration $R_2 = 1$ recorder division. Therefore

$$\text{Each recorder division} = \frac{3 \times 225}{96 - 1} = 7 \cdot 11 \text{ nmoles oxygen.}$$

From this relationship reaction rates are easily provided in suitable units.

Total oxygen consumption. The calculation of the oxygen consumed during substrate oxidation by suspensions of micro-organisms is complicated by two parameters. First, it is often difficult to assess the contribution made by the endogenous respiratory activities of cell when they are exposed to exogenous substrates (Dawes and Ribbons, 1962). A similar situation occurs when P/O ratios are determined for mitochondrial preparations; i.e., does the "uncontrolled respiration" (absence of ADP) occur at the same rate during respiration in the controlled state (presence of ADP), or not. This problem is usually ignored and results are calculated by

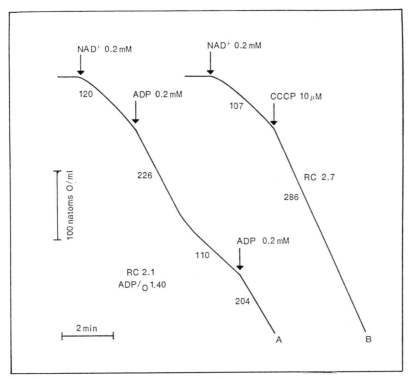

FIG. 14. Effect of ADP and CCCP on the rate of oxygen uptake by particles prepared from *M. dentrificans*. The reaction medium contained 50 mM Tris acetate, pH 7·3, 5 mM Mg acetate, 15 μl. ethanol, 12 units dialysed alcohol dehydrogenase, and 0·1 ml of particle suspension containing 0·63 mg protein. In addition, A contained 3·3 mM sodium phosphate, pH 7·3. Total volume was 3 ml; temperature, 30°C. The numbers along the traces are natoms O/min. Respiratory control ratios, RC, were calculated as in Table I. The ADP/O ratio was calculated by the procedure of Chance and Williams (1955). Adapted from John and Hamilton (1970).

extrapolation of the respiratory rates in the presence and absence of ADP—thus it is assumed that the uncontrolled rate of respiration (analogous to endogenous respiration) occurs at the same rate in the absence and presence of ADP (analogous to substrate respiration). This is the usual practice adopted for manometric experiments of microbial respiration. However, if endogenous respiratory values are subtracted from those that are exhibited in the presence of substrate, the endogenous rates should be quoted.

Examples. In Fig. 13 washed suspensions of *Pseudomonas testosteroni* are exposed to limiting quantities of protocatechuate, and cell extracts to NADH and vanillate. The total oxygen consumption that occurs is calculated by extending the slopes of lines as indicated and determining the difference in scale divisions as they intersect, points marked A and B on each figure. Protocatechuate added (125 nmoles), oxygen consumed (238 nmoles) or 1·91 moles of oxygen are consumed/mole of protocatechuate supplied to cell suspensions.

Vanillate added (125 nmoles), oxygen consumed (268 nmoles) or 2·14 moles of oxygen are consumed/mole of vanillate supplied to extracts in the presence of excess NADH.

Figure 14 (John and Hamilton, 1970) provides a similar example, but of respiratory control by ADP. The ratios of oxygen consumed to ADP added are calculated in the same way.

It becomes immediately clear from the examples presented that oxygen electrode measurements are ideally suitable for the study of multiple additions of substrates (and/or inhibitors and activators) to the reaction mixtures; the rate limiting function of these experiments unfortunately becomes the time consuming analysis of the yards of recorder traces.

D. Combination measurements

The convenient size and geometry of the oxygen electrodes makes it possible to measure simultaneously oxygen and other parameters such as pH, absorbance, fluorescence, etc. Such combination measurements have been widely used in studies of mitochondrial oxidations but have received little attention in microbial systems (Ribbons, Hewitt and Smith, 1968; Peterson, 1969).

VI. CONCLUSIONS

Electrode measurements of oxygen consumption and evolution offer several advantages over manometric procedures (a) reaction periods are usually of short duration; (b) some economy on the use of expensive substrate reagents is achieved; (c) multiple additions of substrates and/or inhibitors or effectors are readily made within a single experiment of short duration; (d) calculation of results and calibration procedures are much less time consuming; (e) measurements made reflect oxygen exchange by chemical reaction and not gaseous exchange; i.e. pressure or volume change; (f) measurements are made without removal of carbon dioxide. There is however usually no economy in the amounts of biological material used.

Manometric procedures allow the use of higher substrate concentrations where these may be rate limiting, and further advantages for the study of slow reactions of long duration; i.e., 1–10 h.

REFERENCES

Brown, D. E. (1970). *In* "Methods in Microbiology", (Eds J. R. Norris and D. W. Ribbons), Volume 2, p. 125. Academic Press, London.

Chance, B., and Williams, G. R. (1955). *Nature, Lond.*, **175**, 1120.

Chappell, J. B. (1964). *Biochem. J.*, **90**, 225.

Davis, P. W. (1962). *In* "Physical Techniques in Biological Research", (Ed. W. H. Nastuk), Volume 4, p. 137. Academic Press, New York.

Davis, P. W., and Brink, F. Jr. (1942). *Rev. Sci. Instr.*, **13**, 524.

Dawes, E. A., and Ribbons, D. W. (1962). *Ann. Rev. Microbiol.*, **16**, 241.

Estabrook, R. W. (1957). *J. Biol. Chem.*, **230**, 735.

Hagihara, B. (1961). *Biochim. Biophys. Acta*, **46**, 134.

Harris, E. D., and Lindsey, A. J. (1948). *Nature, Lond.*, **162**, 413.

Hill, A. V. (1928). *Proc. Royal Soc. (London)*, **B104,** 36.

Hooper, A. B. (1969). *J. Bact.*, **97**, 968.

John, P., and Hamilton, W. A. (1970). *FEBS Letters*, **10**, 246.

Jordan, J., Ackerman, E., and Berger, R. L. (1956). *J. Am. Chem. Soc.*, **78**, 2979.

Kolthoff, I. M., and Lingane, J. J. (1952). *In* "Polarography". Interscience, New York.

Laitinen, H. A., and Kolthoff, I. M. (1941). *J. Phys. Chem.*, **45**, 1061.

Lessler, M. A., and Brierley, G. P. (1959). *Methods in Biochem. Analysis*, **17**, 1.

Lindsey, A. J. (1952). *J. Phys. Chem.*, **56**, 439.

Longmuir, I. S. (1954). *Biochem. J.*, **57**, 81.

Peterson, J. A. (1969). *Arch. Biochem. Biophys,*

Ribbons, D. W. (1970). *FEBS Letters*, **8**, 101.

Ribbons, D. W., Hewitt, A. J. W., and Smith, F. A. (1968). *Biotechnol. and Bioeng.* **10,** 238.

Robinson, J., and Cooper, J. M. (1970). *Anal. Biochem.*, **33**, 390.

Umbreit, W. W., Burris, R. H., and Stauffer, J. F. (1961). Manometric "Techniques, 4th ed. Burgess Publishing Co., Minneapolis, Minn., U.S.A.

CHAPTER III

Electrode Measurements of Carbon Dioxide

D. G. NICHOLLS

Department of Medicine, University of Nottingham, Nottingham, England

AND P. B. GARLAND

Department of Biochemistry, University of Dundee, Dundee, Scotland

Carbon dioxide electrodes have been described by Stow, Baer and Randall (1957), and also by Severinghaus and Bradley (1958). Such electrodes have a relatively slow response time and a logarithmic relationship between the variable actually measured (pH) and the concentration of carbon dioxide. Nicholls, Shepherd and Garland (1967) introduced an analogue convertor that gave a recorder output linearly related to the concentration of carbon dioxide, and also decreased the response time by using a silicone rubber membrane. The major applications of carbon dioxide electrodes have been in the field of clinical biochemistry and physiology, but there is no reason to suppose that they cannot be successfully used for many microbiological purposes. A block diagram of the apparatus is given in Fig. 1.

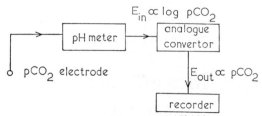

FIG. 1. Block diagram of apparatus for continuous recording of pCO₂.

I. CONSTRUCTION OF THE CARBON DIOXIDE
ELECTRODE

Fig. 2 shows a carbon dioxide electrode similar to those described by Stow *et al.* (1957) and Severinghaus and Bradley (1958), and to that available from Radiometer, Copenhagen, Denmark. A flat-ended glass pH electrode (Radiometer type G.8520) was mounted in a Perspex cylinder machined to the shape shown in Fig. 2, and a reference electrode provided by a 3 in. length of 0·0012 in. diam. silver wire electrolytically coated with AgCl by immersion in 0·1N HCl and passage of 1 mA for 30 min. A groove

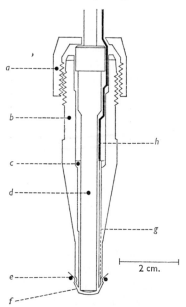

FIG. 2. Vertical section through the carbon dioxide electrode. Components are: (a) electrode retaining cap; (b) Perspex electrode holder; (c) electrolyte (0·1M–NaCl–0·1 mM NaHCO₃); (d) Radiometer G. 8520 pH electrode; (e) rubber "O"-ring; (f) silicone rubber membrane; (g) groove in the Perspex holder to accommodate (h), the silver reference electrode. (*Reprinted from Nicholls* et al., 1967.)

at the tip held a rubber "O" ring that fastened a piece of silicone rubber membrane (type TC 156, Esco Rubber Ltd., London, E. 8, or from Radiometer Ltd, Copenhagen, Denmark). These types of silicone rubber have a slightly granular surface and there is no requirement for a layer of tissue paper or cellophane between the membrane and the glass electrode. For measuring carbon dioxide output or uptake in suspensions of cells, the electrode may be mounted as described by Nicholls *et al.* (1967). The *in situ* use of the electrode to measure carbon dioxide concentrations in growing batch cultures would present two difficulties; first, that of sterilization and, secondly, that arising from the dependence of the partial pressure of CO_2 on the pH of the medium (see below). The carbon dioxide electrode can be more readily applied in controlled pH cultures. The partial pressure of carbon dioxide in the effluent gas phase is equal to that within the culture vessel, and the electrode can be used in the gas phase in a non-sterile position downstream from the culture itself. Measurements of the rates of carbon dioxide output also require accurate measurement and control of the rate of gas flow into the apparatus.

II. THEORY OF THE CARBON DIOXIDE ELECTRODE

CO_2, H_2CO_3, HCO_3^- and CO_3^{2-} are used in this discussion in their strict chemical sense, and the phrase "total carbon dioxide" is used for the sum of the activities of all these species. "pCO_2" refers to the partial pressure of CO_2. CO_2 diffuses from the incubation medium across the silicone rubber membrane and dissolves in, and equilibrates with, the thin layer of electrolyte between the membrane and the pH-sensitive tip of the glass electrode (Fig. 2). The resultant hydration (1) and dissociation (2, 3) reactions cause a change in pH of the electrolyte that is proportional to the change in log pCO_2 (Severinghaus and Bradley (1958)).

$$CO_2 + H_2O \rightleftharpoons H_2CO_3 \tag{1}$$

$$H_2CO_3 \quad \rightleftharpoons H^+ + HCO_3^- \tag{2}$$

$$HCO_3^- \quad \rightleftharpoons H^+ + CO_3^{2-} \tag{3}$$

The proportionality constant relating change of pH to change of pCO_2 is the electrode sensitivity S defined by:—

$$S = \frac{\Delta pH}{\Delta \log pCO_2} \tag{4}$$

where the pH referred to is that of the electrolyte layer between the membrane and glass electrode. Severinghaus and Bradley (1958) (who should be referred to for a more complete description of the theory) showed that the value of S lies between 0.5 and 1.0, its exact magnitude being determined by the concentration of bicarbonate in the electrode electrolyte. It follows from eqn. (4) that:

$$\frac{pCO_2''}{pCO_2'} = \left(\frac{[H^+]''}{[H^+]'}\right)^{1/S} \tag{5}$$

where pCO_2' and pCO_2'' are two arbitrary values of pCO_2 and $[H^+]'$ and $[H^+]''$ are the corresponding values of $[H^+]$ that satisfy eqn. (4). Since the current or voltage available from the recorder output of a pH meter is proportional to pH, it is necessary to convert the recorder output signal into a function that is proportional to $[H^+]^{1/S}$ in order to obtain a linear relationship between pCO_2 and recorder response.

III. THEORY OF THE ANALOGUE CONVERTOR

This device is readily and inexpensively constructed from commercially available operational amplifiers, and converts the pH meter output into a form that is proportional to pCO_2 rather than $\log pCO_2$. The mode of action of the convertor is best explained by referring to the generalized circuit for an antilogarithmic amplifier (Cowell and Gordon (1965)) (Fig. 3) and the forward characteristic of a logarithmic diode (Mullard Ltd

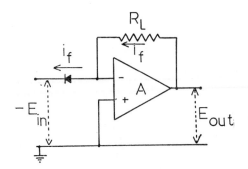

FIG. 3. Generalized circuit for an antilogarithmic amplifier.

(1963)) (Fig. 4). The SX640 diode (Mullard Ltd, London W.C.1) exhibits a forward characteristic that follows a logarithmic law over four decades of current in the range 10^{-9}–10^{-5} A (Fig. 4). In this region the change of forward voltage required for a tenfold change in current is assigned the value D, i.e. the slope of the linear portion of the characteristic is $1/D$. When a voltage $-E_i$ is applied to the input of the antilogarithmic amplifier and therefore across the diode, the diode current $+I_f$ flows through the

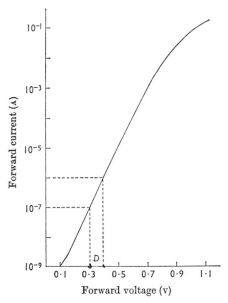

FIG. 4. Forward characteristic of Mullard SX640 diode at 35°.

loop resistance R_L resulting in an output voltage (E_0) of $+R_L.I_f$. Within the operating range of the diode, a change in log I_f is proportional to the corresponding change in E_i. Thus:

$$\Delta \log E_0 = \frac{\Delta E_i}{D}$$

Adopting two values of input voltage E_i' and E_i'' respectively:

$$\log\left(\frac{E_0''}{E_0'}\right) = \frac{E_i'' - E_i'}{D} = \frac{\Delta E_i}{D} \qquad (6)$$

Now suppose that ΔE_i arises from a change in the output of the pH meter, and that this output has been attenuated or amplified such that:

$$\Delta E_i = -\frac{D\Delta \text{pH}}{S} \qquad (7)$$

or

$$\frac{\Delta E_i}{D} = -\frac{\Delta \text{pH}}{S}$$

Substituting in eqn. (6)

$$-\frac{\Delta \text{pH}}{S} = \log\left(\frac{E_0''}{E_0'}\right)$$

Taking antilogarithms of this equation:

$$\frac{E_0''}{E_0'} = \left(\frac{[H^+]''}{[H^+]'}\right)^{1/S} \tag{8}$$

Combining eqns. (5) and (8):

$$\frac{E_0''}{E_0'} = \frac{pCO_2''}{pCO_2'} \tag{9}$$

E_0' corresponds to a nominal value of pCO_2 derived from the pCO_2 at the starting conditions of the experiment and from the bias voltage needed to bring the operating point of the logarithmic diode into the appropriate region. Thus for any given set of operating conditions, E_0'/pCO_2 is an arbitrary constant that determines the overall sensitivity of the electrode and convertor system according to eqn. (11).

$$E_0'' = \left(\frac{E_0'}{pCO_2'}\right)pCO_2'' \tag{11}$$

It is for this reason that the carbon dioxide electrode is suitable for measuring changes in pCO_2 rather than the absolute value of pCO_2, and alternative methods are required for measuring the starting pCO_2 if its magnitude is important.

IV. CIRCUIT FOR THE ANALOGUE CONVERTOR

Although a practical circuit has been published (Nicholls et al., 1967), it would seem preferable to outline the electronic manipulations in general rather than for the particular case for a certain combination of pH meter, operational amplifier and its power supply. The description that follows is applicable to pH meters where one side of the recorder output can be earthed.

In Fig. 5, the generalized circuit can be discussed in the conventional manner for operational amplifiers used in this configuration, namely, that the non-inverting input of each amplifier is effectively at earth potential and does not draw any current (Burr-Brown, 1963; Philbrick-Nexus, 1968). R_1 is chosen to conform with the maker's specification for the load that should be applied to the recorder output of the pH meter, and R_2, R_3 and $VR1$ have values such that if the pH meter output yields a change of N volts per pH unit, then:

$$\frac{R_3}{R_2+VR1} = \frac{D}{NS}$$

where D and S are as defined above. This ensures that eqn. (7) is met.

Although D is known (93 mV per decade), S lies between 0·5 and 1·0. $VR1$ should therefore be a preset potentiometer that can encompass the extreme limits corresponding to $S = 0·5$ or $S = 1·0$.

The power supply to the amplifiers ($+15$ V), VR_2 and R_4 provide a bias current i_b to the summing point of amplifier $A1$, and i_b is adjusted to define the starting bias across the diode $D1$. A suitable value for the SX640 diode, measured at the testpoint 1 (output of $A1$) is around $-0·27$ V.

Amplifier $A2$ acts as an antilogarithmic amplifier, with the modification that advantage is taken of the presence of a summing point to introduce a zero suppression current i_z through VR_3 and R_5.

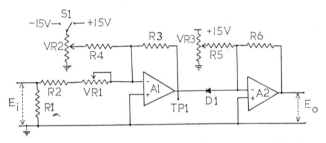

Fig. 5. Generalized circuit for obtaining a linear relationship between pCO_2 and recorder response. E_i is the output voltage of the pH meter across load R_1. The sum of R_2 and $VR1$ should be at least a hundredfold greater than the value of R_1. $S1$ enables an appropriate bias to be set across the logarithmic diode $D1$. $A1$ and $A2$ are operational amplifiers. E_0 is the output to a potentiometric recorder, and $TP1$ is a test point for measuring the bias voltage across $D1$ (which is equal to the output voltage of $A1$).

V. OPERATING PROCEDURE FOR THE CARBON DIOXIDE ELECTRODE

The simplest means of setting $VR1$ to the correct value for linearity between pCO_2 and output voltage of the convertor is to make successive additions of a bicarbonate solution to a buffered medium and plot recorder response against the concentration of bicarbonate added. If the resultant curve is convex upwards, $VR1$ should be increased, and conversely so. Once an acceptable linearity has been obtained $VR1$ need not be reset unless S is altered by changing the electrode conditions (Severinghaus and Bradley, 1958).

VI. CALIBRATION OF THE CARBON DIOXIDE ELECTRODE

The sensitivity of the overall electrode and convertor system is defined by eqn. (11), and it is essential to calibrate the electrode against either standard solutions of bicarbonate (at constant pH, Nicholls *et al.*, 1967) or, in the gas phase, with known partial pressures of CO_2. This calibration is relevant only to the initial conditions defined by the bias voltage across the diode, and must be repeated if the sensitivity is altered by starting with a different bias voltage.

VII. PERFORMANCE OF THE CARBON DIOXIDE ELECTRODE

A. Response time and stability

The system described by Nicholls *et al.* (1967) requires 23 sec for 90% completion on a linear scale, and this time has since been halved by the use of thinner silicone rubber (e.g. 20 μm). However, stability must be sacrificed to obtain an improved response time, and for many longer term applications it may be preferable to use a thicker membrane and also a more concentrated electrolyte solution in the electrode (Severinghaus and Bradley, 1958).

B. Temperature sensitivity

The characteristics of the SX640 diode are temperature sensitive. This is of small significance for short term (5–10 min) experiments. Longer term measurements may require that the diode be placed in a temperature regulated block or solution.

C. Specificity

The electrode is sensitive to any volatile acid or base that can penetrate the silicone rubber membrane. At pH 7·2, the electrode was insensitive to acetate (5 mM), butyrate (1 mM), ammonium chloride (1 mM), but gave a large off-scale signal in response to potassium cyanide (1 mM) and sodium dithionite (1 mM).

D. Sensitivity

Nicholls *et al.* (1967) reported a noise level corresponding to 1 μM total carbon dioxide in experiments where the total carbon dioxide concentration changed from approximately zero to 0·1 mM.

ADDENDUM

Since this article was written, an electrode with holder has become commercially available (Radiometer type E5036) which is as compact as that illustrated in Fig. 2.

REFERENCES

Burr-Brown Research Corp. (1963). "Handbook of Operational Amplifiers". Burr-Brown Research Corp., Tucson, Arizona.

Cowell, T. K., and Gordon, M. (1965). *Electron. Engng.*, **37**, 180.

Mullard Ltd. (1963). "Reference Manual of Transistor Circuits", p. 271. Mullard Ltd., London.

Nicholls, D. G., Shepherd, D., and Garland, P. B. (1967). *Biochem. J.*, **103**, 677.

Philbrick-Nexus Research (1968). "Application Manual for Operational Amplifiers" Philbrick-Nexus Research, Dedham, Mass.

Severinghaus, J. W., and Bradley, A. F. (1958). *J. Appl. Physiol.*, **13**, 515.

Stow, R. W., Baer, R. F., and Randall, G. F. (1957). *Arch. Phys. Med.*, **38**, 446.

CHAPTER IV

Ionization Methods of Counting Radio-Isotopes

G. W. CROSBIE

Department of Biochemistry, The University, Hull, England

I. INTRODUCTION

This chapter is concerned with those techniques of radioactive isotope assay which are based on the ability of the emitted radiations to induce ionization in a gas molecule. The techniques of liquid scintillation counting are discussed elsewhere in this volume. In principle the gas-ionization assay technique is applicable to all radio-isotopes but in practice there are serious limitations both in the ease of detection and in the ease of sample preparation of those isotopes having weakly energetic radiations (e.g. ^{3}H, ^{55}Fe). For the high-efficiency counting of these and other isotopes (notably ^{14}C) the liquid scintillation technique is now the method of choice.

Although no survey of tracer methodology in biology would be complete without mention of the early work of Hevesy and of Schoenheimer and Rittenberg, the main impact of the technique was only made through the ease of access to radioactive isotopes following the Second World War which saw the development of the atomic pile in which the following type of autocatalytic reaction proceeds:

$$^{235}_{92}U + ^{1}_{0}n \rightarrow [^{236}_{92}U] \rightarrow ^{148}_{57}La + ^{85}_{35}Br + 3^{1}_{0}n$$

The neutron flux so generated can be used to initiate the following process:

$$^{14}_{5}N + ^{1}_{0}n \rightarrow ^{14}_{6}C + ^{1}_{1}H$$

If a $(NH_4)NO_3$ target is employed the ^{14}C can be easily removed as a mixture of $^{14}CO_2$ and ^{14}CO which can be combusted to yield only $^{14}CO_2$ from which a large variety of labelled organic molecules can be synthesized. The cyclotron is also used in the preparation of selected isotopes, e.g.

$$^{55}_{25}Mn + ^{1}_{1}H \rightarrow ^{55}_{26}Fe + ^{1}_{0}n$$

A very large number of radio-isotopes are now available relatively cheaply in upwards of millicurie (mCi) amounts.[1] In the current catalogue of the Radiochemical Centre, U.K.A.E.A., Amersham, sodium bicarbonate and many derived organic molecules are listed with specific activities of up to 50 mCi per millimole. Tritium gas (isotopic abundance $> 90\%$) is available in upwards of 100 Ci amounts and tritiated organic molecules are available at activities as high as 15,000 mCi per millimole. The radiochemical purity for ^{14}C compounds is in excess of 97%.

There is an abundant literature on the assay and biological applications of radioactive isotopes to which the reader is referred (e.g. Aronoff, 1956; Calvin et al., 1949; Faires and Parks, 1958; Francis, Mulligan, and Wormall, 1959; Kamen, 1957; Price, 1958; Taylor, 1950). For general information reference should also be made to the Radiochemical Manual (ed. B. J. Wilson) published by the Radiochemical Centre, U.K.A.E.A., Amersham, before commencing radiochemical studies. The investigator ought also to be aware of the potential health hazards involved in radio-chemical work and should consult the relevant regulations. In Great Britain a "Code of Practice for the Protection of Persons Exposed to Ionizing Radiations in Research and Teaching" (HMSO, London, 1964) has been drawn up by the Ministry of Labour and the use of radio-isotopes in University Laboratories is additionally governed by "Radiological Protection in Universities" (The Association of Commonwealth Univer-sities, London, 1966) drawn up by a Committee of Vice-Chancellors and Principals of the Universities of the United Kingdom. Boursnell (1958) should also be consulted.

There is a great diversity both in commercial instrumentation and in the nature of available radio-isotopes and it is proposed in this chapter to do little more than discuss the rationale of the various assay procedures so that the investigator can by applying the principles in his limited sphere of operation readily obtain meaningful results. The biologist is primarily concerned with atoms of low atomic number and no apology is offered

---

[1] 1 Curie (Ci), originally defined as a standard for radium, is that amount of any radio-isotype giving $3 \cdot 7 \times 10^{10}$ disintegrations per second.

for referring in this text to a limited range of isotopes, notably, tritium (^{3}H), radio-carbon (^{14}C), radio-phosphorus (^{32}P) and radio-sulphur (^{35}S).

II. TYPES OF RADIOACTIVE DECAY

The assay methods for radio-isotopes depend upon the properties of the characteristic radiations emitted during the random disintegration of radionuclides. Disintegration may occur in the first instance in any one of the following ways:

A. Alpha (α) particle emission. This involves the ejection from the nucleus of a positively charged helium nucleus. α Particles are only emitted from radionuclides of high mass number and are consequently of relatively little biological interest.

B. Beta (β^-) particle emission due to the nuclear transformation of a neutron into a proton:

$$^0_1n \rightarrow ^1_1p + ^0_{-1}e$$

C. Positron (β^+) emission due to the conversion of a proton to a neutron:

$$^1_1p \rightarrow ^1_0n + ^0_1e$$

Positron emission is always accompanied by γ-ray photons arising from the following annihilation reaction:

$$^0_1e + ^0_{-1}e \rightarrow 2\ hv$$

$^{11}_6$C (half-life 20·5 min) is a positron emitter.

D. Electron Capture (K-capture) in which an orbital electron is captured by the nucleus resulting in a proton to neutron conversion. This transition is characterized by the emission of X-rays.

E. Isomeric Transition in which an unstable nucleus isomerizes with no alteration in the proton/neutron complement of the nucleus. This change is accompanied by γ-ray emission.

In cases **A.–D.** above there may additionally be γ-ray production where the energy of the emitted particle or X-ray does not account for the energy difference between the initial and final states. In certain cases the emitted γ-rays may interact with the orbital electrons leading to the expulsion of homo-energetic electrons (e^-). This process is known as Internal Conversion.

There is no fundamental difference between X-rays and γ-rays other than the greater energy and hence shorter wavelength of the latter. Both form part of the electromagnetic spectrum and have strong penetrative powers. The absorption of γ-rays and X-rays in matter leads to the secondary production of β^- particles and hence enables the detection of γ- and X-rays by gas-ionization devices primarily designed for the detection of β particles.

β^- Particles carry a charge of one electron unit ($4 \cdot 803 \times 10^{-10}$ absolute electrostatic units) and have a rest mass of $9 \cdot 107 \times 10^{-28}$ g. The energies of β^- particles are quoted in terms of the electron-volt (eV) unit which is defined as the kinetic energy gained by an electron when under the influence of a 1 V potential gradient. The commonly used units are the MeV and the keV, being, respectively, one million and one thousand electron volts. β^- Particles have velocities approaching that of light and the following is the relationship between kinetic energy (E) and velocity (v):

$$E \text{ (MeV)} = 0 \cdot 511[\{1/(1 - v^2/c^2)^{0 \cdot 5}\} -]$$

The energy of a γ- or X-ray is given by Planck's relationship:

$$E = hv = hc/\lambda$$

where h = Planck's constant

                v = frequency of the radiation

                λ = wavelength of the radiation

                c = velocity of light.

The energy of a γ- or X-ray in terms of electron-volts is given as follows:

$$E = 0 \cdot 012354/\lambda$$

where λ is expressed in Ångstrom units.

The β^- particles emitted from radio-isotopes are not generally homo-energetic, but rather occur with a continuous distribution of energies from near zero to an upper maximum (E_{max}) characteristic of each isotope. Typical β spectra are given elsewhere in this Volume (J. H. Hash, p. 109). The energy of the β^- particle determines its penetrating power in matter and, in consequence, is a determinant in the choice of the assay technique. β^- particles are classified either as "soft" or "hard". Typical "soft" β^- particles are those of ^{3}H(E_{max} $0 \cdot 018$ MeV), ^{14}C(E_{max} $0 \cdot 155$ MeV), ^{35}S(E_{max} $0 \cdot 167$ MeV): typical "hard" β^- particles are those of ^{59}Fe(E_{max} $0 \cdot 46$, $0 \cdot 27$ MeV), ^{131}I(E_{max} $0 \cdot 61$ MeV), ^{24}Na(E_{max} $1 \cdot 39$ MeV), and ^{32}P(E_{max} $1 \cdot 71$ MeV). ^{59}Fe, ^{131}I, and ^{24}Na are also γ-emitters. ^{55}Fe has a very soft K capture X-ray ($0 \cdot 0065$ MeV). A table giving the particle-type, E_{max} values and half-lives of a variety of biologically important isotopes is given elsewhere in this Volume (J. H. Hash, Table I, p. 113).

The absorption of non homo-energetic β^- particles is found to approximate fortuitously to an exponential process, so that the intensity (I) of radiation emerging from a uniform sheet of an absorber is related to the intensity (I_0) of the incident beam in the following way:

$$I = I_0 \exp\left(-\mu s\right)$$

where s = thickness of the absorber

μ = a constant (linear absorption coefficient) the units of which depend upon those in which s is expressed.

The dependence of μ upon the nature of the absorber is largely avoided by expressing thickness in terms of surface density, i.e. as mg/cm². The above relationship does not, however, apply at large values of s. There is a limiting thickness of any material which will cut off completely the β^- particles from any particular radio-isotope. The maximum ranges in aluminium of the β^- particles from ${}^3H$, ${}^{14}C$ and ${}^{32}P$ are 0·23, 28·5 and 800 mg/cm² respectively (Glendenin and Solomon, 1948). The following empirical relationships between E_{max} and the maximum range (R) of β^- particles have been described:

for E_{max} values greater than 0·6 MeV:

$$R = 542\, E_{max} - 133 \quad \text{(Coryell, 1948)}$$

for E_{max} values less than 0·6 MeV:

$$R - 407\, (E_{max})^{1·38} \quad \text{(Coryell, 1948)}$$

The absorption of γ- and X-rays is very dependent upon the nature of the absorber and gas ionization tubes used in their detection have wall materials of high atomic weight to optimize the electron production consequent upon γ- or X-ray absorption. γ- and X-ray emitters are, however, better assayed by the liquid scintillation technique.

III. ASSAY OF RADIOACTIVITY

A. Basic phenomena

The basic phenomenon upon which radiochemical assays depend is essentially the ability of ionizing radiation to interact with atoms or molecules causing both excitation and ionization of orbital electrons. The number of ion-pairs so produced depends on the energy and charge of the incident particle. The basic detecting equipment is a gas ionization chamber which consists essentially of a gas of low electron attachment characteristics (usually an inert gas) contained in a chamber housing two well-insulated electrodes. There are four main types of assay equipment: the Lauritsen electroscope, the electrometer ionization chamber, the Proportional counter and the Geiger-Müller counter. These instruments differ essentially in the voltage range over which they are operated. Fig. 1 shows the dependence of the charge collected at the anode of a gas ionization chamber as a function of the applied voltage when a β^- particle of high (A) or low (B) specific ionization power traverses the chamber. In the region 0–*ca.* 50 V, ion-pair

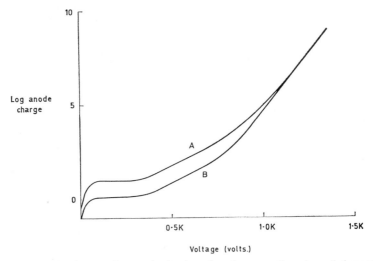

FIG. 1. Anode charge of a gas-ionization chamber as a function of the applied voltage.

production is immediately followed by more or less extensive recombination. When the voltage is raised to *ca.* 50–250 V, the electrons of the ion pairs have a sufficiently high velocity to avoid recombination with the positively charged species. The anode charge is, therefore, independent of voltage and related only to the specific ionizing power of the β^- particle traversing the chamber. This voltage region is that of the electroscope and electrometer devices. In the region *ca.* 350–750 V the electrons of the initially-produced ion-pairs are accelerated to sufficiently high energies to induce secondary electron production through interaction with further gas molecules. The amplification effect is a direct function of the applied voltage but independent of the number of initial ion-pairs. This region is known as the Proportional region. As the voltage is further raised there arises a situation (at *ca.* 1100–1500 V) where the amplification factor is very large (up to 10^8 electrons being collected per single incident β^- particle) and the magnitude of the collected charge is independent of the number of initial ion-pairs. This is the Geiger-Müller (G.M.) region.

Electroscopes and electrometers are not in general use in radio-biochemical laboratories. The reader is referred to other sources (e.g. Calvin *et al.*, 1949) for a description of these instruments and only Proportional and Geiger-Müller counters will be described here.

B. Geiger-Müller and Proportional counters

1. *Construction and operation*

The G.M. tube is the most frequently used gas ionization device due to the following characteristics:

(a) the high operating voltage ensures a sufficiently large amplification factor to give an anode line pulse of 0·1–0·5 V which requires only modest amplification (up to 5 V) to operate the scaling circuits.

(b) the counters are very simple and robust and may be cheaply constructed.

Before use the voltage characteristics of the tube must be determined. Fig. 2 shows a typical count rate/applied voltage curve. The curve is characterized by a starting (threshold) voltage below which no anode line pulses are of sufficient magnitude to actuate the associated pulse counting circuitry. With increasing voltage the internal amplification phenomena of the tube ensure an increasing number of countable pulses until a plateau region is reached where the independence of count rate and voltage reflects a situation where all the pulses are of sufficient magnitude to trigger the

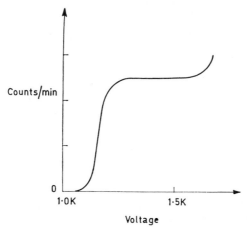

FIG. 2. Voltage characteristics of a typical Geiger-Müller tube showing the Geiger-Müller plateau.

counting stages. The G.M. counter is normally operated at the mid-point of the plateau which, in a good tube, may be as long as 250–300 V. The plateau should preferably be not less than 50 V long. The slope of the plateau should not exceed 0·5% per V and is usually *ca.* 0·1% per V. At voltages above the G.M. plateau the tube goes into spontaneous discharge and damage rapidly ensues if the tube is left under these conditions.

G.M. tubes are generally cylindrical in shape and of glass or metal (brass, copper, aluminium) construction. In glass tubes an evaporated metal film or colloidal graphite deposit on the wall is used as the cathodic element. The anode is usually a thin wire of tungsten or platinum mounted symmetrically in the tube and well insulated from the walls, which in the case of metal tubes serve as cathodes. It is customary to have a "window" in the tube through which the β^- particles enter. The window must be mechanically rigid, thin enough to admit a significant proportion of weak β^- particles and impermeable to the gas phase of the tube and to air. For ^{14}C and ^{35}S assay a 2 mg/cm^2 mica window may be employed albeit at relatively low efficiency. For more energetic β^-'s windows of mica, aluminium or duralumin *ca.* $5–10 \text{ mg/cm}^2$ may be used. It is customary to coat mica windows with a thin layer of graphite to obviate electrostatic charge accumulation. Tubes so treated have the additional advantage for some purposes of being light-insensitive.

G.M. counters may be of two types—"slow" or "fast"—depending upon the composition of the gas phase of the counter. In "slow" tubes the filling is an inert gas (e.g. argon or helium) or some convenient gaseous derivative (e.g. $^{14}CO_2$ or $^{14}CH_4$) of the material to be assayed. In such tubes the energetic collisions of the positively charged gas species with the cathode result in a secondary production of electrons which initiate a new round of ion-pair production thereby prolonging the time interval during which the tube will not respond to a second β^- particle in the sense that the arrival of the second β^- particle will not be registered as a discrete pulse in the anode circuit. In "fast" tubes a polyatomic gas is incorporated in the gas phase, fillings such as helium (60 mm Hg)/ethyl formate (0·7 mm Hg), argon/ propane, or $^{14}CO_2/CS_2$ being commonly employed. The polyatomic component serves to dissipate by collision the energy of the positively charged species and so prevents secondary electron production from cathode collisions. The net effect is to shorten the dead time of the tube to about $50–250 \, \mu\text{sec}$ as compared to upwards of $750 \, \mu\text{sec}$ for "slow" tubes. It should, however, be noted that the life of the "fast" tube is limited and is related to the initial number of polyatomic gas molecules which are, of course, decomposed during the collisions. In a typical counter a life of *ca.* 5×10^8 counts may be expected. Tubes with a halogen (bromine) component have an indefinite life. They have a low operating voltage (*ca.* 400–

500 V) but have a long dead time (*ca.* 800 μsec). Fig. 3, shows a cross-section of a typical end-window G.M. tube used in the assay of solid ^{14}C samples. The tube (EHM2S, General Electric Co., England) has a 1-in. diam mica window (of *ca.* 2 mg/cm^2 thickness) in a nickel-plated copper body. The

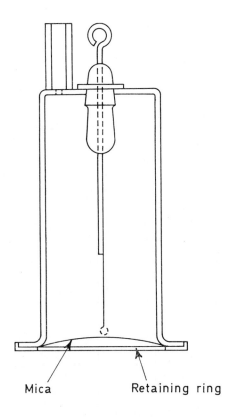

Mica   Retaining ring

EHM2S

FIG. 3. Cross-section of the Geiger-Müller tube EHM2S. (*Reproduced by kind permission of G.E.C. Ltd., Magnet House, Kingsway, London, W.C.2.*)

anode wire (0·08 mm diam.) is mounted coaxially and the gas phase consists of helium, argon, ethyl formate (at 60·0, 4·3 and 0·7 cm Hg respectively). The tube is also available with aluminium and other thin metal windows (*ca.* 7 mg/cm^2) for assay of the more energetic β particles, e.g. those of ^{32}P and ^{131}I. Fig. 4 similarly shows sectional diagrams of tubes used in the counting of liquid specimens. Typical of these is the M6 tube (20th Century Electronics, England) which has a borosilicate-walled G.M.

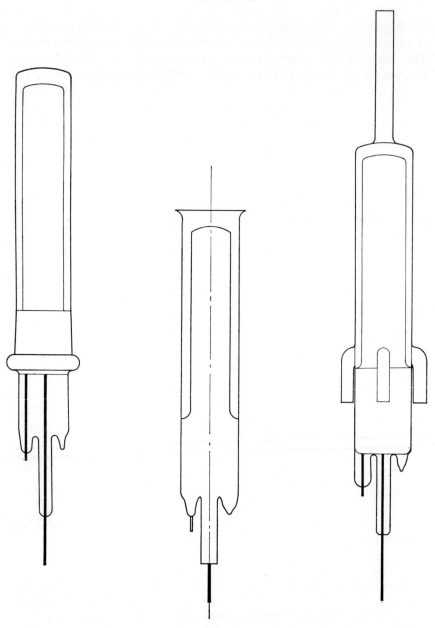

DM 6   M6   FM6

FIG. 4. Geiger-Müller tubes M6, DM6 and FM6 for counting liquid samples. (*Reproduced by kind permission of* 20th *Century Electronics Ltd., Croydon, Surrey, England.*)

tube surrounded by a jacket, the sample being contained in the annular space. For mechanical stability the walls of such tubes have to be relatively thick (20–30 mg/cm²) and accordingly the tubes are most suitable for the assay of energetic β^-'s (e.g. the β^-'s from ^{32}P). They are not recommended for the assay of ^{14}C and other weak β^- emitters. Tube DM6 has a detachable glass jacket and FM6 is a modification of M6 to allow the continuous moni-

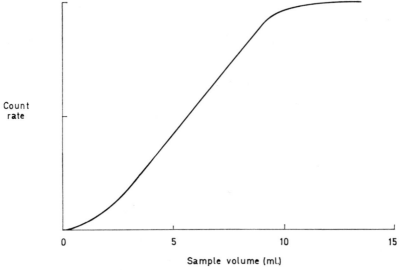

FIG. 5. Activity/volume relationships for a G.E.C. M6 counter.

toring of liquid samples. Fig. 5 shows the count rate/sample volume relationship in an M6 tube. The shape of this curve should be determined for each counter so that appropriate corrections may be made for varying sample volumes.

Assay techniques involving end-window or liquid counters although convenient and inexpensive in operation suffer the defect of being relatively insensitive. Thus in solid sample assay of ^{14}C employing a 2 mg/cm² end-window tube the sensitivity is limited by the less than 2π geometry of the counting arrangement coupled with absorption losses in air and in the window. It may be seen from Fig. 6 that for ^{14}C (E_{max} 0·155 MeV) a 2 mg/cm² window will impose a 40–50% loss of β^-'s giving a maximum efficiency of *ca.* 30%. In practice this drops to less than 10% due to air absorption and obvious geometrical factors. Increased efficiency may be achieved by eliminating window absorption. In the internal gas counter the sample to be assayed forms the gas phase of the counter. ^{14}C Samples may be combusted to and counted as $^{14}CO_2$ (with CS_2 as quenching agent). Tritiated samples may likewise be combusted and the resulting ^3H_2O treated with Al_4C_3 or methyl (or butyl) magnesium iodide to yield [^{3}H]

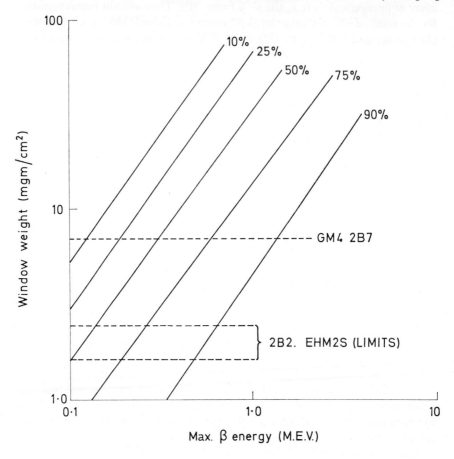

PERCENTAGE TRANSMISSION OF β PARTICLES

FIG. 6. Percentage transmission of β^- particles by windows of Geiger-Müller tubes. (*Reproduced by kind permission of G.E.C. Ltd., Magnet House, Kingsway London.*)

methane (or [^{3}H] butane). Counting efficiencies may be as high as 85% for ^{14}C and better than 25% for ^{3}H. The internal gas counting method how-ever suffers from many disadvantages and is not recommended as a routine procedure. The vacuum line equipment required to manipulate the gaseous samples requires some expertize in operation and is not commonly available. The method is tedious in operation and is not adaptable for the daily handling of a large number of samples (more than ten). For full details of the technique specialist manuals should be consulted (e.g. Glascock, 1954).

The windowless gas flow counter is the most commonly used high efficiency G.M. system. In this technique the solid sample is introduced directly into the sensitive gas space of the G.M. tube. The filling gas—e.g. helium/butane or argon/ propane for G.M. counting; argon/methane for proportional counting—is allowed to flow through the counter continually thus expelling air inadvertently introduced with the sample and preventing access of air during the counting operation. The theoretical counting efficiency of this system is slightly in excess of 50% due to 2π geometry and back-scatter and efficiencies approaching 45% may be observed in practice with infinitely thin ^{14}C samples. The method is not ideal for ^{3}H where the low $E_{\max}$ (0·018 MeV) implies problems in the preparation of infinitely thin samples. Instruments typical of this class are the SC16 counter (Tracerlab) and the Model D47 (Nuclear Chicago) a sectional drawing of which is shown in Fig. 7. The D47 instrument is designed for use with automatic sample changing and data recording facilities (Nuclear Chicago System 4306). The D47 counter has a detecting chamber with a trochoidally shaped profile and a concentric loop anode of tungsten wire (0·002 in. diam.) provides a uniform field within the sensitive volume of the chamber. The counting gas enters through four symmetrically placed orifices at the top of the chamber. The chamber is closed by sealing with a rubber "O" ring to the sample pan and the counting gas is exhausted through ports in the sample pan adapter. The windowless counting technique is prone to chamber contamination, electrostatic charge effects on the sample (giving rise to a decreasing count rate on successive measurements) and to vapour transmission from less than well prepared samples (giving a shift in the detector plateau). These difficulties may be conveniently surmounted through the use of an ultra-thin ("Micromil") window consisting of a fragile metal-coated membrane (ca. 150 μg/cm^2 thick) mounted in a metal ring designed to fit over the open end of the detecting chamber. The window thickness coupled with the 60 μg/cm^2 air layer between the sample and the window combine to offer little loss of efficiency for ^{14}C β^- particle counting. The ultra-thin windows are not impermeable to air and demand a gas flow mode of operation. There is, however, an obvious diminution in the gas requirements and the consequential economy is a not insignificant advantage of the ultra-thin window technique as compared with the windowless technique.

Proportional counters are fundamentally of similar design to G.M. tubes and the Nuclear Chicago DM4, for example, is capable of use in either

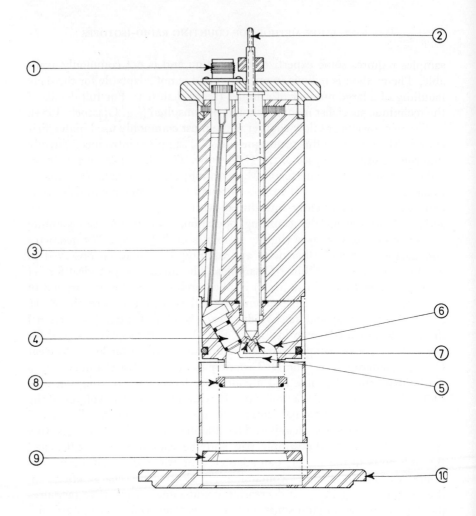

ASSEMBLED VIEW OF DETECTOR

FIG. 7. Cross-sectional diagram of the Nuclear-Chicago Gas-Flow detector D47. (*Reproduced by kind permission of Nuclear-Chicago Corporation.*)

Key No.	*Description*
1.	Co-axial connector.
2.	Counting gas input.
3.	Conductor rod.
4.	Anode and insulator assembly.
5.	Anode loop.
6.	Trochoidally-shaped cross-section of the detector chamber
7.	Counting gas entry ports to detector.
8.	Micromil window assembly with "O" ring.
9.	Sample pan adapter.
10.	Base plate.

mode. In the case of the internal gas counting of $^{14}CO_2$ proportional counting is customary due to the very high voltage (upwards of 4000 V) required for G.M. operation. The use of a counter in the proportional region allows one to assay simultaneously two (or more) isotopes of differing E_{max} provided a multi-channel pulse height analyser is incorporated in the circuit. The proportional counter has an advantage of a very low resolving time—of the order of 0·5 μsec as compared to 50–100 μsec for a self-quenched G.M. counter—thus enabling count rates as high as 10^5 counts/min to be handled without recourse to coincidence correction. It should be noted that the pulse size generated in the proportional region is of the order of only a few millivolts and that a high quality high-gain linear amplifier is required to give a pulse capable of actuating the scaling circuit. The cost of the ancillary equipment required to make full use of the characteristics of the proportional counter approaches that of modern reliable multi-channel liquid scintillation counters, the advent of which is rapidly rendering much G.M. and proportional counting equipment redundant.

2. *Associated equipment*

The basic G.M. counting assembly consists of a G.M. tube powered by a H.V. supply and connected to a scaler which recognizes and records individual voltage pulses in the anode line of the G.M. tube. In practice one usually employs a more elaborate system and, depending upon circumstances, the auxiliary equipment may include a timer, a quench unit, a pre-amplifier, a high-gain linear amplifier, a discriminator or a multi-channel pulse height analyser, anti-coincidence circuitry and a ratemeter. There may also be facilities for the automatic presentation of samples to the detector and for the automatic recording of data by a printer, punch-tape or teletype-unit. The G.M. tube is usually housed in a lead castle which both screens the tube from cosmic radiation and offers facilities for convenient and reproducible sample location with respect to the G.M. tube. A typical assembly for G.M. counting is shown in Fig. 8. In this diagram Ekco components are specified, but equivalent units are available from manufacturers either in the form of modular or integrated units.

It is beyond the scope of this article to discuss the electronics of the various ancillary devices. Only a brief outline of the functional characteristics of the ancillary equipment will be given and the reader is referred to the appropriate manufacturers' instrument manuals for further details.

(a) *The high-voltage supply.* The H.V. supply is normally continuously variable from 200–2000 V in most G.M. systems. The voltage should be highly stabilized and a good specification is better than 0·005% variation for a constant load within $+5\%$ to -15% variation in mains voltage

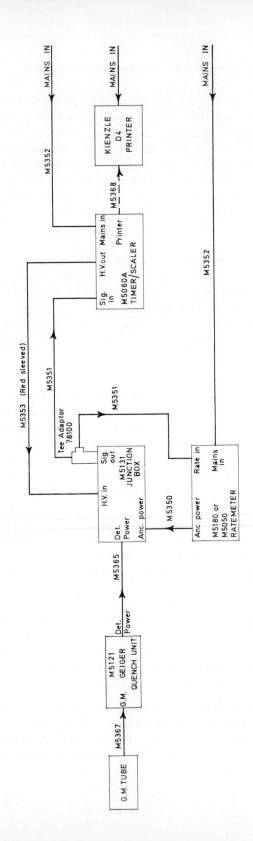

QUENCHED G.M. TUBE SYSTEM

FIG. 8. Diagrammatic representation of a Geiger-Müller assay system. The Ratemeter and Printer units are dispensable. (*Reproduced by kind permission of Ekco Electronics Ltd., Southend-on-Sea, England.*)

although 0·1% variation for ± 10% mains variation suffices for most G.M. counting systems.

(b) *The pre-amplifier.* Most G.M. tubes give a pulse of at least 0·1 V and most scalers have a built-in amplifier with a gain of × 50 to raise the signal to a level capable of triggering the scaling circuit. For most satisfactory operation of the G.M. tube, it is recommended that a pre-amplifier with maximum gain of × 50 to be fitted close to the G.M. tube, thereby minimizing the capacitance across the tube through reduction in cable length.

(c) *The quenching probe unit.* This is complementary to the pre-amplifier and provides facilities for pre-amplification and for pulse sign reversal. The unit also provides a paralysis time device which lowers the anode line voltage by about 200 V for a set interval following the detection of an incident β^- particle, thereby fixing the duration during which the counter is insensitive to the arrival of a subsequent β^- particle. It is convenient to set the paralysis time (between 200–500 μsec) in excess of the resolving time of the G.M. tube thereby obviating the necessity of re-determining the dead time (τ) when a replacement G.M. tube is fitted. The use of the Quench unit has the added advantage of improving the plateau characteristics of the G.M. tube. When a G.M. tube is used in the proportional region a high gain linear amplifier capable of an amplification factor of up to 50,000 (e.g. Nuclear Chicago Logic 8150) is required in order to deal with the millivolt pulse obtained in this region. The dead time of the proportional counter is in the region of 2–20 μsec. Count rates of 10^5/min can be easily handled and no pulse quenching facilities are required.

(d) *The discriminator.* Most commercial scalers have a discriminator circuit following the G.M. input amplifier circuit (or after the external pre-amplifier for direct input). The discriminator enables the counting of pulses having an amplitude in excess of a pre-set value. The acceptance level is usually continuously variable between 5 and 50 V and is normally set to 5 V for G.M. counting. Discriminator circuits find their greatest value in proportional counting where the pulse height is directly related to the energy of the β^- particle initiating the primary detector events. By suitable adjustment of the discriminator threshold it is possible to reject most of the pulses from sources other than the radionuclide under assay. It is thus possible to reduce greatly the background count relative to the sample counts and so increase the accuracy of the analysis. It is also possible, where the β spectra of two isotopes are substantially non-overlapping, to screen off the pulses arising from disintegration events in one of the radionuclides when present along with the other. Discrimination between energies may also be achieved, as in the Beckman Widebeta II, by operation on different voltage plateaux and with absorbers inserted between sample and detector to limit the β energy cut-off. The full potentialities of proportional counting are realized in the simultaneous counting of two or more isotopes when the discriminator is replaced by a multi-channel pulse height analyser which passes pulses to the scaling circuits only when the pulse amplitudes fall between variable pre-set lower and upper limits. The rationale of this technique is essentially that of simultaneous assay using a multi-channel scintillation counter. This is discussed in detail in a succeeding chapter by Hash and will not be dealt with more fully here.

(e) *Anti-coincidence circuitry*. For a sample count of given magnitude the accuracy of the net count after background subtraction is greater the smaller is the background. It is useful particularly when samples of very low activity are being assayed to be able to reduce the contribution of natural background radiation to insignificant proportions. This may be achieved by the use of an anti-coincidence circuit in conjunction with one or more guard detectors through which a cosmic particle has to pass before entering the sample detector. The guard detectors are themselves effectively screened from the sample. The anti-coincidence circuit is so designed that no response to an ionizing event in the sample detector occurs if a pulse be simultaneously recorded by the guard detector(s). Typical background counting rates achieved in this manner are in the range 0·5 cpm (Beckman Lowbeta/Widebeta II with a $1\frac{1}{4}$ in. diam. detector) to 2 cpm (Nuclear Chicago Model C115 with a $1\frac{1}{8}$ in. detector).

(f) *The scaler*. The scaler is the terminal circuit into which the pulses originating in the detector tube are fed. Most scalers operate with pulses in the range 5–50 V and classically the pulses may be used to drive a simple electromechanical register. The high resolution time of such devices (up to 120 msec) allows maximum count rates only of the order of 500 pulses per min. or 25 cpm for a count loss not exceeding 5% and it has been common practice to precede any mechanical register with an electronic counting stage. The basis of such a device is a "scale-of-two" unit (Wyn-Williams, 1932) consisting of a pair of triodes each having its anode connected to the grid of the other. These connections take place through a resistor and capacitor arranged in parallel. The system is symmetrical and has two stable states each with one valve conducting and the other not. Negative-going pulses fed for example from a double diode to the two anodes will go to the more positive anode thus initiating a train of events resulting in transition from one stable state to the other. A subsequent pulse again inverts the conducting states. If the anode output of one triode is used to feed a similar scale-or-two unit it can readily be seen that n linked scales-of-two will provide a system producing an output pulse for every 2^n input pulses. Simple modification enables the system to work on a scale-of-ten basis.

Modern instruments make great use of the cold cathode "dekatron valve" (e.g. Ericsson GC10B) which consists of a central anode with 10 cathodes radially equispaced around it. Cathodes 1–9 are taken to a common base and cathode 0 to a separate outlet. Each cathode is flanked by a guide 1 and a guide 2 electrode, both sets being taken to a common base and normally biased 25 V above the cathode. The discharge glow tests upon the most negative electrode and for each ingoing pulse the glow is transferred from cathode to cathode by time-dependent voltage variations in the intervening guides. The dekatron is thus a self-indicating tube. Early dekatrons had a relatively long resolving time (150–200 μsec) and were normally not used in the first two decades which were counted by hard valve circuits, the data presentation often being by tubes (e.g. Ericsson GR10A) designed to simulate the dekatron. Fast dekatrons (resolving time 50 μsec or better) are now available. Hard valve circuitry is, in general, now obsolescent and equivalent transistorized and integrated circuits are available (e.g. Ekco scaler-timer M5024).

(g) *The timing unit.* It is common practice to include a timing unit in the counting assembly and commercial units may typically have facilities for counting to either a pre-set time or a pre-set count. A low sample activity reject may be incorporated as may facilities for counting to a pre-set error and for automatic background subtraction.

(h) *The ratemeter.* For certain purposes a ratemeter may replace the scaler. A ratemeter gives moment to moment estimates of the sample counting rate. In this intrument the G.M. input pulses are transformed to square wave pulses of constant amplitude which are fed to a condenser (capacitance C) which discharges through a resistance (R) connected in parallel. If x pulses/sec are fed to the condenser each pulse putting a charge q on the condenser the voltage across the condenser is given by the expression:

$$V = V_{\infty}[1 - \exp(-t/RC)]$$

where V_{∞} is the steady stage voltage (equal to xqR). It may readily be seen from this relationship that the time (t) taken effectively to reach V_{∞} depends on the magnitude of RC (the time constant) and that it takes 2·3 and 4·6 time constants to reach 90% and 99% of V_{∞}, respectively. There is no special advantage in the use of a ratemeter for quantitative studies. If a low value of RC is employed the randomness of the decay phenomenon precludes ready accurate estimates of the count rate being made: if large values of RC are employed the random fluctuations are in effect smoothed out, but V_{∞} (and hence the estimate of x) is approached slowly. Further, the accuracy of a ratemeter reading is dependent upon the scale calibration, whereas in a scaler the valve circuits are used merely as on-off switches.

The ratemeter, in conjunction with a chart recorder, is, however, of great value in continuous monitoring of, for example, the activity of the effluent from a chromatographic column. Ratemeters are also of value for personnel and laboratory monitoring.

C. Statistical considerations

It is well-known that no physical measurement can be made without error and in reporting a quantitative measure it is normally incumbent upon the experimenter to offer an estimate of the probability of the reported figure being within stated limits of the correct figure. This consideration is particularly important in radiochemical assays in which, owing to the random nature of the nuclear phenomena, there is no uniquely "correct" assay figure but only an "ideal mean" around which an infinite number of estimates would group.

In any series of measurements of a variable x, the frequency of occurrence of the mean and of the infinite other possible values will be describable by a probability function. A probability distribution function, F_x, and a probability density function, $f(x)$, can be defined such that the probability of finding a value within the limits x and $x + dx$ will be given by the expression:

$$dF_x = f(x).dx$$

A function $f(x)$ will be a probability density function provided:

$$f(x) \geqslant 0$$

$$\int_{-\infty}^{+\infty} f(x).dx = 1 \tag{1}$$

The normal theory of errors is based on the *Normal Distribution* which applies to measures of a continuous variable, x, falling around a mean value m. For this distribution:

$$dF_x = [1/\sigma(2\pi)^{0 \cdot 5}] \exp - (\overline{x-m}^2/2\sigma^2).dx$$

where σ = the standard deviation, a quantity defined (see below) to give information about the breadth of scatter of observations about a population mean. The distribution has two independent parameters, m and σ, and is symmetrical about the mean. Figs. 9 and 10 show for this distribution dF_x/dx and the integral

$$\int_{-\infty}^{x} f(x).dx$$

as functions of x respectively. This definite integral gives the area under the probability density curve between the limits $-\infty$ and x and it follows that

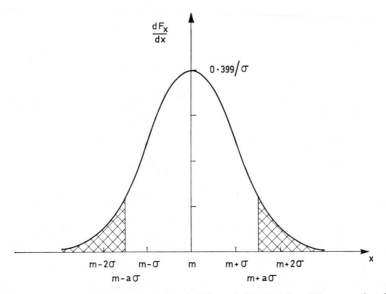

FIG. 9. Probability density curve for the Normal distribution. The cross-hatched area gives the probability in a single trial of finding a value of x lying outwith the limits $m \pm a\sigma$.

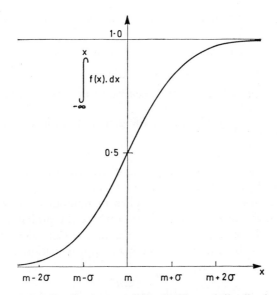

FIG. 10. Probability distribution curve for the Normal distribution. The ordinate gives the area under the probability density curve between the limits $-\infty$ and x.

the proportion of measures lying outwith the limits $m \pm a\sigma$ would be given by the expression:

$$2 \int_{-\infty}^{(m-a\sigma)} (1/\sigma(2\pi)^{0\cdot5}) . \exp - (\overline{x-m}^2/2\sigma^2) . dx$$

The following table gives some useful values of areas (A) under the probability density function outwith the limits $m \pm a\sigma$

a	0·5	0·6745	1·0	1·96	2·0	3·0
A	0·6171	0·5000	0·3173	0·0500	0·0455	0·00272

It may be seen that *ca.* 32% of the area under the probability density function falls outwith the limits $m \pm \sigma$. An equivalent statement is that there is a 68% chance in one trial of finding a value of x within the limits $m \pm \sigma$. Similarly there is a 95% chance of finding a value lying within the limits $m \pm 1\cdot96\sigma$ in a single trial.

In radioactive assays, the variable x is not continuously variable, being restricted to integer values only. A fundamental distribution for a non-continuously variable, x, is the *Binomial Distribution* for which the following relationships obtain:

$$(p+q)^n = \sum_{x=0}^{n=x} P_x = 1$$

where p = the constant probability of the occurrence of an event in a single trial.

$q = 1-p$ = the probability of the non-occurrence of the event.

n = the number of independent trials.

P_x = the probability of the occurrence of x events in n such trials.

$= \dfrac{n!}{x!(n-x)!} . p^x(1-p)^{n-x}$, the general term in the binomial expansion.

It should be noted that the Binomial distribution has two independent parameters p and n and applies where $0 \leqslant x \leqslant n$.

The *Poisson Distribution* which applies to random nuclear events is a limiting case of the Binomial distribution where the probability p is small and constant and n is large ($m = pn$). Taking the general Binomial distribution term and substituting the following approximations:

$$\frac{n!}{(n-x)!} \simeq n^x$$

$$(1-p)^{n-x} \simeq e^{-p(n-x)} \simeq e^{-pn}$$

we get

$$P_x = \frac{n^x \cdot p^x}{x!} \, e^{-pn} = \frac{m^x}{x!} \, e^{-m}$$

This is the Poisson distribution. It should be noted that this distribution is assymetric about m and has only one parameter, m. By definition the standard deviation for the Poisson distribution is given by

$$\sigma^2 = \sum_{0}^{+\infty} (x-m)^2 P_{x'}$$

hence,

$$\sigma^2 = \sum_{0}^{+\infty} (x-m)^2 m^x \, e^{-m}/x! = m$$

i.e. $\sigma = m^{0 \cdot 5}$

For values of $m \geqslant 10$ the Poisson and Normal distributions are virtually identical for all practical purposes provided that the variable σ in the Normal distribution is assigned the value $m^{0 \cdot 5}$. It is common practice, therefore, to apply the data implicit in Fig. 9 to radioactive assay measurements.

In practice m is, of course, not known and the best estimate of m is $\bar{x}$, the numerical average of n observations $x_1, x_2 \ldots x_n$. The standard deviation, σ, implicitly defined as

$$\sigma^2 = \frac{1}{n} \sum_{i=1}^{i=n} (x_i - m)^2$$

becomes

$$\sigma^2 \simeq \frac{1}{n-1} \sum_{i=1}^{i=n} (x_i - \bar{x})^2$$

When only one observation, x_1, is made $m \simeq x_1$ and σ, although indeterminate, is assigned the value $x_1^{0 \cdot 5}$. In these circumstances σ has a significance reflected in the statement that there is approximately a 68% or 95% chance of the true mean falling within the limits $x_1 \pm x_1^{0 \cdot 5}$ or $x_1 \pm 1 \cdot 96$ $x_1^{0 \cdot 5}$, respectively.

The error of a count, x_1, is related to $kx_1^{0 \cdot 5}$ and various errors are defined as follows, depending on the value of k:

Error	*k*
Reliable error	0·5000
Probable error	0·6745
Standard error	1·0000
"95/100" error	1·9600

Thus an observed count of 1000 can be stated to have a "95/100" error of

$2(1000)^{0.5} \simeq 64$ counts, i.e. the true mean has a 95% chance of falling within the limits 1000 ± 64.

A proportional error can also be defined as $\pm 100 \, k x_1^{0.5} / x_1 = \pm 100 \, k / x_1^{0.5}$. It is strongly recommended that in assay work a "95/100" proportional error not greater than $\pm 5\%$ should be aimed at. It may be seen from Table I that at least 1600 counts have to be registered in order to satisfy this recommendation.

TABLE I

"95/100" Proportional error as a function of count magnitude (x_1)

x_1	$x_1^{0.5}$	"95/100" Proportional error
100	10	20%
1000	32	6·4%
1600	40	5·0%
10,000	100	2·0%

It rarely happens in practice that one is interested in the magnitude of a single count: rather is one interested in the net count after subtraction of the background count or in the resultant of some arithmetical combination of counts so corrected. As sample and background counts have their own errors it becomes important to consider the ways in which errors are propagated. Where A and B are observed counts and a and b are errors of the type $kA^{0.5}$ and $kB^{0.5}$, respectively, then the corresponding errors for sums, differences, products and quotients are given as follows:

$$(A \pm a) \pm (B \pm b) = (A \pm B) \pm (a^2 + b^2)^{0.5}$$

$$(A \pm a)(B \pm b) = AB \pm AB\left(\frac{a^2}{A^2} + \frac{b^2}{B^2}\right)^{0.5}$$

$$(A \pm a)/(B \pm b) = A/B \pm A/B\left(\frac{a^2}{A^2} + \frac{b^2}{B^2}\right)^{0.5}$$

In order to stress the importance of these considerations it is instructive to consider a sample giving a count of 125 in an interval during which background was measured at 100 counts. The net count, 25, has, therefore, a "95/100" proportional error of $\pm 120\%$. It is customary in statistical analysis to reject a hypothesis falling below a 5% significance level and accordingly it follows that no evidence has been obtained that the sample is radioactive. The same sample, however, on being counted for a longer interval gave 1200 counts, the background count for the same interval being determined at 990 counts. The corresponding error for the net count of 210 is now calculated to be $\pm 44\%$. The sample can, therefore, be said to be radioactive although an accurate assessment of its activity would demand counting over a still longer interval to reduce the "95/100" proportional error to within $\pm 5\%$.

It occasionally happens that factors other than randomicity introduce variability into observed count rate measures and it is accordingly useful to be able to detect (and hence reject) unreliable data. It is a common, though non-rigorous, practice to reject figures which differ from the population mean by more than three times the numerical average of the deviations of all the data.

In the assessment of the reliability of G.M. counting data it is useful to compare values of σ as derived from $\bar{x}^{0.5}$ and from

$$\left[\frac{1}{n-1} \sum_{i=1}^{i=n} (x_i - \bar{x})^2 \right]^{0.5}$$

Vastly disparate values of σ so obtained lead to the conclusion that the data do not have the requisite degree of randomness. A more quantitative test of the acceptability of the data is based on Pearson's "chi-square test" (Pearson, 1900). Briefly, one defines a quantity, χ^2, as follows:

$$\chi^2 = \frac{\sum_{i=1}^{i=n} (x_i - \bar{x})^2}{\bar{x}}$$

By entering standard tables with a value for χ^2 and for F, the number of degrees of freedom of the system ($F = n-1$), one obtains a value of the probability, P, that a repetition of the measurements would show greater variability amongst the individual observations. It is customary to reject data for which P is greater than 0·98 or less than 0·02. It is recommended when setting up a counting assembly that sample data should be subjected to this test.

The reader is referred to Evans (1955) for a more extensive and authoritative discussion of the statistical aspects of nuclear processes.

D. Corrections to an observed count

All observed counts require to be corrected successively in one or more of the following ways:

1. Correction for dead time

All counting systems have some element of time in the counting interval during which the system is incapable of recording the second of two near coincident events. G.M. tubes are of two types, "paralysable" and "non-paralysable". In the former the arrival of the second β^- is not separately recorded but is responsible for elongating the dead time of the tube. In the latter, the second β^- is not recorded and does not influence the dead time (τ) of the tube following the arrival of the first β^-. The relationship between observed count rate (n_0) and the true count rate (n) for this "paralysable" tube is given by the expression:

$$n_0 = ne^{-n\tau}$$

from which it can be easily shown that n_0 has a maximum value of $1/e\tau$ when $n = 1/\tau$. The corresponding relationship for the "non-paralysable" tube is:

$$n = n_0/(1-n_0\tau)$$

$$\simeq n_0(1+n\tau) \text{ when } n_0\tau \ll 1$$

Self-quenched tubes are of the non-paralysable type and have τ values in the region 100–200 μsec. It may be seen from the above equation that for a count rate of 5000 cpm and a τ value of 300 μsec a correction of 2·4% is required. It is not customary to apply dead time corrections for G.M. counting rates below 2000 cpm (for τ values in the region 250–300 μsec determined by a quenching probe) as the errors from this source are small and much the least of the errors in the radiochemical assay. It is recommended that dead time corrections in excess of 10% should be avoided by dilution of the sample and re-counting. In proportional counting where τ values of the order of 5 μsec obtain count rates of up to 10^6 cpm can be handled without exceeding a 10% dead time correction.

In the absence of knowledge of the τ value for any counting assembly it is possible to determine the correction empirically by counting a very active sample and a series of dilutions prepared therefrom. A plot of count rate versus amount counted will be curvilinear and a tangent to the curve at the origin gives the theoretical relationship between amount plated and counting rate and can be used in the correction of high observed count rates. The method is useful but erroneously assumes that the lower count rates are associated with no dead time correction. The single paired-source method is preferable and will be found adequate for most purposes. In this method two sources A and B are counted separately and together. For end-window counting the sources are mounted on half planchets and the counting performed in the order: sample A (plus blank half planchet), sample A plus sample B, sample B (plus blank half planchet). This sequence ensures that no problems arise due to variable geometry in the successive counting operations. For liquid counters an equivalent procedure can be employed by counting a sample and an accurate 1 : 2 dilution. If n_a is the observed count rate for sample A and so on and b is the background count rate we have:

$$n_a[1-n_a\tau]^{-1}+n_b[1-n_b\tau]^{-1}-b = n_{(a+b)}[1-n_{(a+b)}\tau]^{-1}$$

from which τ can be obtained. When $n\tau \ll 1$ the above expression can be simplified and re-arranged to give:

$$\tau = \frac{n_a+n_b-n_{(a+b)}-b}{n^2_{(a+b)}-n^2_a-n^2_b}$$

It should be noted that the accuracy of τ so determined depends critically upon the accuracy of the determination of the individual terms of the expression. The reader is referred to the section on the propagation of errors and invited to consider the high accuracy with which the terms have to be determined so that, for example, the relatively small resultant from the numerator summation has itself a small error.

2. *Correction for variability of counter response*

It is recommended especially when using gas-flow counters that each batch of samples counted should include a reference standard to account for the daily variations in the counter response due to changes in gas composition and pressure and tube voltage.

3. *Correction for background*

In any single determination the observed count is compounded of the counts due to ionizing radiation originating from the sample and from counts arising from detector events having their origin in the background cosmic radiation and in the components of the castle in which the sample and detector are housed. A blank planchet should therefore be counted.

4. *Correction for decay*

It has been found that the decay of radionuclides is an exponential process, the rate of decay being at any instant proportional to the number of unstable nuclei present, i.e.

$$\frac{dN}{dt} = -kN$$

from which it simply follows that

$$N_t = N_0 \exp(-kt)$$

and

$$\left(\frac{dN}{dt}\right)_t = \left(\frac{dN}{dt}\right)_0 \exp(-kt)$$

where N_t and N_0 are the number of unstable nuclei present at times t and zero, respectively, and where

$$\left(\frac{dN}{dt}\right)_t \text{ and } \left(\frac{dN}{dt}\right)_0$$

are the corresponding instantaneous rates of decay. The constant k is the decay constant and is related to the half-life $(t_{\frac{1}{2}})$ of the isotope as follows:

$$\log_e 2 = k\, t_{\frac{1}{2}}$$

$$\text{i.e. } k = 0 \cdot 693/t_{\frac{1}{2}}$$

For radio-isotopes of short half-life it is essential to correct the observed count back to zero or some other standard time. The corrections may be effected by calculation or by a graphical method. In the graphical method count rate as a percentage of zero time count rate is plotted against time using semi-logarithmic paper. A straight line is drawn through points of co-ordinates $(0, 100)$ and $(t_{\frac{1}{2}}, 50)$. One can then read off for any time t the percentage of original radio-isotope present and hence make the appropriate correction to the observed count. It should be noted that, in practice, determinations of the "instantaneous" values of $(dN/dt)_t$ are made on the assumption that no decay occurs during the interval over which the counts are accumulated. This will hold effectively only when the counting interval is less than 3% of the half-life of the isotope.

5. *Correction for self-absorption*

When increasing amounts of a radioactive sample are plated and counted under conditions of constant geometry it is found that there is a fall away from linearity in the relationship between count rate (I) and sample thickness (h). The non-linearity of the curve is due to the self-absorption by the sample of β^- particles arising within it. The curve approaches asymptotically a maximum count rate (I_∞) and the thickness of sample at which $0 \cdot 95\, I_\infty$ is reached is a function of the E_{max} of the isotope. The effective plateau region—the region of "infinite thickness"—represents a situation where the β^-'s arising from that portion of the sample most remote from the detector are completely absorbed by the specimen and succeeding additions cut off as many β^-'s as they contribute. It follows rigorously that corrections for self-absorption are required when comparing activities of samples of differing thickness. This will be particularly so for isotopes of low E_{max} where $0 \cdot 95\, I_\infty$ is reached at a relatively low thickness e.g. in the case of $Ba^{14}CO_3$ where $0 \cdot 95\, I_\infty$ is reached at *ca.* 20 mg/cm². The corresponding figures for $Ba^{35}SO_4$ and tritiated organic compounds are *ca.* 25 mg/cm² and $0 \cdot 7$ mg/cm², respectively. A typical saturation curve is shown in Fig. 11. It should be emphasized that published data are not generally reproducible as the shape of the curve is affected by the nature of the detector, by backscattering from the mount, and by geometrical and other factors. Accordingly specimen data e.g. for $Ba^{14}CO_3$ (Yankwich et al., 1946; Calvin et al., 1949), for $Ba^{35}SO_4$ (Hendricks et al., 1943) and for $[^{35}S]$ benzidine sulphate (Henriques et al., 1946), are not reproduced here. The saturation curve in Fig. 11 may be divided into three regions,

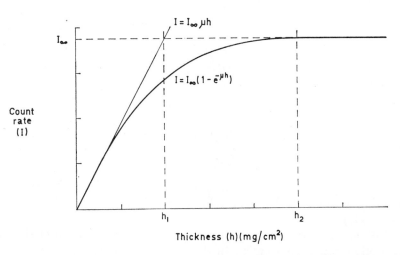

FIG. 11. An ideal activity saturation curve ($I = I\infty[1 - \exp(-\mu h)]$) together with the tangent ($I = I\infty\mu h$) at $h = 0$. The tangent gives the count at thickness h corrected for self-absorption lossess.

(i) a region of "infinite thinness" corresponding to that range of low thicknesses over which the curve is effectively linear. For $[^{14}C]$-labelled compounds this situation obtains below ca. 100 $\mu g/cm^2$, (ii) a region of "infinite thickness", i.e. the region where the curve effectively plateaus and (iii) the region intermediate between (i) and (ii).

Corrections for self-absorption need not, by definition, be made when working in the region of "infinite thinness". The main problem when working in this region arises from poor sample preparation resulting in a distribution of material on a planchet sufficiently non-uniform to give rise to significant localized self-absorption. It is therefore imperative when setting up an assay procedure, if not routinely thereafter, to check the linearity of the dependence of count rate upon amount counted.

In the region intermediate between "infinite thinness" and "infinite thickness" one of several approaches to self-absorption correction may be made. It is possible to attempt to plate a constant amount in a standard procedure thereby obviating the requirement to correct for the constant self-absorption losses. This is not, however, a recommended procedure due to the great difficulty of achieving the required reproducibility. It may, however, be possible to correct by calculation. Assuming that absorption of the β^- particles in the sample is exponential it can readily be shown that the count rate (I) at any thickness (h) is related to the count at "infinite thickness" (I_∞) in the following way:

$$I = I_\infty [1 - \exp(-\mu h)]$$

where μ is a constant (the absorption coefficient), the units of which depend upon the units in which h is expressed. It follows that the equation of the tangent at $h = 0$ is

$$I = I_\infty \mu h$$

and that the corrected count rate (I_c) is obtained from the relationship

$$I_c = I\mu h / 1 - \exp(-\mu h).$$

For ^{14}C β^- particle absorption in $BaCO_3$ μ has been found for one G.M. counting assembly to have the value 0.285 ± 0.008 cm^2, mg^{-1} (Yankwich et al., 1947).

It often happens however that the value of μ is not known or that the absorption is not exponential. In these situations the saturation curve is plotted out and the tangent at $h = 0$ drawn thereby implicitly establishing correction factors. It may be found convenient to draw a self-absorption curve (Fig. 12) relating count rate as a fraction of that at zero thickness to sample thickness. The accuracy of this method depends upon the accuracy of delineation of the saturation curve at low thicknesses, which in turn depends upon the accuracy of quantitation of the amounts being counted. It must be stressed that the self-absorption curves for typical organic compounds containing elements of low atomic number (e.g. H, O, N, S) are not within acceptable error different one from another but that they differ appreciably from that of $Ba^{14}CO_3$ particularly above 5 mg/cm^2 due due to the influence of the heavy metal on the back-scattering properties of the samples.

A fourth approach is to use the upper portion of the saturation curve, to limit variability of sample thickness and to correct to the count rate at a standard thickness (usually about the mean of the range of thicknesses used) or to the count rate at "infinite thickness".

It may be seen from Fig. 11 that the count rate at "infinite thickness" is the count rate corrected to zero thickness for a sample of thickness h_1.

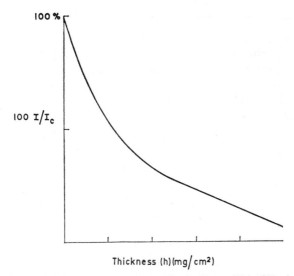

FIG. 12. Self-absorption correction curve. The ordinate (100 I/I_c) gives the count at thickness h as a percentage of the count at zero thickness.

The specific activity of a sample counted at "infinite thickness" is therefore given by I_∞ divided by the constant molar amount corresponding to the thickness h_1. It follows for constant geometry of counting that I_∞ being proportional to the specific activity can be used effectively as a specific activity. Equally it also follows that this method is only applicable when the radionuclide is present in related samples in the same chemical form. For ^{14}C and ^{35}S the preferred forms are $BaCO_3$ and $BaSO_4$, respectively. Work at "infinite thickness" has the considerable advantage of relative ease of sample preparation. Further, the error of the effective specific activity, I_∞, is not compounded of the errors of the observed count rate and of the assay of the amount counted as it is for example in the region of "infinite thinness'. The method suffers however from the obvious disadvantage of requiring relatively large amounts of material, although in certain circumstances the sample can be diluted with inactive carrier prior to counting.

6. Corrections for backscatter and geometry

It rarely if ever happens in radio-biochemical work that estimates of the absolute disintegration rates are required and accordingly corrections for backscatter and geometry are not made. It is obvious however that backscatter and geometrical factors must be held constant. The reader is referred to Calvin et al. (1949) for a discussion of methods of correcting for backscatter and for geometry. It is worth noting in this context that standard reference sources are available from the U.K.A.E.A., The Radiochemical Centre, Amersham. There are two types, (a) sources calibrated by methods for absolute ($4\pi\beta$) determination of activity and (b) reference solutions calibrated by comparison with absolutely standardized solutions. Poly-(^{14}C-methyl)-methacrylate prepared as discs or sheets is available for use either as a solid reference source or as material for combustion to $^{14}CO_2$ of reproducible specific activity. Poly-(^{3}H-methyl)-methacrylate is also available.

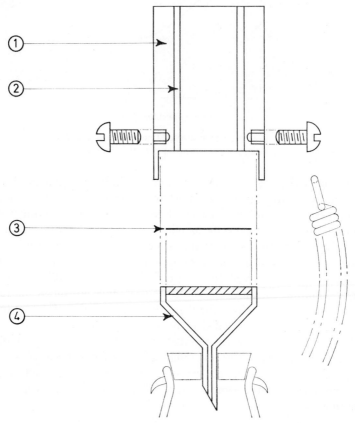

FIG. 13. Cross-sectional diagram of an assembly for solid sample (Ba^{14}CO$_3$) plating.

Key No.	Description
1.	Cylindrical brass castle (outer diameter 2·5 cm).
2.	Stainless steel lining with highly polished inner surface (inner diameter 1·3 cm, height 3·5 cm).
3.	Filter paper disc (2·0 cm diameter).
4.	Filter stick with sintered glass disc (outer diameter 2·2 cm).

IV. PREPARATION AND MOUNTING OF SOLID SAMPLES

β^--Emitting isotopes when assayed using a gas-ionization detector are most commonly counted as solid samples spread on the surface of a metal planchet. The accuracy of the entire assay operation particularly in the case of low energy β^- particles is critically dependent upon the quality of the plating technique. It is true to say that there is as much art as science in solid sample preparation and accordingly only some general observation will be made about procedures. In practice each worker has to establish and validate his own plating techniques.

The essence of solid sample preparation is to ensure high reproducibility of geometrical, self-absorption and backscatter factors. Dry powders may be spread mechanically with a spatula into a cup-shaped planchet. This method yields good results only with infinitely thick samples and is greatly improved if a plunger is employed to compress the material (Poják, 1950). The avoidance of an uneven surface prevents irreproducibility of counts arising from variations in backscatter. Alternatively, the sample may be suspended in a suitable solvent and filtered through a paper or Millipore filter mounted on a porous surface. A variety of filtration devices have been described (Popják, 1950; Calvin et al., 1949; *Nuclear Chicago Technical Bulletin*, No. 7, 1964; see also Mulligan Volume 1 this Series). Fig. 13 shows one such assembly used in the author's laboratory for $Ba^{14}CO_3$ counting. The filter paper is mounted on a filter stick the surface of which has been ground smooth on a glass plate with carborundum powder. The stick sits neatly into the base of a brass castle fitted with a highly polished stainless steel lining. The $BaCO_3$ suspension in water is filtered by suction and washed successively with water, ethanol or acetone and ether. The sample is transferred to a brass planchet (Fig. 14), fitted with a collar to prevent curling and dried slowly where necessary under an infrared lamp. The tendency of infinitely thick samples to crack during drying can be largely eliminated by building up the disc by successive filtration operations rather than by the collection of the entire $BaCO_3$ sample in one operation. The counts obtained on duplicate infinitely thick samples so prepared agree within 2–3%. $BaCO_3$ in suspension may also be plated satisfactorily by evaporation at 40–60° in shallow metal dishes. The slurry is continually stirred by a fine glass rod. Good reproducibility ($\pm 2\%$) is achieved provided more than 3 mg $BaCO_3$ per cm^2 is plated. The method has the advantage of constancy of support tare weight in contrast to the weight loss suffered by paper discs in filtration and drying operations. Yankwich et al. (1946) have described a similar method in which the sample is evaporated on a metal disc placed in the base of a cup and held in position by a concentric sleeve which defines the area over which material is deposited. Thin

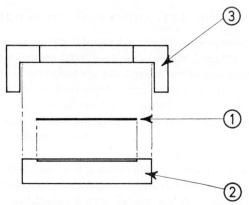

FIG. 14. Assembly for solid samples counting.

Key No.	Description
1.	Filter paper disc supporting labelled material ($Ba^{14}CO_3$).
2.	Base plate (diameter 2·5 cm) recessed concentrically to hold filter paper disc (2·0 cm diameter).
3.	Brass retaining ring (outer diameter 3·1 cm, inner diameter 1·8 cm).

plates are best prepared from fine particles obtained, if necessary, by grinding the sample in a mortar under a suitable solvent. Ethanol (95%) has been found to be an excellent medium in which to manipulate $BaCO_3$. Methanol must be avoided because of the toxicity problem. The grinding of dry powders should preferably be avoided owing to the potential radiation hazards following aerial dispersal of fine insoluble particles.

The counting of ^{14}C samples prepared by filtration and evaporation of solid sample suspensions is most satisfactory in the region of infinite thickness. In the region of infinite thinness the preferred method is by evaporation of solvent from a solution of the labelled substance. Evaporation should not be carried out in dish-shaped planchets owing to capillarity effects which result in a concentration of the solute at the junction of the base and wall. The main problem is to ensure a uniform disposal over a reproducible area. In the case of aqueous samples this can be effectively achieved provided that the surface of the planchet is suitably de-greased e.g. by scrubbing with a detergent powder followed by washing (a) with water, (b) with ethanol and drying in air or under a lamp. The volume plated must be limited so that no overspill on to the shoulders or walls of the planchet occurs. The evaporation is most conveniently conducted under an infrared lamp placed at a sufficient distance to ensure slow drying without "spattering". It is best to use a solvent in which the solute is very soluble. Successive evaporations on to the same planchet are not advisable. For ^{14}C the technique is most suitable at levels less than 0.1 mg/cm^2. Bacterial suspensions may be treated in an analogous manner and acceptable linearity for most purposes obtains up to this thickness. A careful examination of an infinitely thin ^{14}C plate prepared by solvent evaporation reveals that the material is distributed in a series of more or less concentric rings. It is important, therefore, to check continually that significant self-absorption through adventitious local concentration is either absent or within acceptable limits.

Reproducibility of both sample area and of self-absorption factors may be achieved conveniently by dispensing the sample on to the centre of a dished planchet and covering with a standard lens paper (or other absorbing material) of diameter less than the base of the planchet. The addition of a few drops of either ethanol or acetone aids in the wetting process. Little difficulty is usually encountered in drying such a sample but, where necessary, some organic material or collodion adhesive may be added. This method works well for hard β^- particles, but with soft β^-'s there is obviously a significant loss of counting efficiency.

The choice of planchet material is governed by cost and stability under the conditions of plating. Aluminium planchets are generally used owing to their cheapness. When solutions of strong volatile acids (e.g. HCl) are being evaporated nickel-plated planchets are preferred. If trichloroacetic acid has been used for sample preparation it should be removed before plating by ether extraction. The planchet diameter should be less than the G.M. end-window diameter and in any one series of experiments the type of planchet used should not be varied in order to standardize the back-scatter factor.

The reader is referred to Calvin *et al.* (1949) for a fuller discussion of sample preparation and for details of the techniques of sample combustion to $^{14}CO_2$. Combustion techniques are also discussed elsewhere in this Volume (J. H. Hash, p. 132).

V. ANALYTICAL USES OF RADIO-ISOTOPES

This Chapter is concerned with the basic methodology of isotope assay and not with applications of isotopes in microbiological and biochemical work which are, in general, considered elsewhere in this work. Two applications not covered, however, are Isotope Dilution Analysis and Isotope Competition Methods.

A. Isotope dilution analysis

Standard analytical procedures depend upon the quantitative isolation of a compound or upon the measurement of some chemical or physicochemical attribute not common to other molecular species present. When working with complex mixtures or when working on a small scale these methods, however, break down. In such instances the isotope dilution technique is the preferred analytical approach. Isotope dilution analysis in general offers high accuracy and a sensitivity not approached by other methods.

The basic dilution method is simple and consists of the addition to the unknown amount (x mols) of compound to be assayed of a known amount of labelled compound (y mols) of known specific activity (S_1 counts/min/mol). After thorough admixture a pure specimen is isolated without regard to yield and the specific activity (S_2 counts/min/mol) determined. The unknown amount (x mols) originally present is then given simply by the expression:

$$S_2(x+y) = S_1 y$$

i.e. $$x = y(1 - S_1/S_2)$$

The great advantage of the method is that the determination of S_2 does not depend upon quantitative isolation of the compound and hence advantage may be taken of rapid though wasteful methods of purification. It is sufficient that a specimen be isolated which is of adequate radiochemical purity and of sufficient chemical purity to enable a conventional assay (e.g. titrimetric, spectrophotometric) to be performed as part of the determination of S_2. Chromatographic techniques are of great value in the isolation procedures. The success of the method depends upon the chemical and radiochemical purity of the added compound. This important factor may be readily checked by a reverse dilution analysis in which a relatively large amount of pure compound is added to the labelled material and the specific activity (a counts/min/mol) determined. The compound is then exhaustively purified, again without regard to yield, and the specific activity (b counts/min/mol) redetermined. The percentage radiochemical purity of the product is then given by the expression (b/a) 100.

Derivative dilution analysis is a development of the basic technique and may be used when high sensitivity is required or when the isolation procedures result in microgram quantities thereby minimizing analytical accuracy in the determination of S_2. The derivative technique basically involves a quantitative reaction of known stoicheiometry with a labelled reagent of known specific activity followed by the isolation of the derivative in a pure state for total count determination. As stated the method depends upon the quantitative character of the interaction between compound and reagent and also, more critically, upon the quantitative separation of the compound from excess labelled reagent and from other compounds with which the reagent may also react. It is very difficult in general to obtain

the requisite purity of the isolated compound in association with a quantitative recovery and one of the following two procedures may be employed
to surmount this problem. In the first modification, a very large excess of
cold derivative is added to the solution after the initial quantitative interaction of sample and labelled reagent. A pure specimen is isolated again
without regard to yield for the determination of total counts which may be
then corrected for losses in isolation by multiplying by the ratio of added
carrier to isolated compound. This technique has been used successfully
by Keston *et al.* (1946) in the analysis of amino acids in protein hydroly-
sates using [^{131}I]p-iodobenzenesulphonyl chloride as labelled reagent. The
second, and the more powerful, modification employs a second differently
labelled derivative as a means of estimating purification losses. Thus in the
assay of glycine in a protein (Keston *et al.*, 1950) the protein hydrolysate
may be treated with [^{131}I]p-iodobenzenesulphonyl chloride of known specific activity to yield a mixture of labelled pipsylamino acids. The addition
to the reaction mixture of a known amount of [^{35}S]p-iodobenzenesulphonyl
glycine of known specific activity enables losses in purification to be estimated through the observation of the loss of total ^{35}S counts. The success
of the method depends upon using two isotopes with widely differing
β spectra to optimize the ease of analysis of the two isotopes simultaneously
present in the one specimen. Such a radiochemical assay may be performed
most elegantly using proportional or liquid scintillation counting systems.
In the above example differential counting was effectively achieved by
employing a thin aluminium shield (2–3 mils thick) to block [^{39}S]β^-
particles from access to an end-window G.M. counter. In the case of mixed
^{3}H and ^{14}C samples liquid scintillation counting is the method of choice.

The power of the derivative dilution technique is indicated in its application by Riondel *et al.* (1963) to the assay of plasma testosterone. [^{35}S]-
Thiosemicarbazide is here used as the labelled reagent and [^{3}H]testosterone
as isolation loss indicator. The purification of the testosterone semicarba-
zone involves conversion to an acetylated derivative and five chromatographic procedures. The analysis has an error of only 6% at the level of
0·07 μg testosterone/100 ml plasma.

B. Isotope competition methods

Isotope competition methods may be used to follow the pathways of
metabolism in a growing cell and to evaluate the quantitative significance
of these pathways in the metabolic economy of the cell. The method stems
from the observations of Roberts and Roberts (1950) that bacterial cells
growing upon phosphorylated carbohydrates incorporated little ^{32}P from
the inorganic phosphate of the medium. The method was extended to
investigations of the competition between ^{35}SO$_4^{2-}$ and unlabelled cysteine,

homocysteine or methionine for the supply of sulphur for amino acid bio-syntheses. The results of these studies clearly showed (Cowie *et al.*, 1950; Cowie *et al.*, 1951; Bolton *et al.*, 1952) that the sulphur of exogenous homo-cysteine and methionine was used by *Escherichia coli* in the biosynthesis of methionine but not of cysteine, whereas the sulphur of cysteine could be used for all S-amino acid biosyntheses. Extension of the method to the study of pathways of carbon metabolism rapidly followed (Abelson *et al.*, 1953) and are summarized by Roberts *et al.* (1955).

The essence of the isotope competition method is to grow the bacterial cell in a simple defined medium in the presence of a labelled substrate (e.g. [U-^{14}C]glucose, $^{14}CO_2$, [U-^{14}C]acetate, etc.,) which does not affect the metabolic propensities of the system in a significant manner and to add to one of a pair of such cultures an unlabelled compound A. A com-parison is then made of the activity of cell components in such systems. In this way dilution of incorporation into cell component B when cells are grown in the presence of unlabelled supplement A may be interpreted as indicating that compound A (or a closely related metabolic derivative thereof) lies on the pathway of biosynthesis of component B. Table II (Roberts *et al.*, 1955) shows some results relating to pathways of amino acid biosynthesis in *E. coli* obtained by competition experiments involving $^{14}CO_2$ and added unlabelled amino acid supplements. It may be clearly seen from these results that there is strong presumptive evidence for the operation of the following pathways in *E. coli*:

$$\text{aspartic acid} \rightarrow \text{homoserine} \begin{array}{l} \nearrow \text{threonine} \rightarrow \text{isoleucine} \\ \searrow \text{homocysteine} \rightarrow \text{methionine} \end{array}$$

$$\text{glutamic acid} \begin{array}{l} \nearrow \text{proline} \\ \searrow \text{ornithine} \rightarrow \text{citrulline} \rightarrow \text{arginine} \end{array}$$

The technique as described is relatively insensitive to minor contributions from the unlabelled competitor, the more so if non-rigorous analytical methods (e.g. counting of ^{14}C-labelled materials on chromatograms using a G.M. end-window counter) are used. It is recommended that for careful work materials be isolated in a pure state and counted under optimum conditions. In the case of the amino acids above, for example, this would involve conversion to the 2,4-dinitrophenyl (DNP) derivatives followed by purification by two-dimensional paper or column chromato-graphic procedures. In this way, specific activities may be determined with high accuracy, counting having been effected at infinite thinness and chem-ical assays performed spectrophotometrically using the DNP chromophore.

A more sensitive method of detecting minor contributions involves

TABLE II

Synthesis of ^{14}C-labelled amino acids by *E. coli* in the presence of $^{14}CO_2$ and amino acid supplements to the basal medium

Supplement	Concentration (mg/ml)	% Suppression of radioactivity in amino acids						
		Arginine	Aspartic acid	Glutamic acid	Isoleucine	Methionine	Proline	Threonine
Arginine	0·2	100	0	0	0	0	0	0
Aspartic acid	2·0	20	60	60	60	60	60	60
Casein digest	2·0	100	60	90	100	100	90	90
Citrulline	0·2	100	0	0	0	0	0	0
Glutamic acid	2·0	30	60	90	60	60	90	60
Homocysteine	0·2	0	0	0	0	80	0	0
Homoserine	0·1	0	0	0	90	90	0	90
Isoleucine	0·2	0	0	0	100	0	0	0
Methionine	0·2	0	0	0	0	100	0	0
Ornithine	0·2	65	0	0	0	0	0	0
Proline	2·0	0	0	0	0	0	90	0
Threonine	0·1	0	0	0	100	0	0	90

(Reproduced from Roberts *et al.* (1955) by kind permission of the authors.)

growing the cells in the presence of unlabelled carbon source (for example glucose) and labelled supplement (for example [^{14}C]threonine).

The isotope competition method may be used successfully without any understanding of the particular mechanisms underlying the experimental observations. Without doubt feed-back inhibition and enzyme repression together with simple isotope dilution served to explain most of the phenomena. Great care has to be exercised, however, in the interpretation of results. Failure of an exogenous metabolite to influence incorporation patterns may simply reflect non-equilibrium with an internal pool due amongst other possible explanations to a permeability barrier. The presence of an exogenous pool may, through altering the intracellular level of the compound, interfere with the normal homeostatic mechanisms of the cell and lead to the induction of enzymes normally held in a repressed state. Thus in *E. coli*, threonine derived endogenously from glucose does not appear to give rise to glycine, whereas a threonine supplement induces the enzymic capacity to obtain glycine from the exogenous threonine (Abelson, 1945; Roberts *et al.*, 1955). Similarly the normal level of intracellular serine in glucose-grown *E. coli* appears to be capable of repressing an enzyme capable of oxidative decarboxylation of glycine to yield CO_2 (from the carboxyl group) and methylene tetrahydrofolate (from the methylene group) (Bull and Woods, 1963). Exogenous [2-^{14}C]glycine can be shown to give rise to labelling patterns consistent with the operation of the above glycine-splitting enzyme (Crosbie, 1958) and at high exogenous concentration (9000 μM) can in fact function as the sole source of the methylenetetrahydrofolate pool and of serine. (Koch, 1955). By implication, the normal pathway from phosphoglycerate to serine is cut off under these conditions through the operation of the normal feed-back inhibition control of the phosphoglycerate dehydrogenase step (Umbarger and Umbarger, 1962; Pizer, 1963). It should also be emphasized that extensive utilization of an exogenous supplement does not imply that the added material is part of a normal metabolic pathway. Thus uracil (1 mM) will completely suppress utilization of $^{14}CO_2$ for polynucleotide pyrimidine ring biosynthesis in *E. coli* and other bacteria. Uracil is not, however, a normal biosynthetic intermediate but can be converted by the cell to uridine 5′-monophosphate which is on the *de novo* pathway of polynucleotide biosynthesis. Use may be made of this observation in studies of the origin of the methyl group of the pyrimidine thymine. The inclusion of unlabelled uracil in the growth medium ensures that extensive labelling of thymine reflects labelling of the methyl group thereby obviating the requirement for the degradation studies otherwise needed to define the level of activity in the methyl group and in the ring carbon atoms (C-2 and C-6 being labelled via $^{14}CO_2$ fixation reactions).

It is perhaps worth stating that some care has to be exercised in interpreting the results of experiments designed to assess the quantitative significance of a labelled precursor in the biosynthesis of a cell component. Ideally, there should be an amount of labelled precursor present in the medium in excess of the conceivable cell requirements. Taking the following simple model in which the pool of B doubles in the mean generation time of the cells:

$$A \longrightarrow B$$

it can be shown that the specific activity (b_t) of B at time, t, is related to the specific activity (a_0) of the labelled supplement in the following manner:

$$b_t = a_0[1 - \exp(-kt)]$$

where k is a constant defined by the usual relationship between the number (N_t) of bacteria present at time t and the number (N_0) present at zero time:

$$N_t = N_0 \exp(kt)$$

It follows that it takes approximately 4·5 generation times for the value of

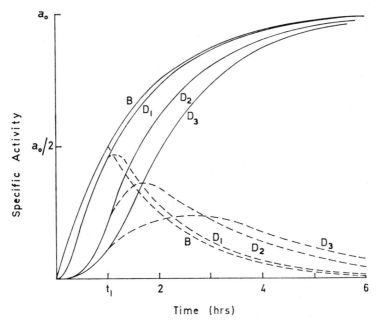

FIG. 15. Specific activity/time curves for the incorporation of a labelled precursor (specific activity a_0) into end products B, D_1, D_2, and D_3 in a bacterial culture growing exponentially with a mean generation time of 1 h. The dotted curves show the activity/time relationships following exhaustion of the precursor at a time t_1.

6

b_t to reach $0.95a_0$. In practice a more complicated model involving one (or more) kinetically significant intermediate pools may have to be considered:

$$A \to C \to D$$

Using analogous notation we have for this system:

$$d_t = a_0[1 + (D/C) \exp(-k\{1 + (D/C)\}t) - \{1 + (D/C)\} \exp(-kt)]$$

where C and D are the cell pool sizes of components C and D respectively. The influence of pools C_1, C_2, C_3, etc., on the specific activity/time curves of the corresponding end products D_1, D_2, D_3, etc., may be assessed by substituting in the above equation different values for the ratios D_1/C_1, D_2/C_2, D_3/C_3, etc. The resultant curves shown in Fig. 15 reveal that the activities of D_1, D_2, D_3, etc., vary considerably one from the other at short time intervals as one would expect and that no valid comparison of the relative activities of A, D_1, D_2, D_3, etc., can be made except at long time intervals. If the added labelled supplement A becomes exhausted at a time t_1, before the activities of D_1, D_2, D_3, etc., attain effectively the value a_0 a different set of specific activity/time curves are obtained (dotted lines Fig. 15). In these circumstances great care should be taken in making any deductions from the relative magnitudes of the specific activities of D_1, D_2, D_3, etc. A qualitatively analogous situation is met in practice when the labelled compound employed (e.g. $^{14}CO_2$) is rapidly diluted by the unlabelled species produced metabolically by the cell.

The reader is referred to Roberts *et al.* (1955) for a more extensive discussion of the isotope competition method.

REFERENCES

Abelson, P. H., Bolton, E. T., Britten, R., Cowie, D. B., and Roberts, R. B. (1953). *Proc. Nat. Acad. Sci.*, **39**, 1020.

Abelson, P. H. (1954). *J. biol. Chem.*, **206**, 335.

Aronoff, S. (1956). "Techniques of Radiobiochemistry". Iowa State University Press, Ames, Iowa.

Bolton, E. T., Cowie, D. B., and Sands, M. (1952). *J. Bact.*, **63**, 309.

Boursnell, J. C. (1958). "Safety Techniques for Radioactive Tracers". Cambridge University Press, Cambridge.

Bull, F. G., and Woods, D. D. (1963). *J. gen. Microbiol.*, **31**, xxiv.

Calvin, M., Heidelberger, C., Reid, J. C., Tolbert, B. M., and Yankwich, P. F. (1949). "Isotopic Carbon". John Wiley and Sons Inc., New York.

Coryell, C. F. (1948). "The Use of Isotopes in Biology and Medicine". University of Wisconsin Press, Madison.

Cowie, D. B., Bolton, E. T., and Sands, M. (1950). *J. Bact.*, **60**, 233.

Cowie, D. B., Bolton, E. T., and Sands, M. (1951). *J. Bact.*, **62**, 63.

Crosbie, G. W. (1958). *Biochem. J.*, **69**, 1P.

Evans, R. D. (1955). "The Atomic Nucleus". McGraw-Hill, New York.

Faires, R. A., and Parkes, B. H. (1958). "Radioisotope Laboratory Techniques". G. Newnes, London.

Francis, G. E., Mulligan, W., and Wormall, A. (1959). "Isotopic Tracers". Athlone Press, University of London, London.

Glascock, R. F. (1954). "Isotopic Gas Analysis for Biochemists". Academic Press, New York.

Glendenin, L. E., and Solomon, A. K. (1948). *Phys. Rev.*, **74**, 700.

Hendricks, R. H., Bryner, L. C., and Thomas, M. D., (1943). *J. Phys. Chem.*, **47**, 469.

Henriques, F. C., Kistiakowsky, G. B., Margnetti, C., and Schneider, W. G. (1946). *Ind. Eng. Chem., Anal. Edn.*, **18**, 349.

Kamen, M. D. (1957). "Isotopic Tracers in Biology". Academic Press, New York.

Keston, A. S., Udenfriend, S., and Cannan, R. K. (1946). *J. Amer. chem. Soc.*, **68**, 1390.

Keston, A. S., Udenfriend, S., and Levy, M. (1950). *J. Amer. chem. Soc.*, **72**, 748.

Koch, A. L. (1955). *J. biol. Chem.*, **217**, 931.

Pearson, K. (1900). *Phil. Mag.*, **50**, 157.

Pizer, L. (1963). *J. biol. Chem.*, **238**, 3934.

Popják, G. (1950). *Biochem. J.*, **46**, 560.

Price, W. J. (1958). "Nuclear Radiation Detection". McGraw-Hill, New York.

Riondel, A., Tait, J. F., Gut, M., Tait, S. A. S., Joachim, E., and Little, B. (1963). *J. clin. Endocrin, Metab.*, **23**, 620.

Roberts, R. B., and Roberts, I. Z. (1950). *J. cell. comp. Physiol.*, **36**, 15.

Roberts, R. B., Abelson, P. H., Cowie, D. B., Bolton, E. T., and Britten, R.J. (1955). "Studies of Biosynthesis in *Escherichia coli*". Carnegie Institute of Washington, Publication 607, Washington.

Taylor, D. (1950). "The Measurement of Radio-sotopes". Methuen and Co. Ltd., London.

Umbarger, H. E., and Umbarger, M. A. (1962). *Biochim. biophys. Acta*, **62**, 193.

Wynn-Williams, C. E. (1932). *Proc. Roy. Soc., London*, A**136**, 312.

Yankwich, P. E., Rollefson, G. K., and Norris, T. H. (1946). *J. chem. Phys.*, **14**, 131.

Yankwich, P. E., Norris, T. H., and Huston, J. L. (1947). *Ind. Eng. Chem.*, **19**, 439.

CHAPTER V

Liquid Scintillation Counting in Microbiology

JOHN H. HASH

Department of Microbiology, Vanderbilt University School of Medicine
Nashville, Tennessee 37203

I. INTRODUCTION

A. General

The use of radioactive atoms to trace the paths of stable isotopes in biological, chemical and physical processes represents one of the most powerful tools of modern science. All of biological science has advanced enormously because of tracer methods.

Radioactivity can be detected and measured by gas ionizing detectors, scintillation detectors, and simply by autoradiography (Wang and Willis, 1965). This article is concerned only with scintillation detection methods, or more specifically with liquid scintillation detection methods and their uses in microbiology.

Bacteria (Luria, 1960) have the following qualitative elemental composition: H, C, N, O, Na, Mg, P, S, Cl, K, Ca, Mn, Fe and occasionally Co, Cu, Zn, and Mo. The first four, H, C, N and O, constitute about 95% of the cell's weight. With the exception of N and O for which no usable radioisotopes exist, the remainder of these elements have radioisotopes that can be used as tracers. The most important tracers in biological systems are ^3H, ^{14}C, ^{32}P and ^{35}S and their measurement by liquid scintillation counting will be the primary concern of this article. In principle, however, the methods are applicable to all nuclides. All of the radioisotopes likely to be encountered in microbiological research can be counted by liquid scintillation techniques.

Counting statistics will not be considered in this article as they are covered elsewhere (Crosbie, this Volume, p. 84) and they have been discussed by Herberg (1961).

B. Basic terminology

In general, the terminology used in this article corresponds to that of Hayes (1958). *Liquid scintillation counting* is a method of detecting radioactivity with a solution of certain chemicals and a photomultiplier tube. A *scintillator* is defined as any material that emits a brief pulse of fluorescent light, or *scintillation*, when it interacts with a high energy particle or quantum. The term *liquid scintillator* refers to the counting system that produces light. The liquid scintillator may be simple or relatively complex but it must have two essential ingredients: solvent and scintillation solute. It may contain more than one solvent or more than one solute and it may even contain compounds that give it a gel structure. In addition to the situation where the sample and scintillator are in true solution, the term "liquid scintillation" is also used where the radioactive sample is in true solution but the scintillator is suspended. Conversely, it is also used where the scintillator is in true solution and the radioactive sample is suspended.

In *external liquid scintillation counting*, the source of radiation is external to the liquid scintillator. These are usually large volume systems. *Internal liquid scintillation counting* applies to the situation where the source of radiation is intimately mixed with the liquid scintillator. These are usually small volume systems. The scope of this article is concerned only with internal liquid scintillation counting and when the term liquid scintillation counting is used without qualification, it is understood to refer to the internal method.

Solvent is used in a broad sense and includes not only those substances whose function is to solubilize the scintillator and sample but also those substances that may be added for favourable effects in energy transfer. Solvents are referred to as primary, secondary, etc., in order of their relative concentration in the liquid scintillator. *Solutes* (or scintillators) are substances whose light emission is actually measured in liquid scintillation counting. Solutes are referred to as primary or secondary according to the sequence in which they participate in energy transfer. Terms like spectrum shifter and wavelength shifter have been applied to the secondary solute but these should be regarded only as second order synonyms (Hayes, 1958).

The term *phosphor* has been used for both the liquid scintillator and the scintillation solute. Hayes (1958) discourages the use of this term because of possible confusion between liquid scintillation and phosphorescence. When used in this article it will mean scintillation solute. The term *fluor* is also used as a synonym for scintillation solute. A *gelling agent* refers to the material added to a liquid scintillator to give it a gel structure, the product then being referred to as a *gel scintillator*. *Sample solute* refers to the radioactive sample that is dissolved in the liquid scintillator and *suspended sample* refers to an insoluble radioactive sample that is suspended in a gel scintillator. The *counting sample* is the system that results from adding the radioactive sample to the liquid or gel scintillator.

Quenching is defined as the attenuation of scintillation pulse heights due to compounds in the liquid scintillator which serves to siphon off some of the energy from the ionizing radiation and cause its emission as heat rather than light (Davidson and Feigelson, 1957). *Cpm* is counts per minute and *dpm* is disintegrations per minute. *Counting efficiency* is the ratio of cpm detected to the dpm theoretically present

$$\left(\% \text{ counting efficiency} = \frac{\text{cpm (observed)}}{\text{dpm (theoretical)}} \times 100\right).$$

For low-level counting the per cent counting efficiency is an insufficient criterion for the sensitivity of the system. The maximum number of counts obtained is greatly dependent on the amount of sample that can be introduced in the counting medium. Therefore in comparing the overall efficiency of various systems a sensitivity criterion should be used that considers these parameters. The following *figures of merit* have been used:

(1) E^2/B where E = counting efficiency and B = background (Hodgson et al., 1958).
(2) $W \times E$ where W = sample weight and E = counting efficiency (Kinard, 1957).

The counting sample which gives the highest figure of merit is considered to have the best liquid scintillator.

C. Historical

The scintillation process has been known for better than half a century and it played an important role in the early years of radiation research (Birks, 1964). Crookes, Rutherford, Geiger and other physicists used zinc sulphide screens to count alpha particles. In this instance the human eye was the detector and counting rates above 100 scintillations/min were physiologically impossible. This method became obsolete as more objective means of detecting radioactivity (Geiger-Mueller counters and ionization chambers) became available. Interest was revived in scintillation counting following World War II by the development of reliable photomultiplier tubes.

The liquid scintillation process for detecting radioactivity was reported independently by Reynolds *et al.* (1950) and Kallman and Furst (1950), who noted that solutions of certain chemicals in aromatic solvents could be used in conjunction whith photomultiplier tubes to detect radiation. Rapid developments in this area soon followed and commercial liquid scintillation counting equipment has been available since 1954. Details of the early history of the scintillation counter are given by Krebs (1955).

The intrinsic advantage of internal liquid scintillation counting over other methods of detection is that it puts the source of radiation in intimate contact with the detector. This juxtaposition of sample and detector has long been a desired goal of investigators working with soft β-emitters because of the various factors encountered in other methods of detection. These factors include self-absorption, geometry, scatter, and absorption by air and counter windows. These problems are eliminated in liquid scintillation counting which in turn has problems of its own, such as quenching and sample solubility, but these problems have been overcome to such an extent that liquid scintillation counting has become the method of choice for counting weak β-emitters. However, it is not restricted to β-emitters and a list of isotopes which may be advantageously counted by liquid scintillation techniques is given in Table I. Sodium-22 is a positron emitter and the weak X-rays of [55]Fe can scarcely be detected by any other

TABLE I

Isotope	Particle type	Energy (MeV)	Half-life
^{3}H	β^-	0·018	12·3 years
^{14}C	β^-	0·156	5745 years
^{22}Na	β^+	0·54	2·6 years
	γ	1·277	
	γ*	0·51	
^{24}Na	β^-	1·39	15·0 hours
	γ	1·37, 2·75	
^{28}Mg	β^-	0·459, 2·87†	21·4 hours
	γ	0·032, 0·40, 0·95	
		1·35, 1·78†	
^{32}P	β^-	1·71	14·3 days
^{35}S	β^-	0·167	87 days
^{36}Cl	β^-	0·714	$3 \cdot 1 \times 10^5$ years
^{40}K	β^-	1·33	$1 \cdot 26 \times 10^9$ years
	γ	1·46	
	X-rays	0·0032	
^{42}K	β^-	2·0, 3·55	12·4 hours
	γ	1·53	
^{45}Ca	β^-	0·254	164 days
^{47}Ca	β^-	0·67, 1·98, 0·44†, 0·60†	4· 53 days
		0·49, 0·81, 1·31, 1·6†	
^{51}Cr	γ	0·325	27·8 days
	X-rays	0·0055	
^{56}Mn	β^-	0·72, 1·03, 2·84	2·6 hours
	γ	0·85, 1·81, 2·11	
^{55}Fe	X-rays	0·0065	2·6 years
^{59}Fe	β^-	0·27, 0·46	45·1 days
	γ	1·1, 1·3	
^{63}Ni	β^-	0·067	92 years
^{65}Zn	β^+ (1·5% of decays)	0·324	245 days
	γ	1·12	
	X-rays	0·009	
^{90}Sr	β^-	0·545, 2·27†	28·1 years
^{125}I	γ	0·035	60 days
	X-rays	0·033	
^{129}I	β^-	0·15	$1 \cdot 7 \times 10^7$ years
	γ	0·038	
^{131}I	β^-	0·335, 0·608	8·08 days
	γ	0·284, 0·364	
		0·637	
^{137}Cs	β^-	0·514, 1·20	30·0 years
^{137}Ba		0·66	

* Annihilation Radiation
† Daughter Radiaton

For detailed decay schemes see: "Table of Isotopes". C. M. Lederer, J. M. Hollander and I. Perlmann, 6th Ed., John Wiley & Sons, N.Y. (1967)

Reproduced and modified with permission of Nuclear-Chicago Corp., Des Plaines, Illinois.

method. α-Particles can also be effectively counted by liquid scintillation counting (Horrocks, 1964, 1966).

II. DETECTION METHODS

A. The liquid scintillation process

While it is not essential that the user of liquid scintillation counting understands all the physics and electronics involved, intelligent use of the equipment requires a familiarity with general principles. For more complete discussions of the theoretical aspects of energy transfer in liquid scintillation counting the reader is referred to Bell and Hayes (1958), Schram and Lombaert (1963) and Birks (1964).

The counting sample consists of a solvent, fluor and the radioactive sample. The radioactive sample provides the emitted particle, the energy of which is intially consumed in ionization and excitation of the electrons in the absorbing material. In the case of a liquid scintillator this material is the solvent. The amount of energy transferred directly to the fluor is negligible. The energy of ionization that leads to ions and free radicals does not contribute to the scintillation process. Rather it is the excitation of electrons in the solvent molecules that leads to light emission. Less than 10% of the energy absorbed by a scintillator system is transformed to light; the remainder is lost as heat or is consumed in chemical reactions (Swank, 1954; Kallman and Furst, 1958).

The excitation energy of the solvent is transferred to molecules of the primary solute or fluor by mechanisms that are imperfectly understood (Birks, 1964) and this process occurs in about one nanosecond (n sec, 10^{-9} sec). The excited molecules of the fluor return to the ground state by emitting quanta of light in the visible of near ultraviolet region of the spectrum. It is these quanta of light or photons that are counted in the liquid scintillation process.

In order to provide a better match between the photocathode that detects the light pulses and the photon emission spectrum, it is sometimes desirable to add a secondary fluor. This compound absorbs the photons emitted by the primary fluor and re-emits them at a higher wavelength. If the absorption spectrum of a scintillator overlaps its emission spectrum some of the light will be reabsorbed by the fluor. However, not all the light that is reabsorbed is lost. The absorbing molecule is merely raised to the same excited state that produced the original photon and a secondary photon is subsequently emitted (Swank, 1958). Light absorption by impurities usually results in loss of energy because most impurities are non-fluorescent. Therefore the purity of solvents and fluors is of some importance. Both fluors and solvents are commercially available in scintillation grade chemicals.

B. Detection of photons

The photons arising from the incident ionizing radiation of the sample are detected by a photomultiplier tube. The photosensitive part of the photomultiplier tube, the photocathode, acts as a producer of primary electrons. The most efficient photocathodes, which contain cesium and antimony, have a low work function and the amount of energy required to release an electron from their surface is rather small. The photons arising from the ionizing radiation strike the photocathode and cause emission of electrons. These photoelectrons, accelerated by an electrical potential, strike the first electrode or dynode and each electron causes the release of 3–5 secondary electrons. These electrons are accelerated to the second dynode where further amplification occurs. Photomultiplier tubes have 10–14 stages of multiplication with a difference in potential of about 100 V between stages. The final is collected by an anode and is converted to a voltage pulse which is counted by a scaler. Overall amplification is by a factor of 10^5–10^6.

C. Pulse height analysis

β-Particles (both positrons and negatrons) are emitted simultaneously with neutrinos which share the total energy of the disintegration in proportions which vary with each disintegration. Consequently, β-emitters have a spectrum of energies with E_{max} representing the total energy of the β-particle and the neutrino. Each β-emitter has a characteristic E_{max} (Table I) and the energy spectra of the four most important isotopes in biological research are shown in Fig. 1. The average energy, E_{mean}, is approximately one third of E_{max}. The dotted portion of each curve represents theoretically calculated rather than experimentally determined values.

When a β-emitter, especially a weak β-emitter, is surrounded by a liquid scintillator the primary particle will be completely stopped by the solution. Consequently all of its energy will be given up to the solution and the number of photons produced will be proportional to the primary energy of the particle. In turn, the size of the voltage pulse or pulse height from the photomultiplier tube will be proportional to the energy of the primary particle. In other words, liquid scintillation counting is essentially a proportional method of detecting radioactivity. The signal from the photomultiplier tube is amplified and fed into pulse height analysers which compare the signal with reference voltages. Discriminator circuits are employed to pass the signal if it falls in a channel between two preselected voltage

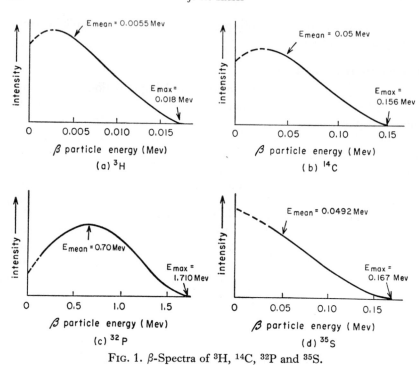

FIG. 1. β-Spectra of ³H, ¹⁴C, ³²P and ³⁵S.

levels. An important advantage of proportional counting and pulse height analysis is the ability to discriminate between signals due to background noise and those produced by the radioactive sample. Discriminators may be set for optimum performance of a particular isotope. Another advantage of pulse height analysis is that, provided their energy spectra are sufficiently different, more than one isotope may be counted simultaneously in different channels with different discriminator settings. A block diagram of a liquid scintillation counter is shown in Fig. 2.

D. Background

In order to get the net counting rate of a sample the background counting rate must be subtracted from the sample counting rate. The background counting rate is obtained by counting a sample with the same chemical composition as the unknown sample but without any added radioactivity. Factors which contribute to background are of several origins.

Inasmuch as the photocathode has a low work function, not only light but also heat will cause the emission of electrons from its surface which may be amplified and counted. Cooling the photomultiplier tube reduces these thermionic emissions and most modern counters have refrigeration units to cool the sample. However, other units count samples at ambient

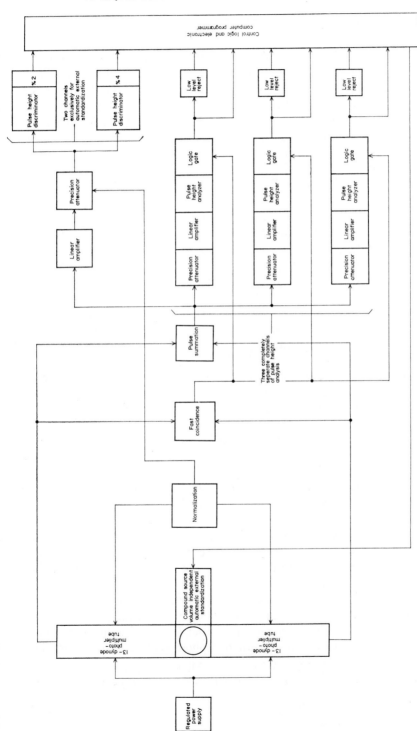

Fig. 2. Block diagram of a modern liquid scintillation counter. Packard Instrument Company Model 3375. Reproduced by permission of Packard Instrument Company.

118   J. H. HASH

temperatures with quite acceptable backgrounds. Another device used to reduce the background attributable to thermal emissions of electrons from the photocathode is to use a coincidence arrangement in which two photo-multiplier tubes view the same counting sample. Thermionic emissions from the photocathode are random events while true scintillation pulses occur simultaneously in both photomultipliers. By feeding the pulses to an appropriate circuit it is possible to screen out the noncoincidental or thermal pulses and pass the coincidental or scintillation pulses. Of course it is possible for two random thermal emissions to occur simultaneously and to be passed by the coincidence circuit. These will be counted by the scalers as legitimate counts. This contribution to the background is quite small.

Another source of background is the naturally occurring radioisotopes in materials used to construct the counter and sample containers and the materials making up the liquid scintillator. A principal offender here is the β- and γ-emitter ^{40}K that occurs in glass, and a special borosilicate glass vial low in ^{40}K is widely used as a counting vial.† These vials are inexpensive enough to be disposable and their use represents an improvement over ordinary glass. Even further improvement is obtained by the use of polyethylene vials‡ (Rapkin and Gibbs, 1963). However, the advantages of plastic vials are somewhat offset by the fact that they are permeable to most liquid scintillators and samples in them must be counted promptly. A natural contributor to the background may be ^{14}C which occurs in contemporary organic materials to the extent of about 15 disintegrations/min/g. For example, Hayes (1958) found that 90 ml of p-cymene, obtained from plant terpenes, gave 600 cpm (50% counting efficiency) but the same quantity of p-cymene synthesized from fossil hydrocarbons had only 60 cpm. Fortunately, most scintillation solvents can be obtained from fossil hydrocarbons in which the ^{14}C content is small.

Other sources of background include external gamma radiation that originates from natural emitters in the air and surrounding structures and from various isotopes in neighbouring laboratories. External sources also include cosmic rays that interact with matter to produce high energy particles which bombard the counter. These interactions may also include some Cherenkov radiation in addition to the usual processes of exciting the liquid scintillator.

Occasionally phosphorescence may be important as a source of background counts. The offenders in this case are sometimes the glass vial which may be excited by certain ultraviolet frequencies and the sample itself which may contain unknown phosphorescent substances. For low

† Wheaton glass vials (T. C. Wheaton Co., Millville, N.J.).
‡ Polyethylene vials can be obtained from most suppliers of counting equipment.

level counting it may be advisable to dark-adapt samples or to prepare samples in a room lighted by an incandescent rather than a fluorescent light. For samples of biological origin that may contain phosphorescent substances, it is important to include as a blank an unlabelled sample of the same chemical composition.

Kaufman *et al.* (1962) investigated the various contributions of the background count rate and concluded that counts from a 56 cpm background came from the following sources:

External gamma radiation	4 cpm
Cosmic radiation	7 cpm
Internal gamma contamination	30 cpm
Random coincidences	1 cpm
Cherenkov radiation and non-rate dependent light interactions	14 cpm
Total	56 cpm

E. Commercial counting equipment

Commercial liquid scintillation counting equipment has been available since 1954 and there have been many modifications and great improvement in instrument design and performance. Modern instruments can handle 25 to 1000 samples automatically in a sequential fashion. Samples are counted to either preset time or preset count and the data are recorded in various ways according to the design of the particular instrument. Most instruments are completely transistorized and are available with multiple discriminators and multiple channels. All instruments to date are of the coincidence type although there seems to be no inherent reason why single photomultiplier systems would not be practicable (Rapkin, 1964). Various optional features such as calculators for data reduction are available on many models.

There have been a number of entries (as well as a number of withdrawals) into the market for liquid counting equipment. For current entries as well as the addresses of the manufacturers, the *Annual Guide of Scientific Instruments*, published by the American Association for the Advancement of Science in *Science*, should be consulted. Instruments are to be used, of course, according to the instructions of the manufacturer.

Several manufacturers of counting equipment, as well as suppliers of radioactive chemicals, publish technical bulletins of excellent quality. Often useful information, tips and hints on the solution of practical problems are to be found in these publications.

III. SOLVENTS AND FLUORS

A. Solvents

The single most important characteristic that a scintillation solvent must possess is the ability to accept energy from incident ionizing radiation and transfer it to a dissolved scintillator. In addition, other characteristics such as proper solvent properties in relation to the sample or a small absorption coefficient for the light the solute emits may be superimposed upon this basic requirement. The ability to accept energy from ionizing radiation is an uncommon property of organic liquids and much effort has been expended to locate suitable scintillation solvents. To date the most efficient organic liquids that have the desired qualities are alkylbenzenes and various ethers (Kallmann and Furst, 1951; Furst and Kallmann, 1955a; Hayes *et al.*, 1955a; and Davidson and Feigelson, 1957). Of the alkyl-benzenes, toluene and xylene are the most efficient. For the physicist and chemist working with organic solvent soluble compounds, aromatic solvents work quite well. For the biological chemist, however, a quite different need arises. The milieu of life is water and consequently there is a need for the scintillation solvent to hold appreciable amounts of water. This requirement has been a principal problem of liquid scintillation counting. While the list of suitable single solvents has probably not been exhausted, the search may be unrewarding (Davidson and Feigelson, 1957). In trying to find a suitable solvent for aqueous samples two approaches may be tried (Hayes, 1958). A better chemical solvent may be made from a good scintillation solvent (addition of methanol to toluene) or a better scintillation solvent may be made from a good chemical solvent (addition of naphthalene to 1,4-dioxane). In practice, the problems attendant to the solubility of both fluors and radioactive sample, freezing point of mixture, cost, etc., have been overcome in many cases by the use of binary, ternary or even quaternary mixtures of solvents. Often the mixture has a greater efficiency of energy transfer than the pure solvent alone. The addition of naphthalene (Furst *et al.*, 1955c; Furst and Kallman, 1955b) to a poor scintillation solvent produces a binary solvent almost as good as toluene in scintillation performance. This discovery has led to a dioxane–naphthalene system for counting tritiated water (Kaufman *et al.*, 1962).

Some solvents tested by Davidson and Feigelson (1957) are shown in Table II.

B. Fluors

The fluor (phosphor, scintillator, scintillation solute) converts the energy of the emitted particle into light pulses or photons. In liquid scintillation counting the fluors are all organic compounds and a common character-

TABLE II

**Counting efficiencies of various solvents tested with 0·3%
diphenyloxazole as fluor**

Compound	Freezes[†]	Efficiency[‡]
Toluene	−95	100
Methoxybenzene (anisole)	−37	100
Xylene (reagent, mixed isomers)	< −20	97
1,3-Dimethoxybenzene	−52	81
n-Heptane	−90	70
1,4-Dioxane	+12	70
1,2-Dimethoxyethane (ethylene glycol dimethyl ether)	−71	60
Benzyl alcohol	−15	38
Diethyleneglycol diethyl ether (Diethyl Carbitol)	−44	32
Acetone	−94	12
Tetrahydropyran	−81	6
Ethyl ether	−116	4
1,1-Diethoxyethane	−100	3
Tetrahydrofuran	−65	2
1,3-Dioxolane	< −10	0
Ethyl alcohol	−114	0
Diethylene glycol monoethyl ether	−10	0
Ethylene glycol monomethyl ether	−85	0
Diethylene glycol	−8	0
Ethylene glycol	−13	0
2,5-Diethoxytetrahydrofuran	−27	0
N,N-Dimethylformamide	−61	0
Diethylamine	−49	0
N-Methyl morpholine	−66	0
2-Ethylhexanoic acid	−117	0
Tri-n-butyl phosphate	< −80	0

† Approximate freezing-points in degrees centrigrade.
‡ Efficiency, on basis of cpm, relative to toluene equalling 100%.
Reproduced with permission of Davidson and Feigelson (1957).

istic is that the scintillator contains conjugated aromatic rings. Extensive surveys of organic compounds suitable for liquid scintillation counting have been made (Hayes et al., 1952; Hayes et al., 1955b; Hayes, 1956a; Furst et al., 1957; Ott, 1958; Kowalski et al., 1967). A majority of 102 compounds listed in one survey (Hayes et al., 1955b) were either oxazole or oxadiazole derivatives. In general, the oxazole derivatives have proven to be the most useful of all compounds tested for liquid scintillation counting.

TABLE III

Some fluors used in liquid scintillation counting

Trivial name	Structure	Chemical name
	Primary fluors	
TP		p-Terphenyl
PBD		2-Phenyl-5-(4-biphenylyl)-1,3,4-oxadiazole
B-PBD		2-(4-t-Butylphenyl)-5-(4-biphenylyl)-1,3,4-oxadiazole
PPO		2,5-Diphenyloxazole
DPS		p,p'-Diphenylstilbene
BBOT		2,5-bis-[5'-t-Butyl-benzoxazolyl (2')]-thiophene
	Secondary fluors	
POPOP		1,4-bis-2-(5-Phenyloxazolyl)-benzene
DM-POPOP		1,4-bis-2-(4-Methyl-5- phenyl-oxazolyl)-benzene
α-NPO		2-(1-Naphthyl)-5-phenyl-oxazole
α-NOPON		1,4-bis-[2-(5,1-Naphthyl-oxazolyl)]-benzene
BBO		2,5-Dibiphenylyloxazole

Numerous compounds, especially compounds with heterocyclic rings, have been examined for scintillation performance and some of these have been discussed by Ott (1958) who concluded that none are likely to replace oxazole as the chief building block of effective fluors.

The emission spectra of most fluors have peaks at shorter wavelengths than the maximum photocathode sensitivity, and secondary fluors are often added to the liquid scintillator to shift the spectrum of the emitted light to longer wavelengths. Some of the most commonly used primary and secondary fluors are shown in Table III. TP (see Table III for abbreviations) is a very efficient and economical fluor and, where a completely organic solvent soluble radioactive source is being measured, may be the fluor of choice. However, it has a limited solubility in toluene and is unsuitable for applications where it is necessary to cool the sample or to incorporate water into the liquid scintillator. PBD is one of the most efficient scintillation solutes yet found but its cost and limited solubility in aqueous samples has limited its usefulness. Of the primary fluors listed, PPO, by virtue of its solubility properties, cost, and longer wavelength emission maximum, has become the most commonly used primary solute in liquid scintillation counting. BBOT is a relatively new entry (as is B-PBD) and suffers from the fact that it has a limited solubility in samples containing water, but has the advantage that its emission maximum is at 4350Å and therefore needs no secondary solute to provide a match for the photocathode.

Of the secondary scintillators, POPOP and its near relative DM-POPOP have established themselves as the favourites. Both are equally effective but the solubility of DM-POPOP is greater. It should be used at twice the concentration of POPOP (Bush and Hansen, 1965).

The synthesis of heterocyclic compounds as potential fluors with more desirable energy transfer and solubility properties continues (Kowalski et al., 1967; and Scales, 1967). Scales (1967) found that B-PBD may be an advantageous replacement for the conventional PPO and DM-POPOP scintillator, especially for quenched samples.

C. Liquid scintillators

The choice of solvents and fluors, as well as their concentrations are generally an arbitrary balance between the factors of performance, solubility (of both fluors and sample) and cost. The investigator may have to devise his own liquid scintillator for his particular needs but the following liquid scintillators (Table IV) are offered as representative of those that have proven useful for a variety of purposes. Additional liquid scintillators have been compiled by Wang and Willis (1965).

IV. PREPARATION OF SAMPLES

A. General

Usually there is a marked contrast in the relative ease of preparing counting samples for liquid scintillation counting and the time and precision required for preparation of planchets for Geiger-Mueller counting or

TABLE IV
Composition of some liquid scintillators

Solvent	Primary (ml)	fluor (g)	Secondary fluor (g)	Comments	Reference
1. Toluene Methanol	1000 ml 100 ml	PPO (6)	POPOP† (0·5)	0·3 ml HOH/10 ml	Hayes and Gould (1953)
2. "Polyether-611" 1,4-Dioxane Anisole 1,2-Dimethoxyethane	750 ml 125 ml 125 ml	PPO (12)	POPOP (0·5)	2 ml HOH/10 ml	Davidson and Feigelson (1957)
3. Naphthalene Methanol Ethylene glycol 1,4-Dioxane to 1 litre	60 gm 100 ml 20 ml	PPO (4)	POPOP (0·2)	3 ml HOH/10 ml	Bray (1960)
4. 1,4-Dioxane Naphthalene	1000 ml 100 g	PPO (6)	POPOP (0·3)	2 ml HOH/10 ml	Kaufman et al. (1962)
5. 1,4-Dioxane 2-Ethoxyethanol Naphthalene	500 ml 100 ml 30 g	PPO (6)	POPOP (0·3)	2·5 ml HOH/10 ml	Bruno and Christian (1961b)
6. Toluene Methanol 2-Phenylethylamine	460 ml 270 ml 270 ml	PPO (5)	POPOP (0·1)	Used for $^{14}CO_2$ counting	Woeller (1961)
7. Toluene 2-Methoxyethanol Naphthalene	600 ml 400 ml 80 g	BBOT (6)		0·4 ml HOH/10 ml	Recommended by CIBA Ltd., makers of BBOT.

† or DM-POPOP.

conversion of samples to gas for ionization chamber assays (Davidson and Feigelson, 1967). In many cases the sample (up to 2 ml) has only to be dissolved in the liquid scintillator (10–20 ml) and the counting sample is ready. However, because of the diversity and complexity of biological material as well as their general insolubility in organic solvents, the problems encountered in sample preparation are not always small. A variety of techniques has been developed for handling biological samples. These include homogeneous methods, heterogeneous methods and, finally, combustion of samples and counting the products of combustion by either homogeneous or heterogeneous methods. Although few of the methods have been designed specifically for microbiological use, most, if not all, of the techniques can be adapted to the needs of the microbiologist. From a knowledge of the techniques available, the investigator can adapt, modify or devise methods on the basis of his own samples and counting equipment. The method of choice will depend on several factors: the number and nature of the samples, the specific activity of the sample, the preparation time required for each sample, and the stability of the sample for counting reproducibility. Also the counting efficiency must be such that the required statistical accuracy can be achieved in a reasonable time.

A useful manual on the preparation of samples for liquid scintillation counting has been compiled (1967).†

B. Solution methods

The widespread interest of biological scientists in liquid scintillation counting is due primarily to the fact that two of the most important tracers in biological science, ^3H and ^{14}C, are weak β-emitters. These β-particles lose their energy rapidly in passing through matter and it is here that the intrinsic advantage of liquid scintillation counting is manifest. When the counting sample is homogeneous (i.e., in the same phase) there is no loss of energy between the sample and detector. In heterogeneous samples (i.e., in different phases) there is a loss of energy and therefore much effort has been directed towards achieving true solution of the sample in the liquid scintillator. Another advantage of homogeneous counting is that counting efficiencies are more easily determined in homogeneous than in heterogeneous systems.

In those few cases where the biological sample in question is organic solvent-soluble (e.g., fats, sterols, etc.) there is no problem. The material is extracted with an organic solvent and transferred directly to the liquid scintillator which has the highest counting efficiency possible, usually a toluene based liquid scintillator.

† "Preparation of Samples for Liquid Scintillation Counting", Nuclear-Chicago Corporation, Des Plaines, Illinois, 1967.

In the majority of cases where the biological material in question is not organic solvent-soluble, efforts have been directed towards improving the water-holding capacity of the liquid scintillator and towards finding solubilizing aids for biological material. The first approach is illustrated by the polyether 611 system of Davidson and Feigelson (1957) and the solution of Bray (1960) (Table IV). Both of these systems contain dioxane and both are capable of dissolving certain biological samples directly. Bray's solution is reported to be capable of dissolving aqueous solutions of amino acids sugars, and even some protein. In many instances, these liquid scintillators or others similar in nature have proven adequate for a variety of biological samples, even in the presence of salt.

The other approach of using solubilizing agents has been the more common and is illustrated by the variety of chemicals used in this regard. These chemicals include inorganic and organic bases, inorganic and organic acids, alcohols, amines, amides and quaternary ammonium compounds. For inorganic isotopes, various chelating agents have been used as solubilizing agents (Rapkin, 1964). Some normally organic solvent-insoluble compounds may be converted to soluble compounds by chemical modification; for example, by alkylation with acid halides or anhydrides.

One class of compounds used as general solubilizing agents has become extremely important; namely, the quaternary ammonium hydroxides. The most prominent such material, Hyamine hydroxide (HyOH), (Passman et al., 1956, Vaughan et al., 1957 has the following structure.

$$\left[\underset{\underset{CH_3}{|}}{\overset{\overset{CH_3}{|}}{H_3C\text{-}C}}\text{-}CH_2\text{-}\underset{\underset{CH_3}{|}}{\overset{\overset{CH_3}{|}}{C}}\text{-}\langle\ \rangle\text{-}O\text{-}CH_2\text{-}CH_2O\text{-}CH_2\text{-}CH_2\text{-}\underset{\underset{CH_3}{|}}{\overset{\overset{CH_3}{|}}{N}}\text{-}CH_2\text{-}\langle\ \rangle \right]^+ OH^-$$

Benzyldimethyl-{2-[2′-(p-1,1,3,3-tetramethylbutyl-o-methylphenoxy)-ethoxy]-ethyl} ammonium hydroxide

Hyamine hydroxide (HyOH)

This organic solvent-soluble quaternary ammonium hydroxide is capable of dissolving diverse biological material such as serum and plasma, amino acids, proteins, tissues, nucleic acids and is also used to trap CO_2. Hyamine carbonate is soluble in toluene. While HyOH has come closer than others to being a universal solubilizing agent for liquid scintillation counting, it suffers from the disadvantage of being a quenching agent, thereby restricting the amount that can be used. It also causes discoloration of some biological materials especially if it is necessary to heat the sample to effect solution. HyOH is commercially available as a 1M solution in methanol.

The mechanism of solubilization of biological samples by quaternary ammonium bases such as HyOH has not been adequately determined. For simple compounds such as CO_2 and acids the mechanism is simply salt formation. But for more complex molecules such as proteins and nucleic acids the mechanisms may not be so simple. Proteins do not generally precipitate from solution when the HyOH is neutralized with glacial acetic acid, indicating that the reasons for solubilization may be complex formation rather than acid-base interactions. It seems quite possible, especially when samples are heated with HyOH, that hydrolysis or esterolysis of the polymeric materials occurs. Proteins dissolved with the aid of HyOH occasionally show phosphorescence that gives spurious counts (Herberg, 1958). These counts are eliminated by allowing the samples to stand in the dark 24 h before counting or neutralizing the HyOH with glacial acetic acid after the tissues have been solubilized in the liquid scintillator.

A more recently developed agent of the quaternary ammonium hydroxide type but of less certain chemical composition is NCS† (Hansen and Bush, 1967). This toluene soluble base is a mixture of bases, in the molecular weight range of 250–600, produced from a commercial mixture of chlorides of the type formula $R_2 R'_2 NCl$, where R is methyl and R' is a straight chain alkyl residue varying from C_6 to C_{20}, with an average of about 12 carbon atoms. According to Hansen and Bush (1967) NCS dissolves soft tissues with higher figures of merit (W × E) than HyOH. Therefore on a molar basis less NCS than HyOH is required to solubilize a given weight of tissues and the quenching is correspondingly reduced. NCS is available commercially as a 0·6N toluene solution.

Herberg (1960) described the use of a KOH-ethylene glycol liquid scintillator for solubilizing various tissue homogenates, compared it to HyOH, and concluded there was little difference between the two. However, Hansen and Bush (1967) found that KOH was inferior to either HyOH or NCS for solubilizing tissues. Other systems using KOH include the one of Petroff et al. (1965) who dissolved tissues in 2N methanolic-KOH and used ethylene glycol monobutyl ether to bring about miscibility of the digest with a toluene based liquid scintillator.

Other liquid scintillators using solubilizing agents for protein and tissue homogenates include formamide-ethanol-toluene (Kinnory et al., 1958), formic acid-ethanol-toluene (Hall and Cocking, 1965), formic acid-ethyl cellosolve-toluene (Bartley and Abraham, 1966) and 2-phenylethylamine-toluene (Francis and Hawkins, 1967). Francis and Hawkins (1967) also found that a liquid scintillator could be made with only 2-phenylethyl-amine and fluors. This scintillator and the one with toluene hold water to

† NCS-Nuclear-Chicago solubilizer, Nuclear Chicago Corp. Des Plaines, Illinois.

about 50% of their volume and protein concentrations up to 20 mg/ml. These samples are counted at room temperature.

For the microbiologist who deals with such diverse organisms as bacteria, protozoa, fungi, algae, etc., the applicability of solution methods in liquid scintillation counting will depend on the nature of the material to be counted. If, for example, he is dealing with fractions of cells such as trichloroacetic acid extracts, lipid solvent extracts or protein or nucleic acid fractions, then the various solubilizing agents mentioned may be adequate. If, however, it is necessary to count label in the entire organism, difficulties arise. The reason is that high molecular weight carbohydrates are not soluble in the solubilizing agents mentioned. These polymers include starch, cellulose, chitin, cell wall murein, etc. On the other hand, the monomers or low molecular weight fragments from these polymers are often quite soluble in liquid scintillators either with or without the aid of solubilizing agents. Hash (1962) accomplished the true solution of the Gram-positive bacterium, *Bacillus megaterium,* by dissolving the cell wall murein with lysozyme and solubilizing the lysate in polyether 611 (Table IV) with HyOH.

The bacteria (2–10 mg dry weight) were collected by centrifugation and were prepared by either washing with 2 ml of 0·05M phosphate buffer pH 7·0 or by first extracting the cells with 2 ml of cold 10% trichloroacetic acid for 10 min and then washing with the buffer. The washed cells were suspended in 0·1 ml of 0·05M phosphate buffer, pH 7·0. Lysozyme was added at a concentration of 10–100 µg in order to dissolve the murein and lyse the cells within 20 min.

In some cases it was possible to carry out this step directly in the counting vial. The lysate was dissolved in a small amount of HyOH (0·1–0·2 ml) and liquid scintillator was added.

The method was extended to the Gram-positive bacterium, *Staphylococcus aureus,* a lysozyme insensitive organism, by dissolving the cell wall murein with a fungal N-acetylhexosaminidase (Hash *et al.*, 1964). The *S. aureus* cells (2–10 mg dry wt) were collected by centrifugation, washed with water and resuspended in 0·1 ml of 0·05M acetate buffer, pH 4·8. The fungal N-acetylhexosaminidase was added at a concentration of 10–100 µg protein so complete lysis would occur within 30 min. The lysate was dissolved in 0·2 ml of HyOH and liquid scintillator was added. In principle, the method is a general one and the only requisite is the necessary enzymes, e.g., cellulase, chitinase, amylase, bacteriolytic enzymes, etc., for dissolving cellulose, chitin, starch and cell wall murein, respectively. The limitation of this method is the availability of particular enzymes.

Another approach to solubilizing bacteria for liquid scintillation counting is that of Neujahr and Ewaldsson (1964) who used formamide to dissolve *Lactobacillus fermenti* and *Streptococcus faecalis* and counted ^{14}C and [35]S. Digestion of cells (10 mg dry wt) was with 1 ml of formamide for 2 h at 60°C. Simple autolysis at 60°C was sufficient for lesser amounts of these cells. Whether formamide is a general solubilizing agent for bacteria and other micro-organisms is yet to be determined.

C. Suspension methods

1. *Suspended samples*

Whenever materials are not conveniently solubilized or their solubility is too low to allow incorporation of sufficient amounts of low activity materials into liquid scintillators for accurate counting, suspension counting may be indicated (Helf, 1958).

Hayes *et al.* (1956b) suspended samples in liquid scintillators and shook them between 1 min counts. Counts decreased as the suspended materials settled and clearly this procedure has disadvantages for the automatic counting of many samples. Fortunately, this disadvantage can be overcome by the use of gelling agents to produce gel scintillators which keep the particles uniformly suspended.

Funt (1956) and Funt and Hetherington (1957) added aluminium stearate to liquid scintillators (2–7% by weight). Gels were produced by heating to 70°C, and the radioactive samples were added either prior to or after gelation. The rigidity of these gels makes it difficult to achieve uniform suspensions.

White and Helf (1956) and Helf *et al.* (1960) introduced the use of thixotropic agents for producing gel scintillators. Thixotropic agents have the property of forming gels when stationary but becoming fluid when agitated. They used Thixin,† a castor oil derivative, for forming gels. The gel is prepared by mixing Thixin with the desired liquid scintillator (25 g/l) in a blender for 2–3 min. The resulting clear mixture will support 1 g of suspended solid in 22 ml of liquid scintillator. The particles do not settle and counting rates are stable over a period of days.

Another thixotropic agent that has been used with considerable success is Cab-O-Sil,‡ a finely divided silicon dioxide (Ott *et al.*, 1959). Cab-O-Sil forms very satisfactory gels in concentrations of 3–12% by weight. The Cab-O-Sil may be added to the liquid scintillator at the desired concentration by vigorous agitation. Concentrations of 12% or more produce gels too rigid for uniform sample dispersion while concentrations of 3% or less may allow the suspensions to settle. It is not even necessary to weigh the

† Thixin, Trade mark of Baker Castor Oil Company, Bayonne, N.J.
‡ Cab-O-Sil, Trademark of Godfrey L. Cabot, Inc. Boston, Mass.

Cab-O-Sil; enough is added to a counting vial to fill it loosely without packing. The liquid scintillator and sample are added and the sample shaken vigorously for dispersion. These gels can hold 2 to 3 g of solids (e.g., BaCO₃) at 4 to 5% concentration of Cab-O-Sil.

Yet another method of suspension involves the formation of emulsions and gels with Triton X-100,† an alkyl phenoxy polyethoxy ethanol (Meade and Stiglitz, 1962; Patterson and Greene, 1965; and Van der Laarse, 1967).

Surprisingly good counting efficiencies have been reported for suspended samples as long as the sample is finely divided and is not coloured. When the particle range becomes comparable to the range of the β-particle, counting efficiency is reduced by self absorption. But by preparing the sample in a finely divided state, self absorption can be largely eliminated for the more energetic isotopes but not for the low energy particles emitted by tritium (Hayes et al., 1956b). Even tritium, however, can be counted in suspensions with about 10% counting efficiency. Solid organic and inorganic salts, water solutions and homogenized tissues have been counted by one or more of these methods of suspension counting.

It is important in suspension counting that the sample be completely insoluble in the liquid scintillator because any that dissolves will be counted at an efficiency different from that in the solid phase, and the overall counting efficiency will be impossible to determine. The determination of counting efficiency in suspended samples demands a solid standard with similar particle size and similar specific activity to the sample being counted. One advantage of suspension counting over solution counting is the general absence of chemical quenching (Hayes et al., 1956b). In the case of materials that result in considerable quenching in homogeneous samples, the suspension method may be preferable because of lack of quenching and consequently higher counting efficiencies.

Suspension counting also refers to samples that may be deposited on a thin translucent substrate and counted in a liquid scintillator. These deposits must be thin in order to minimize self-absorption of β-particles and photons. The insoluble mount may be filter paper strips or discs, lens paper and glass filter paper (Wang and Jones, 1959; Bosquet and Christian, 1960; Mans and Novelli, 1961; Weg, 1962; and Gill, 1964, 1967). Tritium can best be counted on films, such as membrane filters or glass filter paper, that are completely transparent in liquid scintillators. Gill (1967) recommends glass filter paper for counting tritium by suspension methods.

In this instance, a fluor, insoluble in the solvent in question, is placed in a

2. Suspended fluors

Suspensions of fluors may be used for detecting radioactivity in solution.

† Triton X-100. Trade mark of Rohm and Haas Co. Philadelphia, Pa.

vial and the solution containing the radioactive sample is added. Steinberg (1959, 1960) was the first to apply this technique and he concluded that anthracene was the most efficient scintillator of those tested. The counting sample must contain some detergent to wet the anthracene crystals. With 3 ml of sample (in 0·2% detergent) and 1 g of anthracene, counting efficiencies of 2 and 50% were obtained for ^{3}H and ^{14}C, respectively. One of the principal advantages of this type of counting is the general absence of chemical quenching. Other advantages are that sample preparation is minimal, and the sample can be recovered. Myers and Brush (1962) used the detergent–anthracene method for measuring α-, β- and γ-nuclides. With the exception of ^{3}H, α- and β-emitters had counting efficiencies of 50 to 100%. The counting efficiencies of γ-emitters were poor. A scintillation ion-exchange resin has been developed and used for removing α- and β-emitters from solution (Heimbuch and Schwarz, 1964). The resin is counted directly in the liquid scintillation counter.

Even though suspended fluors may be used for in-vial counting, it would appear that the chief application of this technique lies in monitoring flowing streams for radioactivity. Schram and Lombaert (1957, 1962) were the first to use solid scintillators for the continuous assay of radioactivity in chromatographic column effluents. Other monitoring devices and pro-procedures are those of Funt and Hetherington (1959), Piez (1962), Scharpenseel and Menke (1962), Trachuk (1962), and Elwyn (1965). Many of the procedures have been designed specifically for monitoring column effluents from commercial amino acid analysers.

The column effluent is passed through a flow cell (packed with anthra-cene) which is positioned between the photomultipliers of the counter. Most modern counters have provisions for using flow cells. In the case of amino acid analysers, the effluent is passed first through the flow cell and then through the ninhydrin developer. In general, the ninhydrin peaks are neither displaced nor distorted and recoveries are not affected. After passage of a radioactive amino acid the background returns to normal. Data from continuous flow cells may be either by analog or digital presentation. For analog presentation a rate meter and recorder are needed as accessories. In this case a graphical record is obtained which may be matched with a suitable analytical method to identify the source of the activity. Quantitation is by the usual methods of graphical analysis (triangulation, height–width, etc.). The digital method employs the print-out mechanism of the counter. The instrument is preset for 2–5 min and the total counts accumulated in that interval of time are recorded. The print-out time must be short to minimize errors due to dead-time during print-out.

In general, it would appear that aqueous solutions of any α- or β-emitter could be monitored by continuous flow scintillation methods, and literature citations are available covering the following isotopes: ^{3}H, ^{14}C, ^{32}P, ^{35}S, ^{45}Ca, ^{90}Sr, ^{131}I, ^{137}Cs and ^{210}Po (Rapkin, 1964).

In addition to monitoring aqueous effluents it is often desirable to monitor effluents from gas chromatographic columns. The problem is complicated by the high temperatures necessary for volatilizing compounds for gas chromatography, whereas counting must be performed at lower temperatures. To meet these opposing demands, both static and dynamic methods have been developed for scintillation counting of gas chromatographic effluents. In the static method, fractions from the column are collected by suitable means and then transferred to liquid scintillators for routine counting. A dynamic method for counting ^{3}H and ^{14}C in gas chromatographic effluents was developed by Karmen et al. (1962, 1963). After passing the gas chromatographic detector, the volatile compounds are combusted to ^{14}CO$_2$ and ^{3}H$_2$O in a heated tube of copper oxide. The ^{3}H$_2$O is reduced to ^{3}H$_2$ by passage through a tube of hot steel wool. The gases, ^{14}CO$_2$ and ^{3}H$_2$, are then passed through a flow cell packed with anthracene. If only ^{14}CO$_2$ is being measured the H$_2$O can be frozen out in a dry ice trap. In the dynamic system, the radioactive data is obtained as rapidly as the mass data from the gas chromatographic detector, and the radioactive trace is similar to the mass trace. To date, only ^{3}H and ^{14}C have been monitored by dynamic techniques.

D. Combustion methods

1. General

When a sample cannot be solubilized directly in liquid scintillators or is highly coloured or cannot be reduced to fine enough particles for suspension counting, there is no alternative to combustion methods. On the other hand combustion methods have sufficient advantages that they may be the method of choice even when the sample could be counted by one of the other ways.

There are some disadvantages to combustion of samples for liquid scintillation counting. The preparation of samples is time-consuming and even the most efficient combustion methods cannot compare with the speed and ease of direct solubilization. A minor disadvantage is that the technique is destructive; the sample cannot be used for any other type of analysis. On the other hand the advantages may be appreciable. All of the samples are converted to a single substance and hence the counting samples all have the same chemical composition. Consequently, the degree of quenching in each sample is the same and all samples count at the same efficiency. The samples are clear, colourless and are stable for long periods of time. The major steps involve the actual oxidation of the sample and the specific removal of the desired product. Depending on its nature, the product can be counted either as a homogeneous or heterogeneous sample. Combustion methods have been directed primarily towards the oxidation of samples containing ^3H and ^{14}C and to a lesser extent ^{35}S. In these cases the isotopes are recovered as ^3H_2O, $^{14}CO_2$ and $^{35}SO_4^{--}$, respectively. In principle there appears to be no reason why the method would not work for any isotope. High temperature ashing could be used to recover inorganic nuclides (e.g., $^{22}Na^+$, $^{32}PO_4^{---}$, $^{45}Ca^{++}$, etc.). All that is required is a satisfactory means of combustion and suitable methods for removal of the desired combustion product.

Both wet and dry combustion methods have been utilized for the oxidation of biological samples, and various techniques have been developed for recovery of the oxidation products. ^3H_2O has been recovered by diluting it with water, ethyl cellosolve or methanol, or by freezing it at $-70°C$. $^{14}CO_2$ has been absorbed in aqueous or methanolic KOH, HyOH, NCS, ethanolamine, phenylethylamine or other organic bases. ^{35}S oxidation products have been absorbed with either ethanolamine, phenylethylamine or hydrogen peroxide.

Combustion methods work well for all types of biological materials, including all the various types found in microbiology.

2. Wet combustion

The Van Slyke-Folch (1960) oxidation mixture of fuming sulphuric acid, periodic acid and chromic acid has been widely used for the preparation of Ba^{14}CO$_3$ planchets for Geiger-Mueller counting (see Crosbie, this Volume, p. 97). This procedure has been adopted for liquid scintillation counting by suspending the Ba^{14}CO$_3$ in gel scintillators with Cab-O-Sil (Nathan et al., 1958). Jeffay and Alvarez (1961a) used the Van Slyke-Folch oxidation mixture, trapped $^{14}CO_2$ in ethanolamine and counted with a homogeneous glycol-toluene liquid scintillator. Edwards and Kitchener (1965) trapped $^{14}CO_2$ in HyOH, and Weyman et al. (1967) devised a modified Van Slyke procedure for collecting $^{14}CO_2$ directly into counting vials. Phenylethylamine (Woeller, 1961), which was found to be superior to HyOH, was the CO_2 absorbant.

Persulphate has also been used as an oxidant in wet combustions (Katz et al., 1954). A sample (5–50 mg dry wt) in 5–10 ml HOH is placed in a 50 ml Erlenmeyer flask. Solid potassium persulphate (600 mg) is dissolved in the solution which is then acidified with one or two drops of 1N H_2SO_4. The CO_2 absorbant is placed inside a small beaker in the flask and the reaction is initiated by adding 1 ml of 4% silver nitrate solution. The flask is sealed with a rubber stopper and oxidation is carried out at 70°C for 30 min. After CO_2 absorption is complete the contents of the beaker are transferred to a liquid scintillator for counting. The volumes of reagents are not critical, the apparatus is simple and convenient for water soluble compounds and many samples can be oxidized at once. Several hours may be required for all the CO_2 to be absorbed.

Most organic compounds can be oxidized by a mixture of concentrated nitric acid (3 vol) and 60% perchloric acid (1 vol). Jeffay et al. (1960) added 55 g of magnesium nitrate per 400 ml of this mixture and used it for the oxidation of organic ^{35}S-compounds which were converted to $Mg^{35}SO_4$. The dry salts remaining (after the oxidant was evaporated) were dissolved in hot glycerol and counted in an ethanol-dimethylform-amide-toluene liquid scintillator. This technique was extended (Jeffay and Alvarez, 1961b) to include both ^{35}S and ^{14}C. These two isotopes have essentially identical energy spectra and cannot be separated by spectrometry. With this oxidation technique the ^{35}S was converted to $Mg^{35}SO_4$ and the $^{14}CO_2$ was trapped in ethanolamine. Both isotopes could be counted as homogeneous samples with high efficiency and no interference from each other. Recoveries of both were quantitative.

Wet oxidation methods have been quite useful for ^{14}C and ^{35}S but are not generally useful for tritium.

3. *Dry combustion in sealed tubes*

Several procedures for the oxidation of organic compounds in small sealed tubes have been developed. Sample size is usually limited to 2–50 mg organic matter but many samples can usually be handled simultaneously.

Buchanan and Corcoran (1959) determined total carbon and ^{14}C in 5–10 mg dry tissue that was mixed with cupric oxide, manganese dioxide and anhydrous cupric chloride (5 : 1 : 1). One g of oxidant is used per 5–10 mg dry weight sample. The samples were oxidized at 850°C. The tubes were broken in an evacuated system and the water collected in an acetone-dry ice trap and the CO_2 in a liquid nitrogen trap. They counted ^{14}C in a proportional counter but the CO_2 could be absorbed in a suitable absorbant and counted by homogeneous liquid scintillation counting. The water could be used for the determination of tritium, if present.

Jacobson et al. (1960) used sealed tubes for the determination of ^3H. To a tube containing 5–25 mg dry weight sample is added 0·75 g copper oxide and 0·25 g of reduced copper. The tube is evacuated, sealed and heated to 650°C for 60 min. Water was collected in acetone-dry ice traps and the samples transferred to a suitable liquid scintillator for homogeneous counting.

Other oxidation methods, while not designed specifically for liquid scintillation counting, could be modified for such (Kirsten and Carlsson, 1960; Koenig and Brattgard, 1963)

4. Dry combustion in oxygen bombs

In special cases where large amounts of material with low specific activity are being measured, the Parr-oxygen bomb may be useful. Payne and Done (1954) combusted dry samples (up to 1 g) in an oxygen bomb and collected the gases in a train. Sheppard and Rodegkar (1962) confirmed the usefulness of this technique. They collected both water and CO_2 and counted Ba $^{14}CO_3$ in a gel scintillator. An absorbant could be used to collect CO_2 and samples could be counted by homogeneous methods. A modification of the oxygen bomb has been used by McFarlane and Murray (1963) who removed H_2O by freezing and collected CO_2 in phenylethylamine. These methods may be especially useful when there are only a few samples of low specific activity. Oxygen bomb combustion methods do not appear to be easily adaptable for large numbers of samples.

5. Dry combustion in a train

The standard combustion train for C and H analysis may be used to produce $^{14}CO_2$ and $^{3}H_2O$ (Peets et al., 1960). A special train was constructed in which up to 2 g of dry sample could be placed in a platinum boat and heated in a stream of flowing oxygen at 700°C with or without inorganic oxide catalysts. The water vapour was removed in a dry ice trap and the CO_2 was absorbed in an organic base. Each was counted in a homogeneous liquid scintillator. The process is slow, requiring 45 min for three samples, but it allows the use of large samples which have low specific activities.

6. Dry combustion in a flask

Schöniger (1955) developed the technique of burning organic compounds in a flask in an oxygen atmosphere and this method has been developed into the most widely used combustion procedure for liquid scintillation counting. In principle, the sample, enclosed in some sort of combustible material, is suspended in a platinum basket in a heavy walled glass flask; the flask is flushed with oxygen and the sample is ignited. Combustion is complete within 30–60 sec and the gaseous products, at least in the case of $^{14}CO_2$ and $^{3}H_2O$, are easy to collect. The method is rapid, the apparatus is simple and economical, the method can be used for handling many samples and a single person can perhaps handle as many as 50 samples per day. The original Schöniger method used electrical ignition of the sample, which required gas tight enclosures for lead-in wires. In recent years, the trend has been towards infrared ignition (Oliverio et al., 1962) which eliminates the need of special heads for combustion flasks. With infrared ignition, the sample is wrapped in a piece of black paper and a beam of infrared light is focused on the sample directly through the walls of the flask. An apparatus using infrared ignition is commercially available.†

Dry combustion in flasks has been widely used for a variety of purposes and a variety of combustion flasks have been developed (Kelley et al., 1961; Eastham et al., 1961; Kalberer and Rutschmann, 1961; Martin and Harrison, 1962; Oliverio et al., 1962; Dobbs, 1963, 1966; Baxter and Senoner, 1964; Conway et al., 1966).

Approximately 300 mg dry sample can be combusted in a 2 litre flask. If the sample is less than 25 mg there is the possibility of incomplete combustion or the products may be difficult to collect. Therefore, when the radioactive sample is small, non-radioactive organic material such as filter paper or sucrose is added to provide sufficient combustion products for efficient collection. All kinds of non-volatile samples may be burned in the apparatus. Liquid samples are pipetted onto filter paper discs and dried, powders are wrapped in filter paper or enclosed in gelatin capsules, and dry tissues are wrapped in filter paper. Labelled micro-organisms can be collected on membrane filters, washed and dried. These burn exceptionally well because of the chemical nature of the membrane filters. Nichrome wire baskets may be used instead of platinum (Conway et al., 1966). The design of the flasks and the method of collecting products has varied. Perhaps the simplest is that of Oliverio et al. (1962) who used an unmodified 2 litre heavy-walled Erlenmeyer suction flask. The flask top was closed with a Neoprene rubber stopper which had a Pyrex glass rod extending through it to support the platinum sample basket. The side arm of the flask was closed with silicone rubber tubing which was clamped with a standard haemostat whose jaws were covered with gum rubber tubing. Samples are ignited in a shielded area† and after complete combustion the sample is cooled. For ^{3}H, Kelly et al. (1961) froze the water of combustion on the bottom of the flask placed in a shallow tray filled with dry ice and acetone. After 30 min, the flask was opened and 20 ml of liquid scintillator (similar to No. 1 in Table IV, but with 200 ml of methanol/litre toluene) was added and the sample allowed to return to room temp. This amount of liquid scintillator is sufficient to dissolve 0·18 ml of H_2O that would result from the combustion of 300 mg carbohydrate. Fifteen ml of the counting sample was transferred to a vial. For ^{3}H Oliverio et al. (1962) cooled the sample to produce negative pressure and attached a volumetric pipette containing 15 ml of liquid scintillator (similar to No. 1 in Table IV, but with 300 ml methanol/litre toluene) to the tubing on the side arm. The haemostat was removed and the liquid scintillator was drawn into the flask by the negative pressure. The fluid was swirled over the bottom of the

† Thomas-Ogg apparatus, Arthur Thomas, Philadelphia, Pa.

flask and the water was then condensed by placing the flask in a shallow cooling bath at $-15°C$. At the end of the condensing period an additional 3 ml of liquid scintillator was passed through the side arm silicone rubber tube to wash it cleanly into the flask. The flask now contained 18 ml of counting sample. Fifteen ml were withdrawn with a volumetric pipette for counting. Total counts are then 6/5 of the sample counted.

For ^{14}C the situation was somewhat different. Kelly et al. (1961) constructed a reservoir on the side arm of the suction flask and after cooling the sample to produce negative pressure a measured amount of CO_2 absorbant (HyOH) was placed in the reservoir and was drawn into the flask by the negative pressure. Thirty minutes was generally sufficient to absorb the CO_2. An aliquot was removed, mixed with a toluene scintillator (No. 1 in Table IV, no methanol) and counted. Oliverio et al. (1962) used the same flasks and procedure as they used for tritium except they used a liquid scintillator containing phenylethylamine as CO_2 absorber (No. 6, Table IV). Recoveries of ^{3}H and ^{14}C were excellent.

Perhaps the most elaborate combustion apparatus is that of Kalberer and Rutschmann (1961). Their flask differs fundamentally from other combustion flasks in that a finger is provided at the base of each round flask. This finger contains the absorbant for the combustion products and is added before combustion. The absorbants used by Kalberer and Rutschmann (1961) were methanol for $^{3}H_2O$ and 12% ethanolamine in methanol for $^{14}CO_2$ and $^{35}SO_4^{--}$. The absorbant is allowed to drain into the finger which is then immersed in a dry ice-acetone bath to reduce the vapour pressure of the methanol. In the original method the samples were ignited with an open flame and then inserted into the flask. Baxter and Senoner (1964) added electrical ignition to this type of flask. After combustion the flask is rotated for 20 min so the gases may be absorbed and then the solution is allowed to drain back into the finger. An aliquot is removed and transferred to a vial containing a suitable liquid scintillator. The principal advantage of this method is that the flask does not have to be opened to add absorbing solution. It is reported that several thousand combustions have been performed safely with this method. In general, Schöniger oxidations are completely safe and literally thousands of combustions have been performed without incident. Nonetheless, an occasional explosion has occurred with this method and the violence of such explosions is appalling. In practically every case the causes have been traced to residual organic vapours in the flask. The mixture of these vapours with pure oxygen provides the ingredients of a small bomb. Even though the vapour pressure of the methanol absorbant in the Kalberer-Rutschmann flask is reduced by cooling to $-70°C$, the potential hazard of the mixture of methanol vapours and pure oxygen in an improperly cooled sample has been

7

sufficient for most investigators to use flasks in which the absorbant is added after the combustion. It should be emphasized that flask cleaning must be adequate to remove residual radioactivity and solvent. The general practice of thorough washing and heating the flasks at 100°C for 16 h prior to re-use is recommended.

Eastham et al. (1961) trapped $^{35}SO_4^{--}$ with 0·5% aqueous H_2O_2, ^3H_2O with H_2O and $^{14}CO_2$ with tetramethyl ammonium hydroxide. Excellent results were reported for ^3H_2O and $^{35}SO_4^{--}$ but tetramethyl ammonium hydroxide was not an efficient absorber for $^{14}CO_2$. Phenylethylamine would perhaps be better.

Gupta (1966) described a system for combusting small samples (2–3 mg dry wt) directly in the vial used for liquid scintillation counting. The sample is mounted in a platinum–irridium coil in the vial which is then flushed with oxygen and sealed. Ignition was by infrared light and the vials were immersed briefly in liquid nitrogen. ^3H_2O was dissolved directly in liquid scintillator and $^{35}SO_4^{--}$ and $^{14}CO_2$ were absorbed first in phenylethylamine and then liquid scintillator was added. This system is restricted to small samples because of the oxygen capacity of the counting vial. It is quick, direct and the entire sample that is combusted is counted. This method might be useful in microbiological procedures for counting label in organisms that had been collected and washed on membrane filters.

At first glance Schöniger oxidation appears quite complex but in practice it is relatively simple and any laboratory that is confronted with counting ^3H and ^{14}C in diverse biological samples will find it to be an exceedingly useful technique.

E. Carbon dioxide from metabolic experiments

$^{14}CO_2$ evolved from either in vivo or in vitro reactions may be collected and counted by liquid scintillation counting. In general, the collection of metabolic $^{14}CO_2$ is an extension of combustion methods and many of the procedures described for combustion could be adapted readily for this purpose. Essentially all that is required is a closed system with a CO_2 absorber and some means of adding acid for the purpose of terminating the reaction and releasing all the CO_2.

The Warburg apparatus, with its constant temperature bath and shaking facility, and the closed flasks with centre wells and side arms, is especially suited for collecting metabolic CO_2, whether from living cells or individual reactions. The CO_2 absorbant is placed on the centre well and acid in a side arm. Because of the difficulty in removing a suitable aliquot of the absorbant for counting, Snyder and Godfrey (1961) described a modified Warburg flask in which the centre well was removable. After terminating the reaction and allowing time for $^{14}CO_2$ absorption, the entire well was removed and placed in a vial containing a suitable liquid scintillator. The presence of the glass well in the counting sample had no effect on total counts. Yardley (1964) used 20% KOH in the centre well and dissolved the $K_2{}^{14}CO_3$ in a methanol–toluene based liquid scintillator.

Kobayashi (1963) devised a procedure for determining the activity of histidine decarboxylase using aqueous HyOH as CO_2 absorbant. $^{14}CO_2$ may also be removed from air streams by passage through an absorber. HyOH and NCS are both particularly effective for this purpose. But whether static or flowing methods are used, various procedures have been devised for conveniently collecting $^{14}CO_2$ directly in counting vials (Godfrey and Snyder, 1962; Baggiolini and Bickel, 1965, 1966; Weyman et al., 1967).

V. QUENCH CORRECTIONS

A. General

The biggest disadvantage of liquid scintillation counting is that quenching occurs and the counting efficiency for a given isotope can vary from sample to sample. Unless the extent of quenching is known, and corrections applied, the counts from one sample cannot be compared with the counts from another. The problem of quenching is most severe for low energy isotopes and is of less consequence with high energy nuclides. Variations in counting efficiencies in homogeneous samples occur because of the presence of varying quantities of quenching agents in the counting sample. Quenching agents are considered to be of two types: chemical and colour. Chemical quenching agents are those that interfere with the transfer of energy from ionizing radiation to the scintillator. Colour quenching agents are those that absorb the photons emitted by the scintillator and reduce the total amount of light reaching the photomultiplier tubes. Simple dilution of the liquid scintillator also attenuates pulse heights and some investigators refer to this as dilution quenching. The effects are similar to chemical quenching. Severe chemical quenching agents include various types of compounds (Guinn, 1958), such as ketones, secondary and tertiary amines, nitro compounds, halogenated and sulphydryl compounds, and phenols. Less severe quenching agents include alcohols, primary amines and nitriles. For a given compound the amount of quenching is proportional to its concentration. In practice, many compounds of biological origin are quenchers.

Oxygen is a universal chemical quenching agent and the problems of oxygen quenching have been discussed by Seliger (1958). The effect is reversible and disappears on removal of oxygen. Solvents, made oxygen-free by distillation under vacuum, can be stored in air-tight containers.

Individual samples may be flushed with nitrogen or argon. Mahin (1966) described a way to reduce oxygen quenching in counting samples by treatment with liquid nitrogen. While these extra precautions may be indicated for precise physical measurements or for increases in counting efficiencies of low activity samples, their general applicability to routine counting samples appears doubtful. For routine counting, samples are prepared in equilibrium with air. Quenching by oxygen is assumed to be constant and is accepted as unavoidable. Chemical quenching may be reduced by careful selection of fluors and solvents and by optimizing the concentrations of each for the samples under investigation (Bush and Hansen 1965), but, in general, the problem of quenching is solved, not by avoiding or eliminating the quenching agent, but by devising methods to estimate the extent of quenching.

In principal, colour quenching can be overcome by removal of the coloured impurities in question, and in a limited number of cases this procedure has been applied successfully. Urine samples containing ^3H_2O have been decolorized with charcoal, or ^3H_2O has been distilled from the coloured impurities. Samples have been bleached with hydrogen peroxide (Herberg, 1960) or chlorine water (Shneour et al., 1962). For intensely coloured samples or where the label is contained in a coloured compound, the best procedure is combustion which eliminates all colour quenching and also reduces chemical quenching.

Various ways have been devised for determining the extent of quenching. The most widely used methods are internal and external standardization procedures and the channels ratio or pulse shift method. Several other lesser used procedures have been proposed and all of the various procedures have been reviewed by Peng (1966).

B. Internal standardization

The simplest way to establish the counting efficiency of a sample is with the internal standard procedure. The unknown sample is first counted, then a reference standard of known disintegration rate is added to the counting sample and the sample is recounted. From the additional counts of the standard, the counting efficiency of the sample may be calculated.

Reference standards are those whose activity has been determined by comparison with one or more absolute standards. Absolute standardization requires the determination of disintegration rate without reference to any other standard. Such procedures requires the use of complex and precise counting equipment and an expert interpretation of results. Absolute standards are thus quite expensive. For internal standardization in liquid scintillation counting, reference standards are adequate. Reference standards are available from some national standardizing laboratories (e.g., National

Bureau of Standards, Washington, D.C. and National Physical Laboratory, Teddington, England) but the usual source is from the normal suppliers of radioactive chemicals and counting equipment.

The counting efficiency is determined from the expression:

$$\text{Efficiency} = \frac{(\text{Int. Std.} + \text{Sample}) \text{ cpm} - \text{Sample cpm}}{\text{Int. Std. dpm}}$$

The corrected counting rate is obtained from the relation:

$$\text{Sample dpm} = \frac{\text{Sample cpm} - \text{background cpm}}{\text{Efficiency}}$$

The corrected disintegration rate of the sample thus obtained is directly comparable with rates of other samples so corrected.

The internal standardization procedure is straightforward and is widely used. According to Rogers and Moran (1966), it is the most accurate method for correcting quenching, provided sufficient care is exercised in adding the internal standard. Where only limited numbers of samples are involved it is probably the method of choice. However, the method is valid only when the sample counting efficiency is not changed by addition of the standard and the internal standard is in the same phase as the radioactive sample. The first condition is met by using small volumes of internal standard, but the volume must not be so small as to prevent accurate measurement. These opposing demands can be met by using 0·10 to 0·20 ml of internal standard per 10 to 15 ml of counting sample. The second demand is met in homogeneous samples by using a form of the label that is soluble in the counting sample (e.g., ^{14}C- or ^{3}H-toluene). For heterogeneous samples a solid standard with similar particle size and specific activity to the sample being counted is required. In practice, this requirement is difficult to meet.

It is important that no additional quenching be introduced into the sample either with the internal standard or from sources such as water of condensation from cooled samples.

Disadvantages of the internal method include the requirement for extra pipeting and resulting pipeting errors, and the necessity to recount samples. Also, the sample is lost for further recounting or any other type of assay.

C. External standardization

External standardization, a purely instrumental method, employs a strong γ-emitter such as ^{226}Ra, ^{241}Am, ^{137}Cs or ^{133}Ba which have radiations capable of penetrating the walls of the counting vial and generating recoil electrons in the liquid scintillator (Fleishman and Glazunov, 1962;

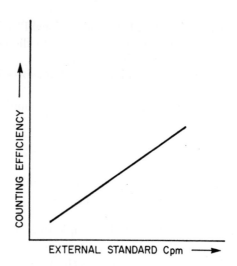

Fɪɢ. 3. Calibration curve for external standardization.

Higashimura *et al.*, 1962). After the sample has been counted, the external standard is brought into position near the vial and the sample is recounted. The number of counts contributed by the external standard is a function of the degreee of quenching of the counting sample.

The method is a graphical one and the graph is constructed in the following manner. Various quenching agents, colour and chemical, are added to liquid scintillators and the same amount of reference standard is added to each sample. The samples are counted and then recounted with the external standard in position. A graph is constructed in which per cent counting efficiency of the standards is plotted against external standard counts. The type of curve obtained is illustrated in Fig. 3. Counting efficiencies of unknown samples are read from the graph. Hayes (1966) has investigated the procedure in detail and found that, with the proper manipulation of counter and a ^{226}Ra source, a remarkably linear relationship between counting efficiency and external standard counts could be obtained.

The advantage of the external standard method is that it is faster and does not irreversibly alter the sample which is still available for recounting. The external standard method does not depend directly on sample counts and low level counts are no harder to standardize than high level counts. Many modern liquid scintillation counters are equipped with external standardization features. The external method does not eliminate the internal method because the calibration of the external standard curve requires the use of internal standards. The calibration curve so constructed should be of the same quenching chemistry as the routinely counted samples

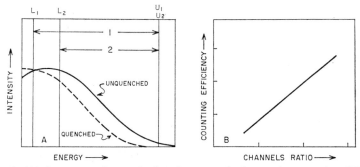

FIG. 4. (A) β-spectra of quenched and unquenched counting samples. (B) Calibration curve for standardization by channels ratio method.

and the calibration curve should be periodically recalibrated. The external method can be as accurate as the internal standard samples used for calibration, but according to Rogers and Moran (1966) it is less accurate than either internal standardization or channels ratio.

D. Channels ratio method

When quenching occurs, the average energy of the pulse height spectrum decreases and there is a downward shift in the pulse height spectrum (Fig. 4A). The channels ratio method, sometimes called the pulse shift method, is also purely an instrumental method for quench correction and requires a two channel instrument. This method, first proposed by Baille (1960), has been refined and modified (Bruno and Christian, 1961a; Bush, 1963). The discriminators of the instrument are set as in Fig. 4A. Channel 1 is set with lower and upper discriminators, L_1 and U_1, respectively, to include most of the pulse height distribution of the isotope being counted. Channel 2 is set with lower and upper discriminators, L_2 and U_2, respectively, to monitor the upper end of the energy spectrum. A ratio of counts in the two channels is thus obtained:

$$\frac{\text{cpm Channel 2}}{\text{cpm Channel 1}} = \text{Channels ratio.}$$

If there is no quenching this ratio will remain constant but if there is quenching the ratio will vary in proportion to the degree of quenching. As in external standardization this method of quench correction is a graphical one and the graph is prepared in a similar fashion. Reference standards are placed in liquid scintillators with various quenching agents, chemical and colour, and the samples are counted in a two channel instrument. The per cent efficiencies are plotted against channels ratio to give a correlation curve. The type of curve obtained is illustrated in Fig. 4B. Colour quenching agents give different correlation curves from chemical quenching agents. For unknown samples, the counting efficiency is read from the graph at the given channels ratio. The method is less accurate for tritium than for more energetic nuclides and also is less accurate than internal standardization for low level quenched samples (Rogers and Moran, 1966). For high level samples the accuracy is as good as or better than internal standardization. As with external standardization the accuracy of the channels ratio method depends on reference standards.

The channels ratio procedure has been modified by Caddock *et al.* (1967) in which the square root of the cpm in one channel is taken as a function of the square root of the cpm in the other channel. According to these workers this modification allows a statistically valid numerical rather than a graphical interpretation of quenching. It also allows estimates of standard errors of the activity. Because of its numerical nature the procedure has been designed for computer evaluation of data from liquid scintillation counting.

VI. DOUBLE LABELLING

A. General

Quite often it is necessary to use two isotopes simultaneously in tracer experiments. The isotopes may be contained in the same or separate compounds. Liquid scintillation counting is especially suitable for the simultaneous measurement of two nuclides. Although the most widely used pair of nuclides in biological experiments has been the weak β-emitters, ^{3}H and ^{14}C, many isotope pairs encountered in biological investigations have been counted by liquid scintillation counting. These pairs include ^{3}H-^{14}C (Okita *et al,,* 1957; Hendler, 1964; Bush, 1964), ^{3}H-^{22}Na (Hiebert and Hayes, 1958), ^{3}H-^{32}P (Doi and Spiegelman, 1962; Bush, 1964), ^{3}H-^{35}S (Weltman and Talmage, 1963), ^{14}C-^{32}P (Hendler, 1964; Bush, 1964), ^{14}C-^{35}S (Jeffay and Alvarez, 1961b), ^{14}C-^{36}Cl (Guinn, 1958), ^{14}C-^{131}I (Nestel *et al.*, 1962), ^{32}P-^{45}Ca (Lerch and Cosandy, 1966), ^{45}Ca-^{90}Sr (Hiebert and Hayes, 1958), ^{55}Fe-^{59}Fe (Dern, 1958; Eakins and Brown, 1966), and ^{90}Sr-^{90}Y (Uyesugi and Greenberg, 1965).

It is possible, in the case of a long lived isotope and a short-lived isotope (e.g., ^{14}C and ^{32}P), to make an initial count and then wait for the short lived isotope to decay. The remaining long lived isotope can be obtained by recount with the difference attributed to the short lived isotope. This would be practicable in only a few instances.

For most isotopes used in biological studies two approaches have been used: spectrometry and chemical separation of the isotopes.

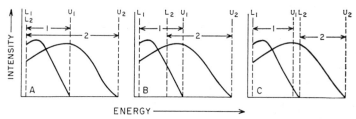

FIG. 5. β-Spectra of ^{3}H and ^{14}C with illustrative discriminator settings.

B. Simultaneous counting by spectrometry

When two isotopes differ in energy by a factor of at least 4, it is possible to discriminate between the counts contributed to the overall count by each isotope. Two different isotopes can be counted in the same vial. Simultaneous counting by spectrometry is thus an instrumental method based on the ability of the scintillation counter to separate the pulses produced by isotopes of different average energies. Because of the requirement for a 4-fold energy difference, isotope pairs like ^{3}H-^{14}C and ^{14}C-^{32}P can be counted simultaneously by spectrometry but ^{14}C-^{35}S cannot (Table I).

In the following discussion, ^{3}H and ^{14}C will be used as examples of lower and higher energy nuclides, respectively, but, in principle, the procedures apply to all pairs of isotopes capable of being counted by spectrometry. The discussion is concerned only with basic principles rather than specific instrument settings, etc. This information should be worked out from basic principles in conjunction with information supplied by the instrument manufacturers.

Okita *et al.* (1957) investigated three methods of counting ^{3}H and ^{14}C in the same sample: (1) screening, (2) simultaneous equations and (3) discriminator-ratios. The screening method can be executed with a single channel instrument; the others require at least a two channel instrument.

Energy spectral curves for ^{3}H and ^{14}C are illustrated in Fig. 5, with various discriminator settings defining channels 1 and 2. Each channel is controlled by its own discriminators. L_1, L_2 and U_1, U_2 are the lower and upper discriminator settings for channels 1 and 2 respectively.

The screening method consists of counting both isotopes together and then through instrumental settings (voltage, gain, etc.) screening out the lower energy isotope and recounting. Because of instrumental manipulation, the necessity of recounting and a high inherent standard error, this method has not found general favour. It is not suitable for automatic counting of many samples.

The simultaneous equation method uses discriminator settings illustrated in Fig. 5A, in which appreciable amounts of both isotopes are counted in two channels. The amount of each isotope is determined by solving the following simultaneous equations:

$$N_1 = D_H E_{H1} + D_C E_{C1} \tag{1}$$

$$N_2 = D_H E_{H2} + D_C E_{C2} \tag{2}$$

The notation is as follows:

N, D, C and E refer to net cpm, dpm, cpm and counting efficiency, respectively. Subscripts C, H, 1 and 2 refer to ^{14}C, ^{3}H and channels 1 and 2, respectively. Thus, $C_{C2} = D_C E_{C2}$ is to be read: the cpm of ^{14}C in channel 2 is equal to the dpm of ^{14}C times the counting efficiency of ^{14}C in channel 2. Solving (1) and (2) simultaneously,

$$D_H = \frac{N_1 E_{C2} - N_2 E_{C1}}{E_{H1} E_{C2} - E_{H2} E_{C1}} \tag{3}$$

$$D_C = \frac{N_1 E_{H2} - N_2 E_{H1}}{E_{C1} E_{H2} - E_{C2} E_{H1}} \tag{4}$$

Counting efficiencies E_{H1}, E_{H2}, E_{C1} and E_{C2} ared etermined in the respective channels with internal reference standards. In principle, the simultaneous equation procedure is applicable to any isotope pair. In practice, it is most useful where only a few unquenched samples are being counted. It is not readily applicable to automatic counting of avriably quenched samples.

Instrument settings for the discriminator-ratio procedure are illustrated in Fig. 5B. They are similar to the settings for the simultaneous equation method and the basic eqn. (5) and (6) are also similar. However, a ratio of isotope counts in each channel is defined by (7) and (8).

$$N_1 = D_{H1} E_{H1} + D_{C1} E_{C1} \tag{5}$$

$$N_2 = D_{H2} E_{H2} + D_{C2} E_{C2} \tag{6}$$

$$a = \frac{C_{H2}}{C_{H1}} = \frac{D_{H2} E_{H2}}{D_{H1} E_{H1}} \tag{7}$$

$$b = \frac{C_{C2}}{C_{C1}} = \frac{D_{C2} E_{C2}}{D_{C1} E_{C1}} \tag{8}$$

where the notation is the same as in eqn. (1) and (2).

Values from (7) and (8) are substituted into (6) which is solved for

$D_{C1}E_{C1}$. This value in turn is substituted into (5) which is solved for D_{H1},

$$D_{H1} = \frac{bN_1 - N_2}{E_{H1}(b-a)} \tag{9}$$

In a similar manner D_{C2} can be obtained,

$$D_{C2} = \frac{b(N_2 - aN_1)}{E_{C2}(b-a)} \tag{10}$$

In practice, the values a, b, E_{H1} and E_{C2} are determined with reference standards. The values N_1 and N_2 are obtained from the double labelled sample. In principle, the discriminator-ratio method is applicable for any isotope pair and, where relatively few unquenched samples (or samples of identical quenching) are being counted, may be the method of choice.

For simultaneously counting weak β-emitters in large numbers of variably quenched samples, especially where ^{3}H is involved, these methods require modification. Because of the attenuation and downward shift of the energy spectrum due to quenching (Fig. 4A), the counting efficiencies of the samples vary. Two things must be determined: the proportion of the net count in each channel attributable to each isotope and the counting efficiency of each particular sample. With discriminators set as shown in Fig. 5C the situation is improved. Channel 1 discriminators are set for maximum counting efficiency of ^{3}H and the L_2 discriminator of the ^{14}C channel is set to exclude 99·9% of ^{3}H in channel 2.

In this case the determination of ^{14}C in channel 2 is relatively simple. All that is needed is the ^{14}C cpm in channel 2 and the counting efficiency of the sample:

$$D_{C2} = \frac{C_{C2}}{E_{C2}} \tag{11}$$

The counts in channel 1 arise from ^{3}H and the ^{14}C that overlaps this channel. The dpm of ^{3}H in channel 1 is:

$$D_{H1} = \frac{N_1 - C_{C1}}{E_{H1}} \tag{12}$$

The difficulty arises from estimating the overlap of ^{14}C into ^{3}H especially when there are variable degrees of quenching. Various methods have been devised to estimate this overlap and to estimate the degree of quenching so that many samples can be counted automatically.

Hendler (1964) used a three channel instrument with the 3rd channel being used as a monitor to establish counting efficiencies of ^{14}C and ^{3}H with the channels ratio method. The Hendler procedure has been adapted

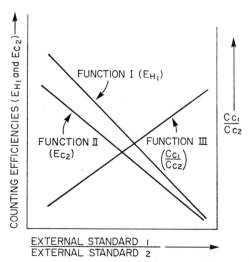

Fig. 6. Calibration curves for counting efficiencies of ^{3}H and ^{14}C, and for estimating the overlap of ^{14}C into the ^{3}H channel. Reproduced with permission of
Heyteni and Reynolds (1967).

to a computer program for automatic handling of large numbers of samples
(Ninomiya, 1966).

Aikman and Patterson (1967) used external standardization to establish
counting efficiencies of the isotopes and constructed a nomograph to determine the overlap of ^{14}C into channel 1. DeWachter and Fiers (1967) also
used external standardization for determination of counting efficiencies for
double labelled or triple labelled samples and estimated overlap through
equations and graphs.

The simplest procedure described to date is that of Heteyni and Reynolds
(1967) who used a two channel instrument with an external standard that
could be counted in both channels. Discriminators are set as in Fig. 5C
with 99·9% of ^{3}H being excluded from channel 2. A set of reference
standards, quenched over the range expected in the counting samples, is
prepared and counted (^{3}H only in channel 1 but ^{14}C in both channels 1 and
2). The external standard is then brought into position and the samples
are recounted in both channels. E_{H1}, E_{C2} and C_{C1}/C_{C2} are all linear functions of the external standard ratio (Ext Std$_1$/Ext Std$_2$) and all three
functions can be plotted on a single graph (Fig. 6).

In practice, after each double labelled sample is counted in channels
1 and 2, the external standard is counted in both channels. Then D_{C2} is
determined by eqn. 11, with E_{C2} being read from Function II. The overlap
of ^{14}C into channel 1 is determined with Function III ($C_{C1}/C_{C2} \times C_{C2} = C_{C1}$).
D_{H1} is then determined by eqn. 12 with E_{H1} being read from Function I.

This procedure is direct, simple and can be programmed for computer analysis.

Each procedure for estimating overlap into the lower energy isotope must be calibrated for each liquid scintillator and counter.

C. Chemical separation methods

An alternative approach to spectrometry for counting dual labelled samples is chemical and/or physical separation of the two isotopes. Isotopes that have similar energies cannot be separated by spectrometry and must be chemically separated. Mention has been made previously of the isotopes, ^{14}C and ^{35}S, which have essentially identical energies. Jeffay and Alvarez (1961b) used combustion techniques for this pair and then separated $^{14}CO_2$ and $Mg\,^{35}SO_4$ with quantitative recoveries of each.

Combustion techniques lend themseves to this procedure and many isotope pairs might be effectively separated and counted. ^3H and ^{14}C could easily be separated. After oxygen-flask combustion the ^3H_2O could be frozen out and $^{14}CO_2$ could be trapped in a suitable CO_2 absorber. For many of the isotope pairs mentioned, separation methods of combustion products would have to be established.

The disadvantage of chemical separation methods (when there is a choice) is the increased time required for each sample. The advantages are less critical instrument settings, simpler mathematical analysis and less complex calibration procedures. Furthermore the range of isotope ratios can be far greater than in spectrometry where the ratios of isotopes are more critical (Okita et al., 1957; Ninomiya, 1966).

VII. CHERENKOV COUNTING

When high energy β-particles pass through a medium with a speed greater than light, photons are produced. This bluish-white light or Cherenkov radiation, has a wavelength band between 3000 and 7000 Å (Jelley, 1958). The most familiar example of this type of radiation is seen in photographs of "swimming-pool" reactors in which a bluish-white light surrounds the core of the reactor. Cherenkov photons can be detected with photomultiplier tubes in the same fashion as in liquid scintillation counting.

In practice, Cherenkov radiation makes it possible to measure certain nuclides simply by placing solutions in a vial (without liquid scintillator) and counting them directly in an unmodified liquid scintillation counter. Although Cherenkov radiation is technically outside the scope of this article, as it does not require a liquid scintillator, the similarities in the detection process justify a small section on this type of radiation.

In water, an optically denser medium than air (index of refraction is
1·33), the lower energy limit of electrons for producing Cherenkov radiation
is 0·260 MeV. However, for β-emitters the maximum MeV has to substantially exceed this value because of the broad energy distribution
(Haberer, 1965). Because of the requirement for high energy nuclides,
Cherenkov detection will be of limited interest and utility to microbiologists.
However, because it offers the simplest means of detection, Rapkin (1964)
suggested the need for further investigations of Cherenkov counting of
high energy nuclides. Several such reports have appeared (Vemmer and
Guette, 1964; Haberer, 1965; Hoffmann, 1965; De Volpi and Porges,
1965; Parker and Elrick, 1966; Francois, 1967).

Nuclides that microbiologists might advantageously count by Cherenkov
detection include ^{24}Na, ^{32}P, ^{36}Cl, ^{40}K, ^{42}K, ^{47}Ca, and ^{56}Mn, all of which
have β-particles with energies of 0·7 MeV or greater (Table I). Parker and
Elrick (1966) found the following counting efficiencies by Cherenkov
radiation in a commercial liquid scintillation counter: ^{36}Cl, 2%; ^{47}Ca, 8%;
^{40}K, 14%; ^{24}Na, 18%; ^{32}P, 25% and ^{42}K, 60%. Vemmer and Guette
(1964) counted ^{32}P in polyethylene vials with 31% counting efficiency.
They counted ^{32}P and ^{45}Ca in the same sample by counting ^{32}P by Cherenkov radiation, allowing it to decay, and then counting ^{45}Ca by conventional
liquid scintillation techniques. De Volpi and Porges (1965) reported counting efficiencies of 40% for ^{56}Mn and 25% for ^{24}Na. Counting efficiencies
of these high energy nuclides by Cherenkov radiation are invariably lower
than with conventional liquid scintillation techniques where the counting
efficiencies would be better than 90% in most cases. Even so, Cherenkov
counting may offer attractive advantages. Other then placing the sample in
the vial, no preparation is necessary. There are no solubility problems with
fluors and solvents. Whereas 1 to 2 ml of aqueous sample can be incorporated into 20 ml of liquid scintillator, the entire vial can be filled with sample
in Cherenkov counting. In most cases the increased sample volume more
than compensates for lower counting efficiencies. The sample is unchanged
and can be completely recovered. Chemical quenching is virtually absent
and the presence of high salt concentrations has no effect on counting
efficiency. Haberer (1965) found that ^{40}K gave constant counting efficiencies
of 25% over the range of 0·1–14% potassium ion concentration. Parker
and Elrick (1966) counted ^{32}P in perchloric acid concentrations of 0–6·3M
and found chemical quenching of less than 1%.

With nuclides with energies greater than 1 MeV, where sample size is
sufficient and where salts would present problems in liquid scintillation
counting, Cherenkov counting is indicated. As an example, the procedure
would be ideally suited for ^{32}P-compounds eluted from columns with salt
gradients. Hoffmann (1965) found that the sensitivity of ^{32}P counting was

1·5 to 50 times greater with Cherenkov counting than with other means of detection.

To date most of the Cherenkov counting of aqueous samples has been with unmodified liquid scintillation counters and future modifications may improve counting efficiencies. Parker and Elrick (1966) found that the addition of a water soluble fluor (Na, K, 2-naphylamine-6, 8-disulphonic acid) to ^{32}P samples increased counting efficiencies from 25% to 50% but by so doing the major advantage of Cherenkov counting was lost.

It has been previously mentioned that Cherenkov radiation contributes to background counts in liquid scintillation counting. It also contributes to sample counts obtained in a liquid scintillator. Haberer (1965) reported that with a particle of 1 MeV energy, 10% of the total counts are of Cherenkov origin and with a 2 MeV particle 40% of the counts are from Cherenkov radiation.

ACKNOWLEDGEMENT

Assistance from the United States Public Health Service, Grant AI-06712, is gratefully acknowledged.

Note added in proof

A symposium was held at the Massachusetts Institute of Technology in the Spring of 1969 to consider recent developments of liquid scintillation counting. The proceedings were published: *The Current Status of Liquid Scintillation Counting*, ed. Bransome, E. R. Jr. Grune and Stratton, N.Y., 1970, 394 pp. This book contains additional information on theory, preparation of samples, quenching, Cherenkov counting and data reduction.

REFERENCES

Aikman, D. P., and Patterson, B. D. (1967). *Anal. Biochem.*, **18**, 185–190.
Baggiolini, M. (1965). *Experientia*, **21**, 731–733.
Baggiolini, M. (1966). *Anal. Biochem.*, **14**, 290–295.
Baille, L. A. (1960). *Intern. J. Appl. Radiation Isotopes*, **8**, 1–7.
Bartley, J. C., and Abraham, S. (1966). *In* "Adv. Tracer Methodology" (Ed. S. Rothchild), Vol. 3, pp. 69–79. Plenum Press, New York.
Baxter, C. F., and Senoner, I. (1964). *Anal. Biochem.*, **7**, 55–61.
Bell, C. G., and Hayes, F. N. (Eds.) (1958). "Liquid Scintillation Counting". Pergamon Press, New York.
Birks, J. B. (1964). "The Theory and Practice of Scintillation Counting". Pergamon Press, New York.
Bosquet, W. F., and Christian, J. E. (1960). *Anal. Chem.*, **32**, 722–723.
Bray, G. A. (1960). *Anal. Biochem.*, **1**, 279–285.
Bruno, G. A., and Christian, J. E. (1961a). *Anal. Chem.*, **33**, 650–651.
Bruno, G. A., and Christian, J. E. (1961b). *Anal. Chem.*, **33**, 1216–1218.
Buchanan, D. L., and Corcoran, B. J. (1959). *Anal. Chem.*, **31**, 1635–1638.
Bush, E. T. (1963). *Anal. Chem.*, **35**, 1024–1029.
Bush, E. T. (1964). *Anal. Chem.*, **36**, 1082–1089.

Bush, E. T., and Hansen, D. L. (1965). *In* "Radioisotope Sample Measurement Techniques in Medicine and Biology", pp. 395–408, I.A.E.A., Vienna.

Caddock, B. D., Davies, P. T., and Deterding, J. H. (1967). *Intern. J. Appl. Radiation Isotopes*, **18**, 209–214.

Conway, W. D., Grace, A. J., and Rogers, J. E. (1966). *Anal. Biochem.*, **14**, 491–494.

Davidson, J. D., and Feigelson, P. (1957). *Intern. J. Appl. Radiation Isotopes*, **2**, 1–18.

Dern, R. J. (1958). *In* "Liquid Scintillation Counting" (Eds C. G. Bell and F. N. Haynes), pp. 205–210 Pergamon Press, New York.

DeVolpi, A., and Porges, K. G. A. (1965). *Intern. J. Appl. Radiation Isotopes*, **16**, 496–498.

DeWachter, R., and Fiers, W. (1967). *Anal. Biochem.*, **18**, 351–374.

Dobbs, H. E. (1963). *Anal. Chem.*, **35**, 783–786.

Dobbs, H. E. (1966). *Intern. J. Appl. Radiation Isotopes*, **17**, 363–364.

Doi, R. H., and Spiegelman, S. (1962). *Science*, **138**, 1271–1272.

Eakins, J. D., and Brown, D. A. (1966). *Intern. J. Appl. Radiation Isotopes*, **17**, 391–397.

Eastham, J. F., Westbrook, H. L., and Gonzales, D. (1962). *In* "Tritium in the Physical and Biological Sciences", pp. 203–209, I.A.E.A., Vienna.

Edwards, B., and Kitchener, J. A. (1965). *Intern. J. Appl. Radiation Isotopes*, **16**, 445–446.

Elwyn, D. H. (1965). *In* "Adv. Tracer Methodology" (Ed. S. Rothchild), Vol. 2, pp. 115–122. Plenum Press, New York.

Fleishman, D. G., and Glazunov, V. V. (1962). *Pribory i Tekhnika Eksperimenta*, **7**, 55–58.

Francis, G. E., and Hawkins, J. D. (1967). *Intern. J. Appl. Radiation Isotopes*, **18**, 223–230.

Francois, B. (1967). *Intern. J. Appl. Radiation Isotopes*, **18**, 525–531.

Funt, B. L. (1956) *Nucleonics* **14** (8), 83–84.

Funt, B. L., and Hetherington, A. (1957). *Science*, **125**, 986–987.

Funt, B. L., and Hetherington, A. (1959). *Science*, **129**, 1429–1430.

Furst, M., and Kallmann, H. (1955a). *J. Chem. Phys.*, **23**, 607–612.

Furst, M., and Kallmann, H. (1955b). *Phys. Rev.*, **97**, 583–587.

Furst, M., Kallmann, H., and Brown, F. H. (1955c). *Nucleonics*, **13** (4), 58–59.

Furst, M., Kallmann, H., and Brown, F. H. (1957). *J. Chem. Phys.*, **26**, 1321–1332.

Gill, D. M. (1964). *Nature, Lond.*, **202**, 626.

Gill, D. M. (1967). *Intern. J. Appl. Radiation Isotopes*, **18**, 393–398.

Godfrey, P., and Snyder, F. (1962). *Anal. Biochem.*, **4**, 310–315.

Guinn, V. P. (1958). *In*. "Liquid Scintillation Counting" (Eds C. G. Bell and F. N. Hayes), pp. 166–182. Pergamon Press, New York.

Gupta, G. N. (1966). *Anal. Chem.*, **38**, 1356–1359.

Haberer, K. (1965). *Atomwirtschaft*, **10** (1), 36–43.

Hall, T. C., and Cocking, E. C. (1965). *Biochem. J.*, **96**, 626–633.

Hansen, D. L., and Bush, E. T. (1967). *Anal. Biochem.*, **18**, 320–332.

Hash, J. H. (1962). *Anal. Biochem.*, **4**, 257–267.

Hash, J. H., Wishnick, M., and Miller, P. A. (1964). *J. Biol. Chem.*, **239**, 2070–2078.

Hayes, F. N., Hiebert, R. D., and Schuch, R. L. (1952). *Science*, **116**, 140.

Hayes, F. N., and Gould, R. G. (1953). *Science*, **117**, 480–482.

Hayes, F. N., Rogers, B. S., and Sanders, P. C. (1955a). *Nucleonics*, **13** (1), 46–48.
Hayes, F. N., Ott, D. G., Kerr, V. N., and Rogers, B. S. (1955b). *Nucleonics*, **13** (12), 38–41.
Hayes, F. N. (1956a). *Nucleonics*, **14** (1), 42–45.
Hayes, F. N., Rogers, B. S., and Langham, W. H. (1956b). *Nucleonics*, **14** (3), 48–51.
Hayes, F. N. (1958). *In* "Liquid Scintillation Counting" (Eds C. G. Bell and F. N. Hayes), pp. 83–87. Pergamon Press, New York.
Hayes, F. N. (1966). *In* "Adv. Tracer Methodology" (Ed. S. Rothchild), Vol. 3, pp. 95–106. Plenum Press, New York.
Heimbuch, A. H., and Schwarz, W. J. (1964). *Atompraxis*, **10**, 70–74.
Helf, S. (1958). *In* "Liquid Scintillation Counting" (Eds C. G. Bell and F. N. Hayes), pp. 96–100. Pergamon Press, New York.
Helf, S., White, C. G., and Shelley, R. N. (1960). *Anal. Chem.*, **32**, 238–241.
Hendler, R. W. (1964). *Anal. Biochem.*, **7**, 110–120.
Herberg, R. J. (1958). *Science*, **128**, 199–200.
Herberg, R. J. (1960). *Anal. Chem.*, **32**, 42–46.
Herberg, R. J. (1961). *Anal. Chem.*, **33**, 1308–1311.
Hetenyi, G., and Reynolds, J. (1967). *Intern. J. Appl. Radiation Isotopes*, **18**, 331–332.
Hiebert, R. D., and Hayes, F. N. (1958). *In* "Liquid Scintillation Counting (Eds C. G. Bell and F. N. Hayes), pp. 41–49. Pergamon Press, New York.
Higashimura, T., Yamada, O., Nohara, N., and Shidei, T. (1962). *Intern. J. Appl. Radiation Isotopes*, **13**, 308–309.
Hodgson, T. S., Gordon, B. E., and Ackerman, M. E. (1958). *Nucleonics*, **16** (7), 89–94.
Hoffman, W. (1965). *Radiochim. Acta*, **4** (3), 117–119.
Horrocks, D. L. (1964). *Rev. Sci. Instru.*, **35**, 334–340.
Horrocks, D. L. (1966). *Intern. J. Appl. Radiation Isotopes*, **17**, 441–446.
Jacobson, H. I., Gupta, G. N., Fernandez, C., Hennix, S., and Jenson, E. V. (1960). *Arch. Biochem. Biophys.*, **86**, 89–93.
Jeffay, H., Olubajo, F., and Jewell, W. R. (1960). *Anal. Chem.*, **32**, 306–308.
Jeffay, H., and Alvarez, J. (1961a). *Anal. Chem.*, **33**, 612–615.
Jeffay, H., and Alvarez, J. (1961b). *Anal. Biochem.*, **2**, 506–508.
Jelley, J. V. (1958). "Cherenkov Radiation and Its Applications". Pergamon Press, New York.
Kalberer, F., and Rutschmann, J. (1961). *Helvetica Chimica Acta*, **44**, 1956–1966.
Kallmann, H., and Furst, M. (1950). *Phys. Revs.*, **79**, 857–870.
Kallmann, H., and Furst, M. (1951). *Nucleonics*, **8** (8), 32–39.
Kallman, H., and Furst, M. (1958). *In* "Liquid Scintillation Counting" (Eds C. G. Bell and F. N. Hayes), pp. 3–22. Pergamon Press, New York.
Karmen, A., McCaffrey, I., and Bowman, R. L. (1962). *J. Lipid Res.*, **3**, 372–377.
Karman, A., McCaffrey, I., Winkelman, J. W., and Bowman, R. L. (1963). *Anal. Chem.*, **35**, 536–542.
Katz, J., Abraham, S., and Baker, N. (1954). *Anal. Chem.*, **26**, 1503–1504.
Kaufman, A. J., Nir, A., Parks, G., and Hours, R. M. (1962). *In* "Tritium in the Physical and Biological Sciences", pp. 249–261, I.A.E.A., Vienna.
Kelley, R. G., Peets, E. A., Gordon, S., and Buyske, D. A. (1961). *Anal. Biochem.*, **2**, 267–273.
Kinard, F. E. (1957). *Rev. Sci. Instr.*, **28**, 293–294.

Kinnory, D. S., Kanabrocki, E. L., Greco, J., Veatch, R. L., Kaplan, E., and Oester, Y. T. (1958). *In* "Liquid Scintillation Counting" (Eds C. G. Bell and F. N. Hayes), pp. 223–229. Pergamon Press, New York.

Kirsten, W. J., and Carlsson, M. E. (1960). *Microchem. J.*, **4**, 3–31.

Kobayashi, Y. (1963). *Anal. Biochem.*, **5**, 284–290.

Koenig, E., and Brattgard, S. O. (1963). *Anal. Biochem.* **6**, 424–434.

Kowalski, E., Anliker, R., and Schmid, K. (1967). *Intern. J. Appl. Radiation Isotopes*, **18**, 307–323.

Krebs, A. T. (1955). *Science*, **122**, 17–18.

Lerch, P., and Cosandy, M. (1966). *In* "Adv. Tracer Methodology" (Ed. S. Rothchild), Vol. 3, pp. 107–117. Plenum Press, New York.

Luria, S. E. (1960). *In* "The Bacteria" (Eds I. C. Gunsalus and R. Y. Stanier), Vol. 1, pp. 1–34. Academic Press, New York.

Mahin, D. T. (1966). *Intern. J. Appl. Radiation Isotopes*, **17**, 185–189.

Mans, R. J., and Novelli, G. D. (1961). *Arch. Biochem. Biophys.*, **94**, 48–53.

Martin, L. E., and Harrison, C. (1962). *Biochem. J.*, **82**, 18P.

McFarlane, A. S., and Murray, K. (1963). *Anal. Biochem.*, **6**, 284–286.

Meade, R. C., and Stiglitz, R. A. (1962). *Intern. J. Appl. Radiation Isotopes*, **13**, 11–14.

Myers, L. S., and Brush, A. H. (1962). *Anal. Chem.*, **34**, 342–345.

Nathan, D. G., Davidson, J. G., Waggoner, J. G., and Berlin, N. J. (1958). *J. Lab. Clin. Med.*, **52**, 915–917.

Nestel, P. J., Havel, R. J., and Bezman, A. (1962). *J. Clin. Invest.*, **41**, 1915–1921.

Neujahr, H. Y., and Ewaldson, B. (1964). *Anal. Biochem.*, **8**, 487–494.

Ninomiya, R. (1966). *Intern. J. Appl. Radiation Isotopes*, **17**, 355–358.

Okita, G. T., Kabara, J. J., Richardson, F., and LeRoy, G. V. (1957). *Nucleonics*, **15** (6), 111–114.

Oliverio, V. T., Denham, C., and Davidson, J. D. (1962). *Anal. Biochem.*, **4**, 188–189.

Ott, D. G. (1958). *In* "Liquid Scintillation Counting" (Eds C. G. Bell and F. N. Hayes), pp. 101–107. Pergamon Press, New York.

Ott, D. G., Richmond, C. R., Trujillo, T. T., and Foreman, H. (1959). *Nucleonics*, **17** (9), 106–108.

Parker, R. P., and Elrick, R. H. (1966). *Intern. J. Appl. Radiation Isotopes*, **17**, 361–362.

Passmann, J. M., Radin, N. S., and Cooper, J. A. D. (1956). *Anal. Chem.*, **28**, 484–486.

Patterson, M. S., and Greene, R. C. (1965). *Anal. Chem.*, **37**, 854–857.

Payne, P. R., and Done, J. (1954). *Nature, Lond.*, **174**, 27–28.

Peets, E. A., Florini, J. R., and Buyske, D. A. (1960). *Anal. Chem.*, **32**, 1465–1468.

Peng, C. T. (1966). *In* "Adv. Tracer Methodology" (Ed. S. Rothchild), Vol. 3, pp. 81–94. Plenum Press, New York.

Petroff, C. P., Patt, H. H., and Nair, P. P. (1965). *Intern. J. Appl. Radiation Isotopes*, **16**, 599–601.

Piez, K. (1962). *Anal. Biochem.*, **4**, 444–458.

Rapkin, E., and Gibbs, J. A. (1963). *Intern. J. Appl. Radiation Isotopes*, **14**, 71–74.

Rapkin, E. (1964). *Intern. J. Appl. Radiation Isotopes*, **15**, 69–87.

Reynolds, G. T., Harrison, F. B., and Salvini, G. (1950). *Phys. Revs.*, **78**, 488.

Rogers, A. W., and Moran, J. F. (1966). *Anal. Biochem.*, **16**, 206–219.

Scales, B. (1967). *Intern. J. Appl. Radiation Isotopes*, **18**, 1–6.
Scharpenseel, H. W., and Menke, K. W. (1962). *In* "Tritium in the Physical and Biological Sciences". pp. 281–302. I. A.E.A., Vienna.
Schöniger, W. (1955). *Microchim. Acta*, **1**, 123–129.
Schram, E., and Lombaert, R. (1957). *Anal. Chim. Acta*, **17**, 417–422.
Schram, E., and Lombaert, R. (1962). *Anal. Biochem.*, **3**, 68–74.
Schram, E., and Lombaert, R. (1963). "Organic Scintillation Detectors". Elsevier Pub. Co., New York.
Seliger, H. H. (1958). *In* "Liquid Scintillation Counting" (Eds C. G. Bell and F. N. Hayes), pp. 115–122. Pergamon Press, New York.
Sheppard, H., and Rodegkar, W. (1962). *Anal. Biochem.*, **4**, 246–251.
Shneour, E. A., Arnoff, S., and Kirk, M. R. (1962). *Intern. J. Appl. Radiation Isotopes*, **13**, 623–627.
Snyder, F., and Godfrey, P. (1961). *J. Lipid Res.*, **2**, 195.
Steinberg, D. (1959). *Nature, Lond.*, **183**, 1253–1254.
Steinberg, D. (1960). *Anal. Biochem.*, **1**, 23–39.
Swank, R. K. (1954). *Ann. Rev. Nuc. Sci.*, **4**, 111–140.
Swank, R. K. (1958). *In* "Liquid Scintillation Counting" (Eds C. G. Bell and F. N. Hayes), pp. 23–38. Pergamon Press, New York.
Trachuk, R. (1962). *Can. J. Chem.*, **40**, 2348–2356.
Uyesugi, G. S., and Greenberg, A. E. (1965). *Intern. J. Appl. Radiation Isotopes*, **16**, 581–587.
Van der Laarse, J. D. (1967). *Intern. J. Appl. Radiation Isotopes*, **18**, 485–491.
Van Slyke, D. D., and Folch, J. (1940). *J. Biol. Chem.*, **136**, 509–541.
Vemmer, H., and Guette, J. O. (1964). *Atompraxis*, **10** (11), 475–477.
Vaughan, M., Steinberg, D., and Logan, J. (1957). *Science*, **126**, 446–447.
Wang, C. H., and Jones, D. E. (1959). *Biochem. Biophys. Res. Communs.*, **1**, 203–205.
Wang, C. H., and Willis, D. L. (1965). "Radiotracer Methodology in Biological Science". Prentice-Hall, Inc., Englewood Cliffs, N.J.
Weg. M. W. (1962). *Nature, Lond.*, **194**, 180–181.
Weltman, J. K., and Talmage, D. W. (1963). *Intern. J. Appl. Radiation Isotopes*, **14**, 541–548.
Weyman, A. K., Williams, J. C., and Plentl, A. A. (1967). *Anal. Biochem.*, **19**, 441–447.
White, C. G., and Helf, S. (1956). *Nucleonics*, **14** (10), 46–48.
Woeller, F. H. (1961). *Anal. Biochem.*, **2**, 508–511.
Yardley, H. J. (1964). *Nature, Lond.*, **204**, 281.

CHAPTER VI

The Use of Isotopes in Tracing Metabolic Pathways

J. R. QUAYLE

Department of Microbiology, University of Sheffield, England

I. OUTLINE OF THE PROBLEM

In many cases isotopic experiments performed with the object of tracing pathways of cell constituent biosynthesis have either of two main objectives—

(a) The determination of the ultimate fate of an isotopic compound in terms of its incorporation into a particular end product. The end product could be a chemical compound, such as a steroid, or a major cellular fraction, such as protein, or a specific organelle, such as the mitochondrion.

(b) The determination of the more immediate fate of an isotopic compound during its incorporation into, or total biosynthesis of, the pool of intermediary metabolites which are used as precursors of the cellular materials mentioned under (a).

These two kinds of objective usually demand quite different types of experimentation. In (a) the general approach is to administer isotope to the cells, allow a suitable time interval (in many cases this may be a long one or will involve actual growth of the cells), fractionate the cells and determine the distribution of isotope in the resulting fractions. If the biosynthesis of a particular compound is being studied, the compound may be isolated and the intramolecular distribution of isotope determined. Over the entire experiment there may be few techniques involved that result specifically from the use of the isotope beyond its administration, assay and determination of its distribution in a particular compound. The special methods that are needed for this kind of experiment are mainly those of fractionation of cell components and chemical compounds. Such methods lie outside the scope of this Chapter. In (b), however, specialized isotopic techniques are involved. It is the very different time scale between experiments of type (a) and (b) that in the main has dictated the development of these special techniques. This Chapter is devoted to a description of such techniques.

Much of the pioneering work on the use of isotopes for tracing metabolic pathways amongst intermediary metabolites is due to Calvin and his colleagues who have developed the techniques during their studies of the path of carbon in photosynthesis (Bassham and Calvin, 1957, 1960; Calvin and Bassham, 1962). The approaches and techniques they devised may be subdivided under the two following main headings.

A. Study of the variation of isotopic labelling pattern with time

For reasons that will be discussed later, this first approach has been used in a greater variety of problems than has the second one. The approach is basically a simple one, and is illustrated by the following example. If isotope is administered to a metabolic sequence represented by A → B → C → D → E, and the isotope enters the pathway via compound A, then if the percentage of fixed isotope present in each of the compounds A–E is plotted against time of incubation, a family of curves such as that shown in Fig. 1 will be obtained. The shapes and slopes of each of the curves will, of course, vary widely from one system to another; however, one feature remains constant, viz., the slope of the percentage plot for the compound that serves as the port of entry for the isotope is negative, whereas for all compounds derived therefrom the slopes of the plots are positive. An experiment of this type can thus be of great utility in determining, firstly, the point of entry of an isotopic compound into a sequence of intermediary metabolites and, secondly, whether the rate of labelling of compounds is in fact rapid enough for them to be considered as intermediary metabolites on a particular pathway. There are many examples of the use of this simple technique both with photosynthetic and non-photosynthetic organisms (Bergmann et al., 1958; Kornberg, 1958; Quayle and Keech, 1959; Knight, 1962; Trüper, 1964; Fuller et al., 1961; McGilvray and Morris, 1969; Dagley and Nicholson, 1970).

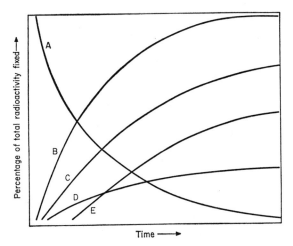

Fɪɢ. 1. Typical isotope-incorporation curves.

There are several limitations and complications of the experiment to be borne in mind.

(*i*) The shapes and slopes of the curves depend on the relative pool sizes of the intermediates. If the pool size of an intermediate is very small, e.g., if the intermediate remains enzyme bound during its transformation to product, it may not show up in the analysis. Hence its function as a port of entry, or even as an intermediary metabolite at all, may be missed. A good example of this can be seen in the initial non-detection by Ljungdahl and Wood (1965) of intermediates between carbon dioxide and acetate in the homoacetate fermentation of *Clostridium thermoaceticum*. Later work, in which 350–400 g (wet weight) of *Cl. thermoaceticum* was incubated with 2 mCi of $^{14}CO_2$, showed that enzyme-bound methyl corrinoids were intermediates in the overall conversion of carbon dioxide to acetate (Ljungdahl *et al.*, 1965; Ljungdahl and Wood, 1969; Sun *et al.*, 1969).

(*ii*) Some compounds may not be stable to the necessary chromatographic analysis.

(*iii*) There may be more than one port of entry for the isotope and hence more than one negative slope in a percentage plot, e.g., carboxylation of phosphoenolpyruvate as well as ribulose 1,5-diphosphate during photosynthesis.

(*iv*) The rapidity of the reactions may result in too many compounds being labelled even in a very short time of incubation. The steepness of the negative slope for the first labelled compound (and hence its diagnostic utility) very rapidly diminishes with time as the isotope spreads into several metabolites. This limitation has led to the development of several rapid sampling devices which will be discussed later.

B. Study of changes in the pool sizes of intermediary metabolites following an environmental change

A completely different approach from the one described above was devised by Calvin and Massini (1952). They pointed out that if a suspension of organisms under steady-state conditions is fed with radioactive growth substrate, all the pools of intermediary metabolites will become radioactive and quickly attain the specific activity of the labelled growth substrate. If the organism is killed rapidly at this stage and its intermediary metabolites separated, then the amounts of radioactivity present in each compound will be in direct proportion to the individual pool sizes. This enables the effect of an environmental change on the pool sizes of a large number of intermediary metabolites to be determined simultaneously. Application of this idea to the problem of photosynthesis led directly to the iden tification of the acceptor compound for carbon dioxide (ribulose 1,5-diphosphate).

The technique demands sophisticated equipment that is capable of maintaining a suspension of micro-organisms in steady-state conditions, of monitoring oxygen tension, carbon dioxide tension and radioactivity, of imposing rapid changes of environment on the culture and of sampling rapidly after the environmental change. (Bassham and Kirk, 1960; Smith et al., 1961; Pedersen et al., 1966.)

C. Comparison of the two approaches

Application of the second approach has been very successful in work with photosynthetic organisms, but there are difficulties in its application to problems of non-photosynthetic metabolism. The reason is that changes in the supply of carbon substrate (CO_2), energy (light) or oxidant (O_2) may be made independently of one another in the case of a photosynthetic organism, whereas in the case of a heterotrophic organism, the sources of carbon, intracellular carbon dioxide, and energy all spring from the substrate itself. Variation of any one of these parameters independently of the others is thus difficult or impossible to achieve. This difficulty, coupled with the complexity of the apparatus required, has resulted in the more widespread use of the first approach for mapping out the immediate fate of a radioactive substrate. For these reasons, this Chapter is devoted mainly to the first technique. It should be noted, however, that rapid sampling devices as well as the chromatographic and autoradiographic systems that will be described are an essential part of *both* approaches.

II. PERFORMANCE OF THE EXPERIMENT

The performance of the whole experiment may be divided into five main stages, each of which will be dealt with in turn.

A. Incubation of the microbial suspension with isotope

The particular procedure to be followed depends on several factors, such as the scale of the experiment, the nature of the organism (whether aerobic, anaerobic or photosynthetic) and the nature of the isotopic compound (whether gaseous or in solution).

1. *Scale of the experiment*

The scale of the experiment is an important factor that must be carefully considered beforehand. The scale chosen is usually a compromise between several mutually opposing requirements. Ultimately, if two-dimensional paper chromatography is to be used as the separation method, then a sample of cell extract has to be applied to a paper chromatogram such that the concentration of salts and metabolites is not too high to upset the chromatography and, at the same time, it must contain sufficient isotope in the metabolites for them to be located and assayed. It may not be open to the investigator to increase the amount of radioactivity in the sample by increasing the time of exposure of the cells to isotope in the initial experiment. The essence of many of these experiments, as explained earlier, lies in very brief incubation times with isotope. Increase of cell density beyond a certain point, apart from causing trouble with chromatography, may lead to establishment of undesirable incubation conditions, such as partial anaerobiosis. Increase of isotope concentration beyond the saturation level with respect to the organism will merely waste isotope to no effect. In the face of these many variables, each particular system may have to be worked out in preliminary trial experiments. Nevertheless it may be useful to give a set of conditions that approximate to those which have been used in several studies of this type with aerobic organisms.

The organisms are harvested in the exponential phase of growth and re-suspended in 9 ml of fresh medium to a cell density of 2–10 mg dry wt/ml. This medium is usually a simplified growth medium, e.g., one merely containing buffer (e.g., 10 mM phosphate) a source of nitrogen and sulphur (e.g., 10 mM $(NH_4)_2SO_4$) and phosphorus, if the buffer is not already a phosphate buffer. If the isotope to be introduced is the same as the primary source of carbon in the medium, then care should be taken that the re-suspending medium does not contain too high a concentration (e.g., in excess of 10 mM) of this unlabelled substrate, such that its excess will dilute the specific activity of the administered isotope too much. The cell suspension is then aerated in a bubbler (see below) for about 5 min to minimize the effect of a lag in growth of the organism, and 1 ml of isotope solution, containing approximately 200 μC of isotope, is then added rapidly. Samples of 1 ml are then withdrawn as detailed below. These conditions are such that, after appropriate treatment of the samples, half of each may be subjected to two-dimensional chromatography, followed by autoradiography, with a reasonable chance of acceptable chromatography and sufficient isotope fixed in the early-time samples.

2. *Nature of the organism*

(a) *Aerobic*. The apparatus necessary for the incubation may be very simple if the isotope is introduced manually and samples are withdrawn by hypodermic syringe. A simple apparatus that has been used for the purpose in several laboratories is shown in Fig. 2. The vessel is partly submerged in a water bath at the appropriate temperature and the experiment is conducted in a well-ventilated fume cupboard. The bacterial suspension (approximately 10 ml) is vigorously aerated by blowing air through the sintered-glass bottom. Isotope is pipetted in at zero time and samples (1 ml) withdrawn by hypodermic syringe. With practice a sample can be withdrawn about every 10 sec. If faster sampling is required, resort has to be made to one of the special devices described in Section II B. Metabolic rates may of course be slowed down by working at lower temperatures.

(b) *Anaerobic*. Incubation under anaerobic conditions calls for more specialized apparatus permitting sampling to be performed without allowing air to enter.

A simple apparatus is illustrated in Fig. 3, which has been used by Knight (1962) to study the kinetics of uptake of radioactive substrates by *Rhodospirillum rubrum* anaerobically in the light. The apparatus was made from a medical flat bottle (50 ml) to the neck of which was cemented a B14 standard socket with a gas inlet and outlet. The gas mixture used for flushing was maintained at a positive pressure of approximately 20 cm of water. A hole, A, was cut into the bottle to accommodate a tap (2-mm bore) for sampling. A second hole, B, cut in the side, was closed with a rubber Subaseal cap, through which the substrate was injected with a hypodermic syringe. The contents of the vessel were stirred by a magnetic stirring bar rotating on the back wall of the vessel. Suspensions of bacteria (40 ml containing 5–10 mg dry wt of bacteria/ml) were placed in the vessel, unlabelled substrate was added, and the suspension stirred for 10 min before injecting in the isotope. Samples were then withdrawn through the tap.

It will be noted that forms of apparatus, such as those illustrated in Fig. 2 and Fig. 3 deliver samples of variable volume depending on the accuracy of rapid handling of a hypodermic syringe or on the amount of liquid allowed through a stopcock. Variability of sample size may not be of importance in construction of percentage plots of the type illustrated in Fig. 1; if

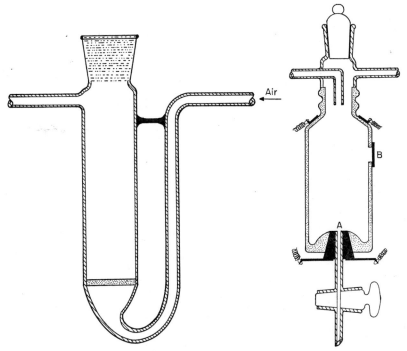

FIG. 2. Bubbler vessel for incubation of aerobic organisms with isotope.

FIG. 3. Apparatus for incubation of photosynthetic anaerobes with isotope. (From Knight, 1962.)

it is of importance, the actual sample size may be determined by weighing the receivers into which the samples are placed. There are however devices that have been designed to deliver rapidly samples of constant volume; as an example, an apparatus designed by Trüper (1964) for studying isotope incorporation by *Chromatium okenii* is illustrated in Fig. 4. The apparatus was made from a Plexiglass chamber, A (inner diameter 12 cm, depth 2 cm), secured to a detachable back plate, B. The chamber possessed three entry ports; C for flushing gas and isotope, D for addition of medium and E for a thermometer. The sampling device consisted of a rod, F (1·4 cm diameter), that could both be rotated and slid backwards and forwards within its barrel, G. A cavity, H (1·4 ml volume), was cut into the rod. The suspension was then sampled by the sequence of operations shown in Fig. 5(a), (b) and (c), in which F was twisted through 90°, slid forward, turned back through 90°, and then returned for the next sample. The sample was blown out of the cavity each time by the flushing gas present under positive pressure in tube I.

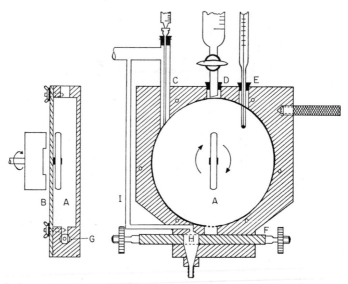

FIG. 4. Apparatus for incubation of photosynthetic anaerobes with isotope, fitted with semi-automatic sampler. (From Trüper, 1964.)

The two kinds of apparatus depicted in Fig. 3 and 4 were both originally designed for anaerobic work. They can of course be used equally well with aerobic organisms if a suitable flushing gas is used.

(c) *Photosynthetic.* Incubation vessels used for photosynthetic organisms must be relatively thin in section so as to allow penetration of the microbial suspension by the light. The simplest form of apparatus is the "lollipop" (Bassham and Calvin, 1960) consisting of a thin cylindrical vessel fitted with a tap at the bottom and openings at the top for gas exchange and addition of medium. The two kinds of apparatus described in Fig. 3 and 4 are also suitable for use with photosynthetic organisms, given an appropriate light source.

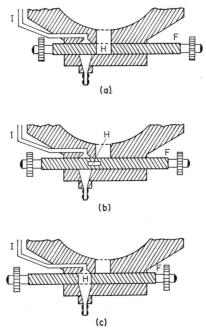

Fig. 5. Detail of semi-automatic sampler. (From Trüper, 1964.)

3. *Nature of isotope*

(a) *Non-volatile.* The addition of isotope at the start of the experiment presents little difficulty when the isotope is non-volatile and in aqueous solution.

(b) *Volatile or gaseous.* Those isotopes that are volatile or can be liberated from solution as gases, e.g., carbon dioxide, may require closed-circuit apparatus, although it should be emphasized that where short-term exposure experiments are being performed, rather than steady-state experiments, such apparatus may not always be necessary. If the gaseous isotope can be condensed *in vacuo* with liquid air, then it may be introduced into closed circuit apparatus by means of the loop shown in Fig. 6. The loop is first incorporated into a vacuum line, cooled in liquid air, and the isotope transferred into it by conventional methods. The four-way tap is rotated into the closed position, the loop is removed from the vacuum line and is then incorporated into the gas line of the closed-circuit apparatus. Circulation of gas in the closed-circuit system may proceed through the tap without entering the closed loop containing the isotope. When the isotope is to be introduced into the system, the stopcock is rotated through $90°$ and the flushing gas drives out the isotope. If the isotope cannot be condensed *in vacuo* with liquid air into the loop, its transfer may have to be made with the use of some form of Toepler pump (see below).

The simplest closed-circuit apparatus must necessarily involve a certain volume of circulating gas and this will mean that the partial pressure of a gaseous isotope within it will be low. If the isotope also has limited solubility in water, it may mean that an unacceptably low amount can be introduced into the microbial suspension in a given short time. Recourse

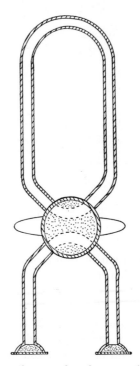

FIG. 6. Loop for transfer of gaseous isotope.

may then have to be made to carrying out the entire incubation in a hypodermic syringe. An example of an apparatus which involved transfer of gaseous isotope by Toepler pump into a syringe is that used by Johnson and Quayle (1965) for studying the uptake of [^{14}C]methane by *Pseudomonas methanica* (see Fig. 7). The [^{14}C]methane (4·2 ml at STP; 500 μC) was contained under reduced pressure in the sealed ampoule, A (internal volume, 14·6 ml). The ampoule, with a soft iron core, B, enclosed, was sealed on to the apparatus. The apparatus was connected to a high-vacuum line via tube C, and flask D was evacuated with tap E shut and taps F and G open to the pump. Tap G was closed, and the glass seal in the ampoule broken by raising iron core B with a magnet and allowing it to drop on to the seal. After allowing 5 min for the [^{14}C]methane to distribute itself throughout the apparatus, tap F was shut. Since the volume of flask D was 150 ml, approximately 90% of the [^{14}C]methane was enclosed between the closed taps E and F. Mercury was now run into flask D from reservoir H until the [^{14}C]methane was enclosed in the upper part of flask D. The gas was then finally led into a 10-ml plastic hypodermic syringe via the tap F and a three-way stainless-steel tap, J. Tap J was then closed off and the syringe removed from the rubber connection K. In the syringe I, before it had been attached to the connection K, was placed 5 ml of air and 5 ml of solution containing 10 mM phosphate buffer, pH 7·0, and 10 mM ammonium

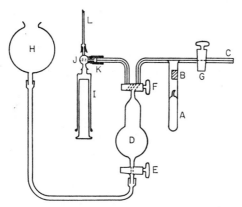

Fig. 7. Modified Toepler pump for transfer of gaseous isotope into hypodermic syringe. (From Johnson and Quayle, 1965.)

chloride. The displacement of the syringe plunger during the entry of [^{14}C]methane into the syringe enabled a check to be made of the completeness of transfer of the gas from the ampoule to the syringe. The detached syringe was then shaken by hand for 5 min to saturate the solution inside with [^{14}C]methane. Meanwhile a culture of methane-grown *Ps. methanica* was harvested in the exponential phase of growth and resuspended in 10 mM phosphate buffer, pH 7·0, containing ammonium chloride (10 mM), to give a bacterial concentration of 8–10 mg dry wt/ml. This suspension was gassed with methane + air (50 : 50) for 15 min and then 5 ml of the suspension drawn into syringe I through a hypodermic needle L attached to one arm of tap J. The tap was closed and the syringe rapidly shaken by hand. Samples (approximately 1 ml) were squirted through L at suitable time intervals into separate 4-ml portions of ethanol.

B. Rapid sampling of the suspension

The apparatuses described in the above Section, with the exception of that shown in Fig. 4, involve sampling by hypodermic syringe or operation of conventional stopcocks. Sampling times below 5 sec are not in general practicable without use of special apparatus. Some of these special devices are somewhat complex, and in the Sections below an indication will be given of their working principles and scope. For full details of construction the appropriate references should be consulted.

It should be noted that some rapid-sampling devices can only withdraw small samples, e.g., 25–100 μl, and hence their successful use may depend on the availability of isotopes of high specific activity in order to give sufficient radioactivity fixed in the short times for subsequent analysis and assay.

1. *Injection through plastic tubing*

A relatively simple but effective form of rapid sampling was used by Calvin and his colleagues (see Bassham and Calvin, 1957) in which a fast-flowing stream of algal suspension was incubated with isotope inside narrow tubing. The algal suspension was contained in a large transparent reservoir that was illuminated and aerated. A stream of cell suspension was then pumped from this reservoir through transparent plastic tubing (1 mm bore) (also illuminated) at a linear flow rate of 57 cm/sec. The time for the algal suspension to traverse the tubing was 20 sec, during which time sufficient carbon dioxide was present in solution to support an unchanged rate of photosynthesis. At selected points along the tubing a solution of $^{14}CO_2$ in water was injected at a constant rate through a hypodermic needle. The time of exposure of the algae to the isotope was determined by the length of tubing between the points of injection and discharge into alcohol. It was varied between 1 and 15 sec.

2. *Rotating stopcocks*

The essential part of a rotating stopcock sampler is illustrated in Fig. 8. Full details may be found elsewhere (Lonberg-Holm, 1959, 1964). The glass barrel has four inlets for cell suspension, A; water, B; vacuum, C; and sample ejection, D. The plug is made of Teflon and is rotated clockwise by electric motor. The cell suspension is maintained with stirring in the chamber above A. The sampling cycle is commenced by evacuation of the bore of the Teflon plug through C, the evacuated bore fills with cell suspension at A, and is then flushed out with distilled water at 2–3 lbs/sq. in from B through D. During the next cycle some air is admitted into the plug bore through a groove, E, and the bore is then sucked empty by final re-evacuation through C.

In the device described by Lonberg-Holm, samples of 25 μl were taken out at 1·6-sec intervals and were ejected with 300–400 μl of water into tubes containing boiling alcohol. These tubes were held in an electrically heated aluminium block which was moved under the sampler by a solenoid. This solenoid was synchronized with the turning of the stopcock plug by means of a microswitch actuated by a cam attached to the axle of the plug.

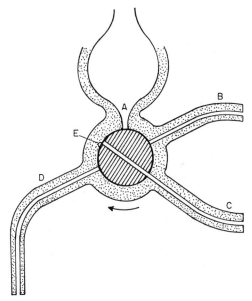

FIG. 8. Rotating stopcock. (From Lonberg-Holm, 1964.)

3. *Sliding valves*

A manually operated sliding valve sampler has already been described (Figs. 4 and 5). A more sophisticated automatic device has been described by Lonberg-Holm (1964) that is capable of taking 70–100 μl samples at 0·7-sec intervals. The essence of the device is shown in Fig. 9. The cell suspension is contained in a smaller chamber, A, through which passes the sampler, B. B is made out of "Lucite"† and in operation resembles a water vacuum pump. Water is passed down the centre of B at a pressure of 18–19 lbs/sq. in, passes through a jet, C (0·028-in diam.), sucks the cell suspension in through inlet D (0·018-in diam.) and discharges a portion through E into a suitable receiver. Sampler B is mounted at its upper end in a piston assembly that can move it rapidly up and down. When the

† "Lucite" is an alternative trade name to Plexiglass or Perspex, i.e., poly(methyl methacrylate).

8

170   J. R. QUAYLE

sampler is in the upper position (Fig. 9a), no water flows through the jet
and the inlet D is above the level of the cell suspension. During the sampling cycle, B moves down, a water valve is opened and water passes through
jet C before inlet D enters the cell suspension. D then dips below the level
of the cell suspension and a sample is sucked in and ejected (Fig. 9b). The
sampler is then raised up to complete the cycle. The device needs complex
supporting equipment to synchronize the movement of the rack containing
the receiver tubes with the operation of the sampler.

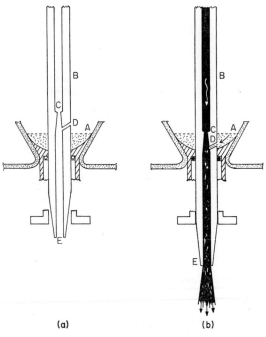

(a)   (b)

FIG. 9. Sliding valve sampler. (From Lonberg-Holm, 1964.)

4. *Rotating sample collector*

   Miettinen (1964) has described a rapid sampling device in which the
samples are collected in tubes mounted on a turntable. The cell suspension
is held under positive pressure in a vessel in which the outlet for ejection
is controlled by an electrically operated valve. When the turntable is rotated,
actuation of the sampling valve is synchronized with the positioning of the
receiver tubes by means of electrical signals from a commutator assembly
on the turntable. The apparatus as described by Miettinen is designed to
withdraw six 1-ml samples at time intervals of 0·1, 0·2, 0·6, 1, 2 and 3 sec
starting from zero time.

5. *Sliding syringe sampler*

Moses and Lonberg-Holm (1964) have designed an apparatus in which samples are rapidly withdrawn from an incubation vessel by successive hypodermic syringes, which are then further filled with alcohol as killing agent. The principle of the method is illustrated in Fig. 10. A row of 2-ml syringes, A, is placed in a Lucite train, D, so that they can be pulled in sequence under an incubation vessel, B, containing the cell suspension, and under a reservoir of the killing agent, C. The syringes fit into standard taper holes, E, machined into a Teflon runner strip secured to D. The syringes are spring-loaded, G, in such a way that the spring is almost completely compressed as in Fig. 10. As the train D is pulled from right to left, the syringe samples from the incubation vessel B when the plunger jumps down the step, F. This is followed by withdrawal of alcohol from C when

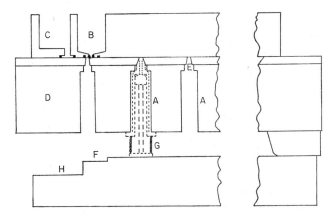

Fig. 10. Sliding syringe sampler. (From Moses and Lonberg-Holm, 1964.)

the plunger encounters step H. In the apparatus described by Moses and Lonberg-Holm the steps were made such that samples of 138 ± 7 μl were withdrawn from B and 0·5–1·0 ml of ethanol from C. The apparatus may be extended so that several syringe trains may be run simultaneously, enabling sampling to be done at the same time from a row of separate incubation vessels.

C. Stopping of reaction

All types of experiments that have been described so far involve sampling a cell suspension to which isotope has been added. It is necessary that metabolism occurring in these samples is stopped as rapidly as possible. The choice of killing agent is usually dictated by the kind of analysis to be carried out subsequently on the samples. In cases where column chromato-

TABLE I

Effective killing time of *Chlorella pyrenoidosa* by alcohol

Alcohol	Temperature	Killing time sec,
Methyl alcohol	Room	0·5
	Boiling	0·25
Ethyl alcohol	Room	1·0
	Boiling	0·5

Data of Bassham and Kirk (1964).

graphy has been used, trichloroacetic acid has sometimes served as the killing agent. (Ljungdahl and Wood, 1965; Campbell *et al.*, 1966). Where paper chromatography has been used, a volatile killing agent, such as methanol or ethanol, that does not interfere with the subsequent analysis has found very widespread application. In general, the sample is killed with 4 volumes of ethanol or methanol. The solvents are used at boiling point, room temperature or chilled to −15° to −40°C. The choice of the actual conditions should be governed by the objectives of the experiment. If the prime objective is to stop the reaction as rapidly as possible, then boiling alcohol should be used. Bassham and Kirk (1964) quote the figures shown in Table I for the effective killing times of *Chlorella pyrenoidosa* by alcohol. These authors state that the pattern and individual amounts of radioactive substances found in control experiments with methanol at room temperature and boiling methanol were essentially similar, this is in accord with similar conclusions drawn by Moses (1964). Hatch and Slack (1966) have noted little difference in labelling pattern in sugar cane leaves killed with boiling 80% ethanol or with methanol–chloroform–formic acid at − 80°C.

There may be special cases where use of boiling alcohol is mandatory, since some phosphatases are notoriously resistant to alcohol. Killing the cells with cold alcohol (at least up to 50% in concentration) may leave some of these enzymes active and enzymatic hydrolysis of phosphorylated compounds may occur in the aqueous alcohol (Ullrich, 1963).

Chilled alcohol (− 15°C) has been used to detect unstable radioactive compounds (Moses and Calvin, 1958).

D. Separation of products

1. *General chromatography*

In most cases the analysis of the samples resulting from the performance of the isotopic experiment needs to be capable of handling a large number of samples and separating a very wide range of compounds: carboxylic acids, amino-acids, sugars, phosphorylated compounds and lipids. Furthermore, it is necessary to be able to locate the radioactive compounds, assay them and often to recover them unchanged. The techniques of paper chromatography or thin-layer chromatography (Randerath, 1964; Stahl, 1965; Goodwin, 1968) offer obvious alternative approaches. The advantages of the latter technique over paper chromatography are—

(a) Faster development times.

(b) Higher loads can be handled in a thin-layer separation.

(c) The small size of the radioactive spots results in a higher intensity of radioactivity and thus enables a shorter exposure time to X-ray film to be used.

(d) Greater resolution of some classes of compound.

However, there are some serious disadvantages to the use of thin-layer chromatography in the first general separation of all the labelled compounds. As mentioned above, any generally useful system must be capable of reasonably separating, in one operation, a wide range of compounds. A large number of very small radioactive spots within the small area of a thin-layer chromatogram poses more difficult problems of radioassay than the larger-sized paper chromatogram. At this early stage of the analysis, the use of liquid scintillation counting, which could obviate this relative disadvantage, is not desirable, as the radioactive compounds will probably have to be identified. This entails their recovery from the liquid scintillator.

Thus, in practice, many investigators have used two-dimensional paper chromatography. Calvin and his colleagues have made an extensive search to find a generally useful solvent system for paper chromatography. A system was finally chosen in which phenol–water (72:28, v/v) is used in the first direction and a mixture of equal volumes of n-butanol–water (1246:84, v/v) and propionic acid–water (620:790, v/v) was used in the second direction (Benson et al., 1950). This system has been used for many years by the Berkeley group and other groups of workers. Recently the phenolic component of this solvent system has been modified by the inclusion of glacial acetic acid to give a more constant pH, and ethylenediaminetetra-acetic acid to eliminate the necessity of washing the chromatographic paper beforehand (Pedersen et al., 1966); the modified system has the composition: 840 ml of "liquefied" phenol (approximately 88% phenol, 12% water), 160 ml of water, 10 ml of glacial acetic acid and 1 ml of M ethylenediamine-tetra-acetic acid. The solvent for running in the second dimension remains unchanged.

Kornberg (1958) introduced a modification of the Berkeley solvent system by using a phenolic system for development in the first direction, composed of 500 g of phenol, 13 ml of 90% formic acid and 167 ml of water. The butanol–propionic acid solvent for development in the second direction was identical with that of Benson *et al.* (1950). This two-dimensional system has been widely used in several laboratories.

The practical value of any solvent system is greatly enhanced if the chromatographic co-ordinates of a large number of metabolites have already been established. This is the case for both the Berkeley solvent system and Kornberg's modified system, and hence detailed data relating only to these two systems are given here. It should be emphasized that these solvent systems do not necessarily provide the best possible separation of individual mixtures of compounds, and further separation often has to be made after the first general separation (see later).

(a) *Preparation of paper.* Whatman No. 4 filter paper (46 cm × 57 cm) is used. It is customary in some laboratories to wash the paper (unless EDTA is present in the developing solvent) by soaking in 0·5% oxalic acid solution for 2 h, rinsing repeatedly with distilled water and then drying.

(b) *Preparation of extract to be chromatographed.* The most common form of extract is one in which a sample has been killed by the addition of 4 volumes of methanol or ethanol. The resulting precipitate should be centrifuged, extracted with 20% aqueous ethanol, and the supernatant solutions combined. They are then concentrated under reduced pressure (the Rotary Evapo-mix evaporator made by Buchler Instruments, New York, N.Y., U.S.A., is especially useful for simultaneously handling many samples) and samples applied to the origin positions of the paper chromatograms. It is important that if a stream of air is used to facilitate the evaporation of the sample on the paper, the area of application should not be allowed to dry out. Artificial drying of the origin results in irreversible adsorption of some compounds by the paper. The amount of extract that is applied is critical for good chromatography; overloading results in streaking. The amount that can safely be applied depends both on the cell density and on the nature of the medium used in the initial incubation with isotope (see p. 000). Bassham and Calvin (1957) recommend that not more than 20 mg wet wt of plant material, including not more than 300 μg of inorganic salts, should be applied to a single chromatogram.

(c) *Development of chromatogram.* The chromatograms are best equilibrated in the chromatography tanks for about an hour before development. If all labelled compounds are of interest then the amount of developing solvent should be limited (approximately 70–80 ml) so that the solvent front does not pass the edge of the paper. This limited development will result in poor separation of the slower-moving compounds, such as phosphates. If the latter compounds are of prime interest, more solvent should be used and allowed to drip off the bottom edge of the paper. The paper is then removed and dried in a stream of air at room temperature in a properly ventilated cabinet. When dry, the paper is developed in the second dimension with the butanol–propionic acid solvent system.

Figures 11 and 12 present chromatographic maps relating to the Berkeley solvent system and Kornberg's modified system, respectively. On these maps no solvent fronts are shown, the chromatographic co-ordinates of each compound being relative ones. The circles represent the centres of the spots and do not represent the size of the spots. In practice it will, of course, be found that chromatographic co-ordinates vary somewhat depending on the exact experimental conditions, and the maps should only be taken as guides.

2. General electrophoresis

One of the disadvantages of the two-dimensional solvent systems described above is that the overall procedure from start to finish is a lengthy one, especially if good separation of phosphorylated compounds is to be achieved. This may be detrimental where the metabolites of interest are unstable. Electrophoresis is a technique that can be used to shorten this time. Rohr and Bassham (1964) have developed a two-dimensional electrophoretic system that accomplishes separations of complex mixtures of cell constituents at least as good as those achieved by two-dimensional chromatography. The buffer system (pH 4·4) used in the first dimension consisted of 150 ml of glacial acetic acid, 90 ml of pyridine, made up to 12 litres with distilled water and 8 g of ethylenediaminetetra-acetic acid. The second system (pH 2·0) consisted of 290 ml of glacial acetic acid, 130 ml of 25% formic acid and 4·5 litres of distilled water. Electrophoresis was carried out on sheets of Whatman 3MM paper (48·4 cm × 46·4 cm) for 75 min at 2·35 kV (53 V/cm) and 105 mA in the first dimension, followed, after drying, by 55 min at 3·35 kV (78 V/cm) and 90 mA. The entire procedure, including drying time, could be completed within 6 h, and hence the advantages for dealing with unstable compounds are obvious. The disadvantages of the method, as compared with the chromatographic method, are that it involves greater experimental complexity and cannot be used to run large numbers of papers concurrently.

3. Further separation of specific groups of compounds

After the initial two-dimensional chromatography certain groups of compounds may need further separation or co-chromatography with authentic

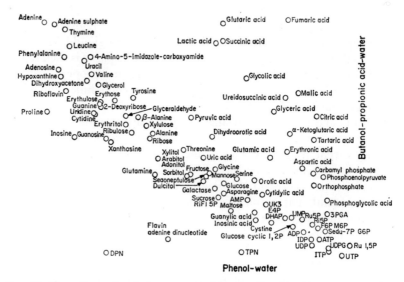

FIG. 11. Two-dimensional chromatographic map for the solvent system phenol: water–butanol : propionic acid. (Reproduced with permission from the Lawrence Radiation Laboratory, University of California, Berkeley.)

FIG. 12. Two-dimensional chromatographic map for the solvent system phenol: formic acid : water–butanol : propionic acid.

carriers, either in the same solvent system (when better separation will almost always result, owing to the lighter loading on the paper) or in a special system. It is beyond the scope of this article to detail the large number of thin-layer chromatographic, paper chromatographic and paper electrophoretic systems that have been used by various authors for separating individual compounds, but a few references to examples of the last two kinds of separation that the author has found particularly useful are given in Table II.

TABLE II

Special solvent systems

Compounds separated	Chromatographic (C) or Electrophoretic (E)	Reference
Amino-acids	C	Hardy *et al.* (1955)
	E	Gross (1955, 1956, 1959 a, b)
Carboxylic acids	C	Long *et al.* (1951)
	C	Hartley & Lawson (1960)
	E	Gross (1955, 1956, 1959 a, b)
Phosphorylated compounds	C	Bandurski & Axelrod (1951)
	C, E	Bieleski & Young (1963)
Sugars, sugar alcohols and anhydro derivatives	C	Hough & Stacey (1963)
	C	Gibbins & Simpson (1964)
	E	Frahn & Mills (1959)
	E	Bourne *et al.* (1960)
	C	Baddiley *et al.* (1957)

4. *Dephosphorylation of phosphorylated compounds*

It is often necessary to dephosphorylate phosphates and re-chromatograph in order to identify the residue. Any non-specific phosphatase may be used, but an acid phosphatase is preferable to an alkaline phosphatase so as to minimize isomerization or oxidation of some sugars, which occur more readily under alkaline conditions A suitable general acid phasphatase is that prepared from potatoes (Boehringer Corporation (London) Ltd, London W.5). A dried lichen preparation (Polidase S, Schwarz Bioresearch Inc. Orangeburg, New York, U.S.A.) has also been found to contain an acid phosphatase that is very suitable for the purpose. It may be purified by precipitation with ammonium sulphate between 83–100% of saturation. A typical purification of the phosphatase is given by Pon (1960). A suspension of Polidase S (10 g) in 10 ml of distilled water is made to 83% of saturation with 63 g of ammonium sulphate. The suspension is centrifuged after standing at 0°C for 10 min and the precipitate discarded. Sufficient ammonium sulphate (12 g) is then added to make the solution saturated. The suspension is allowed to stand for 30 min at 0°C and is then gently swirled and decanted so as to leave most of the crystals of undissolved ammonium sulphate behind. The suspension of protein is centrifuged and the precipitate dissolved in 5–10 ml of water. The resulting solution is dialysed overnight against distilled water in the cold room. The dialysed protein solution is then lyophilized, yielding several hundred milligrams of light brown fluffy powder, which may be stored indefinitely under anhydrous conditions at − 15 °C.

A convenient stock solution of the phosphatase may be prepared by dissolving 1 mg of lyophilized protein/ml of 0·2M acetate buffer (pH 5·0), which contains 0·01 M $MgCl_2$. Samples containing trace amounts of phosphorylated compounds dissolved in up to 0·5 ml of water may be dephosphorylated by incubating with 50μl of the stock phosphatase solution, or 100 μg of the potato phosphatase, overnight at 37 °C. Precautions should be taken to avoid microbial growth taking place, e.g., layering the stoppered incubation tube with toluene.

E. Detection of products

1. *Detection with X-ray film*

Even a short period of exposure of a cell suspension to isotope will result in many metabolites becoming labelled. The chromatogram will thus always consist of several radioactive spots, many of which will run close together. These spots are best located with the use of X-ray film. The paper is folded to the size of the film and a symbol is stamped on the corners with radioactive ink so that the developed film can subsequently be realigned on the paper sheet. The paper sheet and X-ray film are sealed up in a lead-backed folder and stored for a suitable period of time depending on the amount of radioactivity present; 4000 β particles/min emitted from one side of the paper from a radioactive spot of average size could be expected to show a visible darkening of the film overnight, whereas 100 β particles/min from a similar spot would need at least two weeks' exposure to be visible. Exposure times of 1–3 weeks are often involved in the type of experiment described in this article.

2. *Detection with Geiger–Müller tube*

In order to shorten the time delay associated with the use of X-ray film, several kinds of automatic scanners have been devised. The principles behind three main types are summarized below.

(a) *Detectors involving many counting tubes.* Such devices are typified by the Radioactive Multi Counter (Baird & Tatlock (London) Ltd, Chadwell Heath, Essex), which consists essentially of a bank of 31 Geiger–Müller tubes arranged linearly. Each of these tubes simultaneously can count a different small square of the paper. The paper is then advanced so that a further row of squares can be counted. A composite numerical picture of the radioactivity distribution over the paper can thus be built up and an idea can be gained of the positions of the main spots.

(b) *Detectors involving a single counting tube with graphic recording of radio-activity.* The principle behind these instruments is exemplified by that of Perkins and Tyrrell (1961) in a modification of an original design of Aronoff (1956). A Geiger–Müller tube is moved across the chromatogram, which is wrapped around a rotating drum. Simultaneously an electrically energized stylus is moved in the same way over electrosensitive paper wrapped around another rotating drum. A pulse from the Geiger–Müller tube is recorded as a black dot at a corresponding position on the electrosensitive paper. In this way a facsimile of an autoradiogram is built up in a shorter time than would be required for exposure to X-ray film.

(c) *Detectors involving a single counting tube with numerical recording of radio-activity.* These are typified by the design of Frank, Chain, Pocchiari and Rossi (see Pocchiari and Rossi, 1961). The radiochromatogram is mounted in the carriage of an electric typewriter. A Geiger–Müller tube is mounted on the typewriter. The entire area of the chromatogram is aligned, square by square, before the tube by the discontinuous movements of the carriage. The radioactivity present in each position on the paper is then relayed from the counting tube as impulses to a print-out unit. A numerical map of the radiochromatogram is thus obtained. A commercial model based essentially on this design is available (Bi-Dimensional Scanner, Model 460, Packard Instrument Co. Inc., La Grange, Illinois).

3. Comparison of the methods

No scanner can yet achieve the exact delineation of radioactive spots, which is necessary when, as is frequently encountered, different spots run close together or when exact co-chromatography with authentic carrier is being performed. This fact must be weighed against the possible saving of time which use of a scanner might effect; furthermore, only one paper may be scanned at a time, compared to the large number which may be exposed simultaneously to X-ray film.

F. Assay of radioactivity

The final stage of the experiment consists in assaying the radioactivity present in the spots that have been located on the paper. Several methods have been devised for doing this.

1. *Manual Geiger–Müller counting*

The simplest method of radioassay involves the use of a commercially available, wide-end-window Geiger–Müller tube (e.g., GM tube type 2B2, 2-in diameter, Panax Equipment Ltd, Holmethorpe Industrial Estate, Redhill, Surrey) protected by a portable castle.

Construction of a more sensitive counting tube with a thin, easily replaceable Mylar polyester window (0·00025-in thickness) has been described (Fuller, 1956). The tube is machined from brass and the Mylar (E. I. du Pont de Nemours & Co. Inc., Wilmington, Delaware) is fitted over the end and held in position in the same way as a jam-pot cover. Gold sputtering of the Mylar has been used to eliminate build-up of static charge on the window (Moses and Lonberg-Holm, 1963). The window is slightly porous, and hence the tube has to be continually flushed with a slow stream of counting gas. Background counts of 60–70/min with a counting efficiency of 10% for ^{14}C are claimed.

With both kinds of counting tube it will often be found necessary to mask neighbouring radioactive spots with card so that their radioactivity does not contribute to that of the spot actually being assayed. If the greatest accuracy is required it will be necessary to count both sides of the paper. A spot will usually give a slightly different count on either side, owing to unequal rates of drying of the two sides.

In considering the efficiency of this counting procedure, it should be borne in mind that about one-third of the β-particles emitted from the isotope actually escape from the paper, and these β-particles are divided between the two sides of the paper. Thus, a maximum of approximately one-sixth of the β-particles emitted by a radioactive spot in paper could strike the window of a single counting tube.

2. *Automatic Geiger–Müller counting*

Radioassay of the large numbers of radioactive spots usually encountered in experiments involving tracing of metabolic pathways becomes very tedious and time consuming. In Section E some automatic counting instruments have been described. These instruments have been primarily designed to radioassay the entire chromatogram when the positions of radioactive spots are not known. When, however, the position of the radioactive spots has been located by X-ray film, a different approach to automatic counting is possible. Each radioactive spot may be cut out with scissors and the problem then resolves itself into assay of large numbers of small pieces of radioactive paper. Moses and Lonberg-Holm (1963) have devised an instrument for doing this automatically. The paper spots are sandwiched between two strips of Mylar in a linear sequence. The position of each spot is marked by a piece of opaque tape stuck on the strips. The long sandwich is rolled on to a reel, which is then mounted in a counting assembly. The sandwich is fed automatically between two opposed, wide-end-window Geiger–Müller tubes of a design similar to that of Fuller (1956). Positions of the paper spots are sensed by a photoelectric cell that scans for the presence of the pieces of opaque tape. The feeding is stopped by the photo-electric cell and simultaneously radioassay of both sides of the paper spot is then performed by the counting tubes. After counting for a pre-set time or pre-set count, the counts are relayed to printing registers, and the sand-wich is automatically moved on to the next sample.

3. *Scintillation counting*

In cases where the radioactive material contained in the paper spots is not required after radioassay, liquid scintillation counting can be of use. The paper spots may be placed in counting vials and a suitable liquid scintillator added (preferably toluene-based, since paper is translucent in toluene). These vials may then be readily assayed in an automatic scintil-lation counter. Difficulties may arise with radioactive compounds that are soluble in the liquid scintillator, as the efficiency of counting may change with time as they are leached out of the paper. This may of course be over-come by first eluting all the radioactive compounds from the paper spot with water and assaying the eluted radioactivity after blending with a water-tolerant liquid scintillator. Unless there are special advantages to be gained, such as assay of tritium or simultaneous assay of compounds labelled with two isotopes, this procedure may then become more time consuming than counting manually with a Geiger–Müller tube.

REFERENCES

Aronoff, S. (1956). *Nucleonics*, **14**, 92–94.
Baddiley, J., Buchanan, J. G., and Carss, B. (1957). *J. chem. Soc.*, 4138–4139.
Bandurski, R. S., and Axelrod, B. (1951). *J. biol. Chem.*, **193**, 405–410.
Bassham, J. A., and Calvin, M. (1957). "The Path of Carbon in Photosynthesis". Prentice-Hall, Englewood Cliffs.
Bassham, J. A., and Calvin, M. (1960). *In* "Encyclopedia of Plant Physiology" (Ed. W. Ruhland), Vol. V, Pt. 1, pp. 884–922. Springer-Verlag, Heidelberg.
Bassham, J. A., and Kirk, M. R. (1960). *Biochim. biophys. Acta*, **43**, 447–464.
Bassham, J. A., and Kirk, M. R. (1964). *In* "Rapid Mixing and Sampling Tech-niques in Biochemistry" (Ed. B. Chance, R. H. Eisenhardt, Q. H. Gibson and K. K. Lonberg-Holm), pp. 319–331. Academic Press, New York.

Benson, A. A., Bassham, J. A., Calvin, M., Goodale, T. C., Haas, V. A., and Stepka, W. (1950). *J. Am. chem. Soc.*, **72**, 1710–1718.

Bergmann, F. M., Towne, J. C., and Burris, R. H. (1958). *J. biol. Chem.*, **230**, 13–24.

Bieleski, R. L., and Young, R. E. (1963). *Analyt. Biochem.*, **6**, 54–68.

Bourne, E. J., Hutson, D. H., and Weigel, H. (1960). *J. chem. Soc.*, 4252–4256.

Calvin, M., and Bassham, J. A. (1962). "The Photosynthesis of Carbon Compounds". Benjamin, New York.

Calvin, M., and Massini, P. (1952). *Experientia*, 8, 445–457.

Campbell, A. E., Hellebust, J. A., and Watson, S. W. (1966). *J. Bact.*, **91**, 1178–1185.

Dagley, S., and Nicholson, D. E. (1970). "An Introduction to Metabolic Pathways", Blackwells Scientific Publications, Oxford and Edinburgh.

Frahn, J. L., and Mills, J. A. (1959). *Aust. J. Chem.*, **12**, 65–89.

Fuller, R. C. (1956). *Science, N.Y.*, **124**, 1253.

Fuller, R. C., Smillie, R. M., Sisler, E. C., and Kornberg, H. L. (1961). *J. biol. Chem.*, **236**, 2140–2149.

Gibbins, L. N., and Simpson, F. J. (1964). *Can. J. Microbiol.*, **10**, 829–836.

Goodwin, T. W. (1968). *In* "Thin Layer Chromatography", p. 51. United Trade Press, London.

Gross, D. (1955). *Nature, Lond.*, **176**, 72–73.

Gross, D. (1956). *Nature, Lond.*, **178**, 29–31.

Gross, D. (1959a). *Chemy & Ind.*, 1219–1220.

Gross, D. (1959b). *Nature, Lond.*, **184**, 1298–1301.

Hardy, T. L., Holland, D. O., and Nayler, J. H. C. (1955). *Analyt. Chem.*, **27**, 971–974.

Hartley, R. D., and Lawson, G. J. (1960). *J. Chromato.*, **4**, 410–413.

Hatch, M. D., and Slack, C. R. (1966). *Biochem. J.*, **101**, 103–111.

Hough, L., and Stacey, B. E. (1963). *Phytochemistry*, **2**, 315–320.

Johnson, P. A., and Quayle, J. R. (1965). *Biochem. J.*, **95**, 850–867.

Knight, M. (1962). *Biochem. J.*, **84**, 170–185.

Kornberg, H. L. (1958). *Biochem. J.*, **68**, 535–542.

Ljungdahl, L. G., Irion, E., and Wood, H. G. (1965). *Biochemistry, N.Y.*, **4**, 2771–2780.

Ljungdahl, L. G., and Wood, H. G. (1965). *J. Bact.*, **89**, 1055–1064.

Ljungdahl, L. G., and Wood, H. G. (1969). *A Rev. Microbiol.*, **23**, 515–538.

Lonberg-Holm, K. K. (1959). *Biochim. biophys. Acta*, **35**, 464–472.

Lonberg-Holm, K. K. (1964). *In* "Rapid Mixing and Sampling Techniques in Biochemistry" (Ed. B. Chance, R. H. Eisenhardt, Q. H. Gibson, and K. K. Lonberg-Holm), pp. 275–287. Academic Press, New York.

Long A. G., Quayle, J. R., and Stedman, R. J. (1951). *J. chem. Soc.*, 2197–2201.

McGilvray, D., and Morris, J. G. (1969). *Biochem. J.*, 657–761.

Miettinen, J. K. (1964). *In* "Rapid Mixing and Sampling Techniques in Biochemistry (Ed. B. Chance, R. H. Eisenhardt, Q. H. Gibson, and K. K. Lonberg-Holm), pp. 303–307. Academic Press, New York.

Moses, V. (1964). *In* "Rapid Mixing and Sampling Techniques in Biochemistry" (Ed. B. Chance, R. H. Eisenhardt, Q. H. Gibson, and K. K. Lonberg-Holm), p. 347. Academic Press, New York.

Moses, V., and Calvin, M. (1958). *Proc. natn. Acad. Sci., U.S.A.*, **44**, 260–277.

Moses, V., and Lonberg-Holm, K. K. (1963). *Analyt. Biochem.*, **5**, 11–27.

Moses, V., and Lonberg-Holm, K. K. (1964). *In* "Rapid Mixing and Sampling Techniques in Biochemistry" (Ed. B. Chance, R. H. Eisenhardt, Q. H. Gibson, and K. K. Lonberg-Holm), pp. 311–317. Academic Press, New York.

Pedersen, T. A., Kirk, M. R., and Bassham, J. A. (1966). *Physiologica Pl.*, **19**, 219–231.

Perkins, H. J., and Tyrrell, C. (1961). *Can. J. Biochem. Physiol.*, **39**, 1183–1188.

Pocchiari, F., and Rossi, C. (1961). *J. Chromat.*, **5**, 377–394.

Pon, N. G. (1960). University of California Radiation Laboratory Report 9373.

Quayle, J. R., and Keech, D. B. (1959). *Biochem. J.*, **72**, 623–630.

Randerath, K. (1964). "Thin Layer Chromatography". Academic Press, New York.

Rohr, W., and Bassham, J. A. (1964). *Analyt. Biochem.*, **9**, 343–350.

Smith, D. C., Bassham, J. A., and Kirk, M. R. (1961). *Biochim. biophys. Acta*, **48**, 299–313.

Stahl, E. (1965). "Thin Layer Chromatography", Springer-Verlag, Heidelberg.

Sun, A. Y., Ljungdahl, L. G., and Wood, H. G. (1969). *J. Bact.*, **98**, 842–844.

Trüper, H. G. (1964). *Arch. Mikrobiol.*, **49**, 23–50.

Ullrich, J. (1963). *Biochim. biophys. Acta*, **71**, 589–594.

CHAPTER VII

Radiorespirometric Methods

C. H. WANG

Radiation Center and Department of Chemistry, Oregon State University, Corvallis, Oregon, 97331

I. THEORETICAL CONSIDERATIONS

A. Definition of the term

The term "radiorespirometry" (Wang, 1967) refers to a class of methods by which respiratory activity of a biological system is measured by means of radiotracer techniques. More specifically, the rate and the extent of the conversion of a ^{14}C-labelled carbon atom of a given substrate to respiratory CO_2 is determined. It should be noted that the radiorespirometric method is not concerned with the measurement of oxygen uptake by the biological system.

B. Radiorespirometric methods versus manometric methods

Information on the respiratory activity of a biological system has long been recognized as one of the important physiological manifestations and investigations have been much enhanced since the development of the manometric method by Otto Warburg (1923); Umbreit et al. (1964). However, one of the major limiting factors in applying manometric methods, insofar as the data on respiratory CO_2 are concerned, is the fact that the measurement can be made only when a biological system such as micro-organisms, tissue preparation, etc., are incubated in a medium containing the carbonaceous substrate under study as sole carbon source. Such incubation procedures impose an "unphysiological" environment to the organism under study. Thus, micro-organisms require carbon sources of various types such as amino-acids, vitamins, etc., before proliferation can take place. Moreover, the respiratory CO_2 data so obtained represent the overall CO_2 production from the substrate with no possible way to identify the net contribution of individual carbon atoms of the substrate.

C. Unique advantages of radiorespirometric methods

In contrast, one finds that these limitations are not involved in the use of the radiorespirometric method in the study of microbial physiology. Thus, unique advantages of the radiorespirometric method include:

1. Measurement of the production of respiratory CO_2 from micro-organisms utilizing a ^{14}C-labelled substrate in a complex medium consisting of all necessary nutritional requirements.

2. By using ^{14}C-specifically labelled substrates, one can determine the rate and extent of the conversion of individual carbon atoms of the substrate to respiratory $^{14}CO_2$. Such information is of vital importance to the understanding of pathways responsible for the catabolism of the substrates.

3. Not to be ignored is the fact that with the radiorespirometric method, one can trace not only the fate of substrates in the formation of respiratory $^{14}CO_2$ but also in the biosynthesis of cellular constituents and fermentation

products by examining radioactivity incorporated into the cells and incubation medium.

4. With equipment capable of producing data on respiratory $^{14}CO_2$ formation with high resolution, it is possible to gain detailed kinetic information on catabolic pathways in experiments lasting only a few minutes. This feature permits the study of the catabolic behaviour of micro-organisms at different developmental stages. This aspect is elaborated on in a later section.

D. Type of radiorespirometric experiments

Generally speaking, there are two types of radiorespirometric experiments classified according to the manner by which the labelled substrate is administered. The most common type of experiment involves the single-dose administration of substrate at the beginning of a given experiment. More recently, methods have been developed so that the labelled substrate can be administered to the micro-organism, under study, in the nature of continuous feeding. Experiments of this latter type provide one with refined data, valuable to investigators interested in the kinetics underlying the catabolic processes of micro-organisms.

E. Limitations and disadvantages of radiorespirometric methods

Radiorespirometric methods, like any other research tool, have certain disadvantages and limitations. For example, to carry out radiorespirometric experiments, one has to construct necessary apparatus and equipment which are not commercially available. In addition, the instruments for measurement of radioactivity such as liquid scintillation counter or ion chamber-electrometer system are costly items. The relatively more involved procedures associated with radiorespirometry limit the number of experiments one can perform during a given day.

Several other basic limitations in applying radiorespirometry to study microbial physiology are noteworthy. First, some of the ^{14}C-specifically labelled compounds that are of importance to microbial studies are not commercially available. These include such compounds as glucose-5-^{14}C, fructose-2-^{14}C, fructose-3(4)-^{14}C, etc. Most of the available ^{14}C-specifically labelled amino-acids are synthesized by chemical methods and, hence, they are racemic mixtures. It is a well-known fact that many micro-organisms do not utilize D-isomers of amino-acids and thereby making it difficult to interpret the radiorespirometric findings. One also finds that whereas one can obtain much qualitative information relative to the operation of various catabolic pathways, the estimation of concurrent catabolic pathways such as the case of glucose catabolism, remains to be a difficult task. However, it is anticipated that further developments in methodology in this regard will make radiorespirometry a more effective tool.

II. APPARATUS NEEDED TO CARRY OUT
RADIORESPIROMETRIC STUDIES

A. Radiorespirometer for single-dose experiments

The apparatus consists of the following major components:

1. A gas supply system which can be either an air pump for aerobic experiments or a tank of purified nitrogen or helium for anaerobic experiments.

2. A gas-flow meter (Model 36-541-03, Fisher & Porter Company, Warminster, Pennsylvania).

3. The incubation flask, which is a modified version of a conventional Warburg flask. The flask is equipped with an aeration tube inserted through a rubber stopper equipped with a connector (Hamilton needle No. N730, point style No. 3, Hamilton Syringe Company, Whittier, California); a side arm attached to a LUER-LOK female connector No. L/606 (Becton, Dickinson & Company, Rutherford, New Jersey). The female LUER-LOK connector is coupled with an appropriate male LUER-LOK connector which is in turn connected to one of the two CO_2 traps by way of a 3-way stopcock equipped with LUER-LOK connectors (No. MS08). The trap is, in essence, a modified version of a sintered glass filter (Model 36060 15C, porosity C, Corning Glasswares, Corning, New York). The incubation flask and CO_2 trap assembly can be mounted on a holder as depicted in Fig. 1. Attached to the bottom of the holder is a metal base that can be attached readily to the shaker mechanism of a conventional Warburg assembly.

A number of the individual incubation flasks and CO_2 trap assembly can be accommodated by a round Warburg waterbath making use of a common air supply system as depicted in Fig. 2.

Inside the CO_2 trap one can place 10 ml of either 2N NaOH solution or an organic base in organic solvent to trap respiratory CO_2, in the sweeping gas completely, at flow rate as high as 100 ml per min. Several organic bases can be used, and the most common type is a mixture of ethanol and ethanolamine at a ratio of 1 : 2 (v/v). Use of ethanol is recommended instead of methanol or cellosolve used by earlier workers primarily to avoid the possible toxic action of the latter two organic solvents.

B. Radiorespirometer for continuous feeding experiments

Components for this type of radiorespirometer are depicted in Fig. 3. A 25-ml micro-Fernbach flask is used for micro-organism incubation and

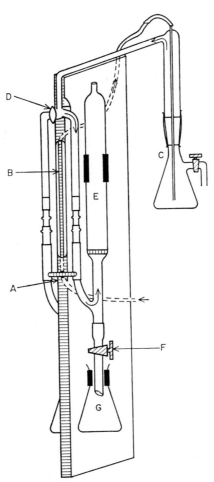

FIG. 1. Incubation flask and dual CO_2-trap assembly. A, three-way stopcock with Luer-Lok connectors (Model MS08, Becton, Dickinson & Company, Rutherford, New Jersey); B, optional individual flow meter (Model 36-541-03, Fisher and Porter Co., Warminster, Pennsylvania); C, respiratory chamber with side arm; D, holders for CO_2 traps; E, CO_2 traps. Sintered-glass filter with extended top and side arm (Model 36060 15C, prosity C, Corning Glasswares, Corning, New York); F, stopcock; G, trap solution collecting flask.

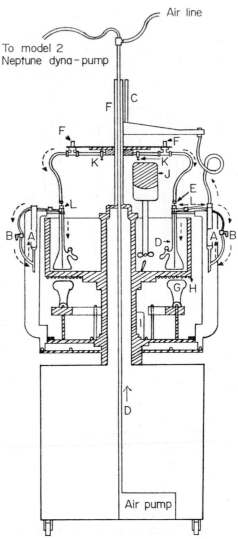

Fig. 2. Multiple radiorespirometry assembly for studies with micro-organisms, cell suspensions, enzyme systems, etc. The direction of air-flow is indicated by — — →. A, CO_2 trap; B, 3-way stopcock equipped with Luer-Lok connectors (No. MS08, Becton, Dickinson & Company, Rutherford, New Jersey); C, flow-meter (Model 36-541-03, Fisher & Porter Co., Warminster, Pennsylvania); D, incubation flask; E, aeration tube, injection needle (H/468L) with male Luer-Lok connector (Becton, Dickinson & Co., Rutherford, New Jersey); F, gas metering valve (Model 4M-305-2, Nuclear Products Company), mounted on standard steel platform; G, light source; H, constant temperature waterbath (Model WBP4, Gilson Medical Electronics, Middleton, Wisc.); I, shaker mechanism; J, stirring motor; K, castaloy screw clamp; L, rubber stopper.

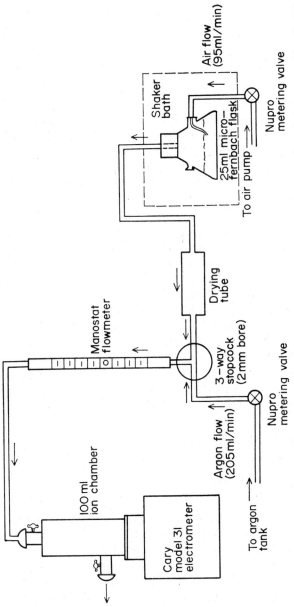

FIG. 3. The gas-flow system of the high resolution radiorespirometer. Designed and constructed by D. W. Jacobsen, 1967.

a drying tube is installed between the incubation flask and the monostat flow meter. With this type of experiment, it is necessary to use a flow ion chamber for the measurement of radioactivity in respiratory CO_2 and any excessive amount of water in the sweeping gas will interfere with the function of the ion chamber.

The optimal volume for the incubation flask is approximately 25 ml to ensure rapid turnover of the atmosphere in the flask. Naturally, for the measurement of $^{14}CO_2$ one would be inclined to use a flow ion chamber having a volume compatible with that of the incubation flask. However, it is also recognized that for adequate detection efficiency of $^{14}CO_2$ in a flowing stream of gas, the volume of the ion chamber should be at least 100 ml in volume. For this reason, in the apparatus designed for radio-respirometric experiments involving continuous substrate feeding, a gas mixing manifold is devised to mix 75 ml of argon (from a cylinder) with 25 ml of gas derived from the incubation flask at any given time prior to entering a 100 ml ion chamber. Such an arrangement makes the true volume of the respiratory gases in ion chamber compatible with the volume of the incubation flask. Moreover, the presence of argon in the flow ion chamber will also increase the detection efficiency of the $^{14}CO_2$.

The ion chamber is connected with an electrometer to measure the current produced by the radioactive $^{14}CO_2$ in the ion chamber. In order to convert the analog signal from the electrometer to digital form, one can make use of a voltage-to-frequency converter. This makes it possible to count the digital data by means of a conventional scaler. One or more of the incubation flasks can be housed in a rectangular Warburg waterbath with a common air supply. A four-flask system equipped with a data programmer and a data printer is depicted as a block diagram in Fig. 4.

III. RADIORESPIROMETRIC EXPERIMENTS INVOLVING SINGLE-DOSE SUBSTRATE ADMINISTRATION

A. General considerations

Radiorespirometric experiments involving administration of substrate as a single-dose is the most common type of experiment practised at the present time. Microbial cells suspended in a proliferating medium, generally at the middle log phase, are harvested by centrifugation, and resuspended in a desirable fresh medium (generally the same growth medium excluding the substrate under study). Such handling naturally disturbs the physiological state of the micro-organism to some extent and, hence, the findings in this type of experiment may not represent exactly true physiological processes. Moreover, the single-dose experiment involves a duration of several hours, during which time the micro-organism is undergoing

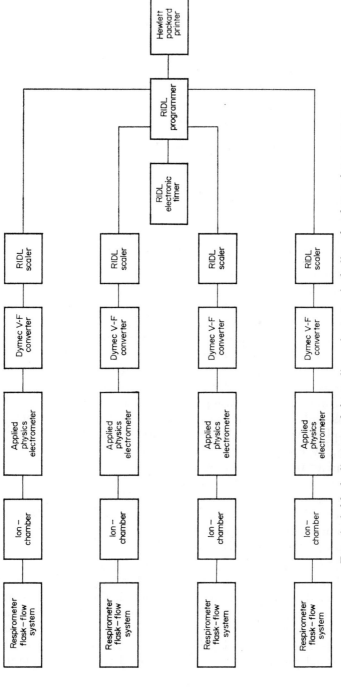

FIG. 4. A block diagram of the radiorespirometer including the data printout system.

change in its physiological state (including cell proliferation), hence the findings represent a rather composite picture of the catabolic mechanism of the micro-organisms.

Nevertheless, single-dose experiments are easy to carry out and the findings, despite that they are semi-quantitative in nature, are useful in understanding the catabolic pathways operating in the micro-organism. The application of radiorespirometric experiments of this type is not limited only to the studies on catabolism, thus it is possible to study the stimulation or inhibition of catabolic pathways by external factors such as nutrients, cultural environment (Wang and Krackov, 1962), etc. Given in the following is a set of general operating techniques in carrying out single-dose radiorespirometric experiments. Incorporated into the description are various facets which are of importance to the concepts of experiment design.

B. Basic concepts underlying experiment design

1. *Preparation of culture*

Microbial cells under study are transferred from stock in the conventional manner to a sterilized growth medium having an appropriate composition contained in an incubation flask.

The flask is equipped with a side arm of appropriate size that can be inserted into the sample holder of a conventional colorimeter or nephelometer for ready measurement of the optical density of the cell suspension and, hence, makes it possible to follow the growth of the micro-organism under study. The relationship between optical density of the incubation medium with cell weight can be established in the conventional manner. In a typical experiment, the cells are harvested, at the middle log phase of growth, by centrifugation. The cell crop is then resuspended with an appropriate volume of the growth medium excluding the major carbon source such as glucose, glycerol, etc. The handling of the culture at this stage need not be done under aseptic conditions since contamination of the micro-organism under study by other micro-organisms would not be a serious problem for at least a period of 8 to 10 h. The exclusion of carbon sources from the medium is necessary since:

(a) If the major carbon source is the substrate under study, the ^{14}C-labelled substrate to be introduced subsequently in the operation would be suffering from an enormous dilution factor, thereby making it necessary to use the labelled substrate having a very high specific activity. Moreover, the concentration of major carbon sources at the level that is typical in cultural media is generally too high and would prevent one to observe a complete time course of utilization of the substrate within a desirable duration of the experiment of between 4 to 8 h.

(b) If the labelled substrate to be used is similar in nature to that of the carbon source, one may encounter the so-called diauxie effect; e.g., glucose is preferentially utilized by yeast, in the presence of such other hexoses as mannose, galactose, etc.

On the other hand, in some instances it may be necessary to introduce a small amount of the major carbon sources, such as glucose, into the medium at this point, since it is known that some micro-organisms will not utilize amino-acids or tricarboxylic-acid (TCA) cycle intermediates, if they were the substrate under study, unless a major carbon source such as glucose is present (Jacobsen and Wang, in press).

For most micro-organisms, the desirable concentration of cell suspension for radiorespirometric experiments is 1 to 2 mg (dry weight basis) per ml of medium. Since the size of the incubation flask is generally 50 ml in capacity, 10 to 20 ml of the cell suspension can be used without concern about whether oxygen supply is ample for cell metabolism. This is true since during the experiment the cell suspension is aerated in addition to the shaking treatment.

For anaerobic micro-organisms, the handling procedures are similar to that as described above except that helium gas or nitrogen gas is used as the incubation environment and as sweeping gas during the radiorespirometric experiment.

2. Selection of ^{14}C-labelled substrates

The ^{14}C-labelled substrate to be used in a radiorespirometric experiment is naturally dependent on the objectives of the experiment. In the case that the catabolic behaviour of the micro-organism is completely unknown, it may be desirable to execute a preliminary set of experiments using such test substrates as glucose-U-^{14}C, gluconate-1-^{14}C, glucuronate-6-^{14}C, acetate-1-^{14}C, DL-glutamate-1-^{14}C, glyoxylate-l-^{14}C, etc. The foregoing given substrates are named since they are the key intermediates or entry compounds of the known catabolic pathways of micro-organisms. If the rate of utilization of the respective substrate by the micro-organism in question is unknown, the substrate level can be arbitrarily set as 0·5 mg (or approximately 2–5 μmoles) per 10 mg (dry weight basis) of cells. With the labelled substrate in the side arm, the incubation flask is attached to the radiorespirometer assembly and placed in a waterbath and the flow rate of the sweeping gas is adjusted to 40 to 80 ml/min. A brief incubation period of 5 min, with the shaking mechanism on, is desirable in order to adjust the temperature of the cultural medium to the desirable level. The labelled substrate, stored in the side arm, is then tipped into the incubation flask and the side arm of the flask is rinsed twice to ensure complete removal of the labelled substrate from the side arm. This operation marks the initiation of the radiorespirometric experiment. The sweeping gas at this time is directed into one of the two CO_2 traps. Inasmuch as the substrate level is low in these preliminary experiments, it is desirable to switch the sweeping gas to the second CO_2 trap by manipulation of the 3-way stopcock at the end of 15 min. The schedule for trap switching can be maintained in 15-min intervals since it is entirely possible to drain the trapping solution into a collection flask, rinse the trap with a small amount of trapping solution and reload the trap with fresh solution within a few minutes.

For this type of experiment, the duration of the experiment can be arbitrarily set at 4 h since by the end of 4 h, the radiorespirometric data collected will provide information on (1) whether a given substrate can be utilized under the prevailing incubation environment; (2) if the given substrate can be utilized, the rate of utilization can be assessed by plotting the $^{14}CO_2$ yield, at 15 min intervals, expressed as per cent of substrate activity in respiratory CO_2 versus time.

The volume of the trapping solution in the CO_2 trap is generally set at 10 ml. This volume in addition to the volume of the rinsing solution will make the total volume approximately 12 to 13 ml in the collection flask. It may be desirable to use a graduated cylinder as collection flask since this will make it easier to dilute the trapping solution and rinsing solution to a defined volume, say 15 ml. Upon shaking of the diluted trapping solution, an aliquot of either 5 ml or 7·5 ml, can be transferred into a conventional 20 ml liquid scintillation counting vial. To the aliquot of the trapping solution is then added a scintillation solution, to make a total volume of 15 ml, consisting of toluene containing an appropriate amount of primary solute and secondary solute (Wang and Krackov, 1962) (e.g., 3 g of terphenyl and 30 mg of 1,4-bis-2' (5'-phenyl-oxazolyl) benzene (POPOP) in 1 litre of toluene).

The counting vial, upon shaking to ensure thorough mixing, can then be counted in a liquid scintillation counter in the conventional manner (Wang and Krackov, 1962; Wang and Willis, 1965).

Generally, duration of the counting should be such that the counting data will carry a standard deviation of no greater than 2% to be compatible with the precisions associated with other procedures involved in the overall experiment. The counting data can then be translated from cpm to dpm and then to yields of $^{14}CO_2$, expressed as per cent of the substrate administered, per unit time. A plot can then be made with the interval yields versus time thereby providing one with the kinetic information relative to the utilization of the labelled substrate by the micro-organisms under study. Such information is of primary importance in designing the experiments for a specific substrate with ^{14}C labelling at individual carbon atoms. The $^{14}CO_2$ yield data should also be plotted on the basis of cumulative yield versus time.

Once the utilizability and the rate of utilization of the substrates are known, efforts can then be directed to the design and execution of radiorespirometric experiments using a chosen substrate, depending on the objectives of the study. In this series of experiments, the substrate level can be determined on the basis of information gained in the preliminary experiment described in the foregoing section. It may also be necessary to carry out additional series of experiments to determine the optimal substrate level. The general guideline calls for the adjustment of the substrate level so that the administered labelled substrate can be utilized within a period of 4 to 6 h with the peak yield of $^{14}CO_2$ occurring between 1 and 2 h after substrate administration. Once the optimal substrate level is known, a series of radiorespirometric experiments can then be implemented using the substrate labelled with ^{14}C at specific carbon atoms. It is important that concurrent experiments with specifically labelled substrates be conducted with a given cell crop to avoid variation derived from physiological differences among different cell crops.

Although the radiorespirometric experiments have been used primarily in the study of carbohydrate catabolism in micro-organisms, the scope of the method actually encompasses the study of any other metabolizable compounds by micro-organisms. The limitation in this regard is really dependent on the objectives of the study and the availability of the ^{14}C-labelled compounds.

3. Radioactivity inventory in a radiorespirometric experiment

Upon termination of a given radiorespirometric experiment, the cell suspension in the flask is chilled with ice and transferred to a centrifuge tube and the cells are separated from the incubation medium by centrifugation. The cells are resuspended in a few ml of fresh incubation medium and harvested again by centrifugation. The cell washings are then combined with the incubation medium and diluted with water to a given total volume. The harvested cells are suspended in a defined volume of water. Aliquots of the incubation medium and the cell suspension (e.g., 1 ml) are taken and mixed with a defined volume of thixotropic gel (White and Helf, 1956) (e.g., 14 ml) in a liquid scintillation counting vial. The gel samples can then be readily counted in the liquid scintillation counter to provide one with information on the radioactivity in the incubation medium and cells respectively. In the event one encounters problems in the measurement of radioactivity in cells by the gel method, the cell crop can be dried and an aliquot can be taken to be counted by means of the Schöniger flask combustion method (Wang and Willis, 1965; Schöniger, 1955; Kalberer and Rutschmann, 1961).

The data so far collected on the substrate radioactivity in the respiratory CO_2, incubation medium, and cells provide one with an inventory of the fate of substrate radioactivity. Generally speaking, if one can account for over 95% of the substrate radioactivity in the respective samples, one is provided with confidence on the reliability of the experiments. However, in the event total inventory of substrate radioactivity does not add up to the desired recovery, it is indicative of several possible happenings; i.e., malfunction of the apparatus such as leakage in the sweeping system; inadequacy of procedures in the counting of cell or incubation medium samples; the formation of gaseous fermentation products that cannot be trapped by the CO_2 trapping solutions, etc.

The information on the radioactivity residing in the cells in the incubation medium is of importance to the interpretation of the radiorespirometric data. One can gain much knowledge of the biosynthetic pathways and fermentation mechanisms upon analysis of the data on substrate inventory.

C. Some typical experiments

To illustrate the typical uses of radiorespirometry, involving single-dose substrate administration, in identifying and estimating catabolic pathways in micro-organisms, three sets of experiments are described briefly in the following, including design concepts of experiment.

1. *Catabolic pathways for glucose utilization by bakers' yeast*

Use is first made of the data obtained in the preliminary experiment for the utilization of glucose-U-^{14}C by yeast. From the radiorespirometric data, one learns that glucose is used at a very rapid pace by yeast; consequently it is necessary to conduct another set of experiments to determine the optimal substrate level. Such an experiment includes the use of glucose-U-^{14}C at a substrate level of 5 mg, 10 mg, 30 mg and 50 mg/10 mg (dry weight basis) of cells suspended in 10 ml of incubation medium. The optimal radioactivity level is set to be 0·01 μc/mg of labelled glucose. The radiochemical level is determined taking into consideration the desirable level of radioactivity in the respiratory CO_2 that can be trapped in a 15-min interval. By "desirable level", it is meant that the radioactivity in the majority of samples of CO_2 trap solution collected during a 15-min interval is such that it would permit one to count the sample in approximately 10 min; i.e., the counting rate of the sample is approximately 1000 to 3000 cpm, to provide adequate accuracy of the data.

Thus, as an educated estimation, if one assumes that 50 mg of glucose can be utilized by yeast in 5 h and 30% of the radioactivity of glucose-$U^{14}C$ will appear in respiratory CO_2, calculation can be readily made to determine the optimal level of radioactivity that should be used in the experiment. Since the desired sampling intervals are 15 min, there will be 20 samples taken during the 5-h experiment. Since the desirable counting rate of a sample is no less than 1000 cpm and one-third (5 ml of a total 15 ml trap solution) of each of the trap solutions will be used for counting, the radioactivity of an average sample of trap solution will then be 3000 cpm $\times$ 20 = 60,000 cpm. Considering that the detection efficiency for the $^{14}CO_2$ samples, by means of a liquid scintillation counter, is 40%, the desired radioactivity in respiratory CO_2 is then 60,000/0·04 = 150,000 dpm and that the radioactivity of substrate glucose (30% of which will appear in CO_2) should therefore be 150,000 dpm/0·30 = 500,000 dpm or 0·23 μc. The latter figure is multiplied by a safety factor of two and hence the total desired level of radioactivity is approximately 0·5 μc in 50 mg of glucose and the specific activity is therefore 0·01 μc/mg of substrate glucose.

The experimental procedures are essentially that as described previously. However, the experiment is allowed to proceed to 10 h. The radiorespirometric data obtained in this set of experiments revealed that 10 mg of yeast cells can utilize 30 mg of glucose in 3 h with the peak $^{14}CO_2$ interval yield (15 min) observed at approximately 2 h after substrate administration. This is followed by a decline of $^{14}CO_2$ yield to a practically insignificant level at the end of 6 h. Based on this piece of information, a series of radiorespirometric experiments designed for the study of catabolic pathways in yeast is designed employing a substrate level of 30 mg each of ^{14}C-specifically labelled glucose substrate for 10 mg of yeast cells (dry weight basis) and the specific activity of substrate glucose is set at 0·01 μc/mg.

The radiorespirometric pattern obtained in this series of experiments is given in Fig. 5. Much information can be acquired by detailed analyses of these data. The conclusions reached from data analysis will be given in a later section.

2. *Detection of the Tricarboxylic Acid Cycle Pathway in* Brevibacterium stationes (*ATCC* 14403).

Inasmuch as the Tricarboxylic Acid Cycle (TCA cycle) constitutes one of the most important catabolic pathways in the utilization of acetyl CoA derived from glucose or other carbonaceous substrates, it is often desirable to examine whether the TCA Cycle pathway is operative in a given microorganism. Radiorespirometry can be readily used for this task. However, it is generally recognized that TCA Cycle acids cannot be readily utilized by most of the micro-organisms due primarily to permeability problems.

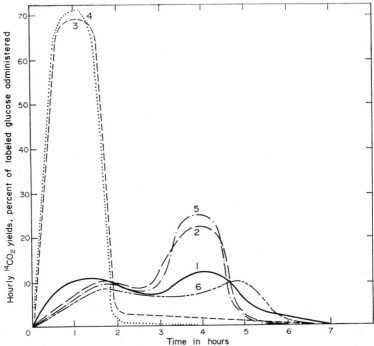

Fig. 5. The radiorespirometric pattern for utilization of ^{14}C-specifically labelled glucose substrate by *Saccharomyces cerevisiae* (OSU Strain 1). Single-dose experiment. Numerals refer to the labelled carbon atoms of glucose. (M. Isono and C. H. Wang, 1967).

To overcome this, one finds that glutamic acid can be used as a suitable substrate for this purpose. This is true for three reasons:

(a) Glutamic acid is permeable to most micro-organisms.
(b) Glutamic acid, upon entering the cells, can be readily converted to α-ketoglutarate, a key intermediate in the TCA Cycle pathway.
(c) ^{14}C-specifically labelled DL-glutamate are commercially available.

It should be noted that many micro-organisms cannot use D-isomers of glutamic acid and, hence, at the end of the experiment, one may find a large amount of radioactivity left over in the incubation medium primarily in the form of D-glutamic acid. However, this physiological characteristic of a given micro-organism does not interfere with data analysis.

With *Br. stationes*, results obtained in the preliminary experiments revealed that with 5·0 mg of DL-glutamate-1-^{14}C and 10 mg of cells, the rate for [14]CO$_2$ production peaked at 1 h after the substrate administration. Consequently, the series of experiments using ^{14}C-specifically labelled

DL-glutamate are designed to have a substrate level of 3·0 mg/5 mg cells (dry weight basis) suspended in 10 ml of incubation medium. The specific activity of DL-glutamate is chosen as 0·05 μc/mg. The results obtained in this experiment are given in Fig. 6. Data interpretation for this particular section will be given in a later section.

3. *Catabolic pathways for glucose utilization in* Arthrobacter globiformis (ATCC 8010)†

With *A. globiformis*, preliminary experiments using a great variety of ^{14}C-labelled substrates revealed that glucose and gluconate can be readily utilized by this organism. Making use of the results so obtained, two sets

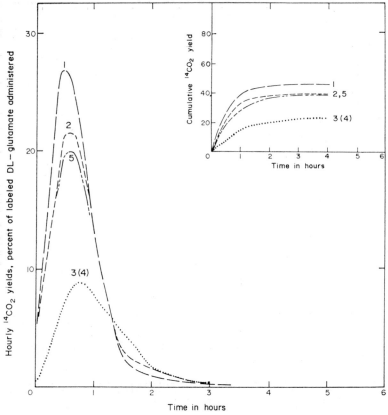

FIG. 6. The radiorespirometric pattern for utilization of ^{14}C-specifically labelled DL-glutamate substrates by *Brevibacterium stationes* (ATCC 14403). Single-dose experiment. Numerals refer to the labelled carbon atoms of glutamate. (M. Ameyama and C. H. Wang, unpublished work).

† Zagallo and Wang, 1967.

9

of experiments were designed with ¹⁴C-specifically labelled glucose as substrate (substrate level 8·0 mg (sp. act. 0·10 μc/mg)/8 mg cells (dry weight basis) suspended in 10 ml medium) in one set and ¹⁴C-specifically labelled gluconate (substrate level 10 mg (sp. act. 0·10 μc/mg)/10 mg cells in 10 ml medium) in the other set. These experiments were carried out for a duration of 6 h and the data obtained are given in Fig. 7 and Fig. 8. Data interpretation for these experiments has been given in a previous paper (Zagallo and Wang, 1967); however, it is enough to say that the use of gluconate as a substrate facilitated much the analysis of data obtained in the glucose experiment.

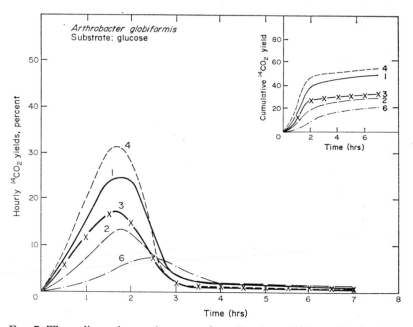

FIG. 7. The radiorespirometric pattern for utilization of ¹⁴C-specifically labelled glucose substrate by *Arthrobacter globiformis* (ATCC 8010). Single-dose experiment. Numerals refer to the labelled carbon atoms of glucose. (A. Zagallo and C. H. Wang, 1967).

IV. RADIORESPIROMETRIC EXPERIMENTS INVOLVING CONTINUOUS SUBSTRATE FEEDING

A. General considerations

The single-dose radiorespirometric experiment, as described in the foregoing section, is easy to carry out. However, the information so collected, while useful, is somewhat crude in nature. To learn details of

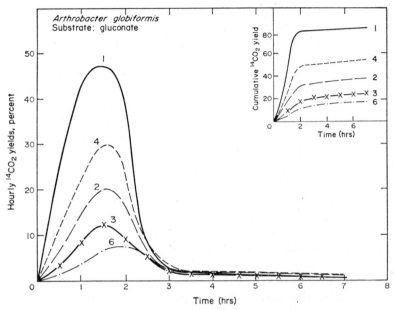

FIG. 8. The radiorespirometric pattern for utilization of ^{14}C-specifically labelled gluconate substrate by *Arthrobacter globiformis* (ATCC 8010). Single-dose experiment. Numerals refer to the labelled carbon atoms of gluconate. (A. Zagallo and C. H. Wang, 1967).

kinetics pertaining to the catabolic mechanism of micro-organisms, one must refine his approach to some basic facets of radiorespirometric experiments. Several concepts underlying the design of such a refined experiment are given in the following.

First, in order to gain information on the kinetics of microbial catabolism, it is important that data on yields of substrate radioactivity in respiratory CO_2 be those observed with micro-organisms utilizing a given substrate under proximate steady states. The term "steady state" is used here to refer to the situation in which substrate turnover in each of the microbial cells follows essentially a constant rate. Such a situation can be realized only when substrates are present in the incubation medium at a reasonably higher level so that any reduction during the course of study is essentially insignificant in magnitude. Consequently, this type of experiment can be considered as involving continuous substrate feeding. Moreover, with this type of experiment, it is possible to use microbial cells cultured in the original growth medium without harvesting. This manoeuvre avoids any disturbance of the physiological state of the micro-organism. At a specific phase of growth of the micro-organism, ^{14}C-labelled substrate with high specific activity but in minute amount, can be introduced into the cell culture, thereby marking the start of the radiorespirometric experiment.

In order to gain kinetic information in fine detail pertaining to the production of $^{14}CO_2$, one must measure the $^{14}CO_2$ by means of a flow ion chamber in conjunction with an electrometer. The analog signal from the electrometer can be either presented on a recorder or converted to digital form presented by a data read-out system. Inasmuch as, under these circumstances, proliferation of microbial cells will continue without interruption, data on the rate or the yields of $^{14}CO_2$ will be best expressed on the basis of unit number of cells. This means that the population of the microbial cells must be determined periodically by frequent sampling and counting of the cells in the cell culture.

However, there are some problems associated with this approach. For example, the use of the ion chamber-electrometer system and associated equipment for the measurement of respiratory $^{14}CO_2$ calls for involved procedures. Also, the dilution factor inflicted on the labelled substrates such as glucose requires a much higher level of radioactivity in a given experiment. Moreover, experiments of this type do not permit one to observe a complete time course of substrate utilization. Upon termination of such an experiment, the majority of the radioactivity will remain in the incubation medium in the form of the labelled substrate and hence one would not be able to determine precisely the amount of substrate that has incorporated in cells or in fermentation products.

B. Basic considerations underlying experiment design

1. *Preparation of culture*

In order to avoid any perturbation of the physiological state of the micro-organisms, inoculum of stock culture of a given micro-organism is transferred aseptically into a sterile micro-Fernbach flask (50–100 ml in size) containing the desired growth medium. The cultures are allowed to incubate in a rectangular Warburg waterbath or similar apparatus with shaking at the desired temperature for the micro-organism under study. At the end of a prescribed incubation period, dependent on the growth phase desired for the experiment, the cotton plug of the incubation flask is removed and aliquots are transferred to smaller micro-Fernbach flasks (25 ml in size). The latter are connected to the sweeping gas system (Fig. 3) followed immediately by the injection of the labelled substrate through the syringe cap-covered side port.

2. *Labelled substrate*

Some consideration should be given to the composition of the growth medium in carrying out this type of radiorespirometric experiment. The composition of the incubation medium for micro-organisms reported by various workers are those that ensure optimal growth and generally contain an excessive supply of various nutrients. This situation does not cause any concern for other types of experiments. In the present case, the presence of an excessive amount of the carbonaceous compound under study in the incubation medium will require proportionately larger amounts of labelled substrates with a proportionately higher level of specific activity so that the specific activity of the respiratory $^{14}CO_2$ evolved by the micro-organism would be high enough for ready detection by means of a flow ion chamber. For example, one may find that for a certain micro-organism the concentration of glucose in the growth medium is as high as 3%. It is entirely possible that even when the micro-organism has grown to the stationary phase, there was still over 2% of the glucose left in the incubation medium. If the mechanism of the glucose catabolism is to be studied by means of the radiorespirometric method, it will be desirable to reduce the initial glucose concentration to a lower level. Hence, the optimal level of unlabelled glucose in the incubation medium should be determined by carrying out a series of preliminary experiments in which the concentration of glucose is determined from time to time during a prescribed course of incubation. From the results so obtained one can then design an experiment so that the concentration of unlabelled glucose at the time of addition of the labelled glucose is such that excessive dilution of the labelled glucose can be avoided.

Similar situations also prevail when one desires to trace the catabolic fate of other ^{14}C-labelled substrates. Thus, if ^{14}C-labelled glutamate is to be used as a labelled substrate, it may be desirable to consider the reduction of the level of peptone or yeast extract in the incubation medium to avoid excessive dilution of the labelled substrate. Naturally, one of the criteria in determining the optimal level of nutrients is that one should not inflict an unphysiological environment upon the micro-organisms.

The specific activity and the level of radioactivity of the ^{14}C-labelled substrate to be used in a given experiment can be determined by considering the following factors: (a) The detection efficiency of $^{14}CO_2$ by means of a flow ion chamber-electrometer assembly as depicted in Fig. 3; (b) The amount of unlabelled substrate present in the incubation medium at the time of administration of the labelled substrate; (c) The rate of utilization of the substrate; (d) The anticipated yield of $^{14}CO_2$ from a specific labelled carbon atom. In the latter regard, one can cite the case of glucose as an example. Thus, if the glucose is catabolized by the micro-organisms exclusively via the EMP–TCA Cycle pathway, one would find that C-3 and C-4 of glucose are converted extensively to respiratory CO_2 while the conversion of C-1 and C-6 of glucose to CO_2 is limited but to cellular constituents is extensive. This understanding implies that one would need to use a higher level of radioactivity in the glucose-1-^{14}C and glucose-6-^{14}C experiments in comparison to that needed to be used in the glucose-3(4)-^{14}C experiment.

3. Execution of experiment

The desirable duration of radiorespirometric experiments of this type is dependent on several parameters. First, if the labelled carbon atoms of the substrates under study can be promptly converted to respiratory $^{14}CO_2$, one should be able to observe that the rate of $^{14}CO_2$ evolution (expressed as dpm or μc/min or per cent of substrate activity) following an acute ascending slope that lasts for a few minutes, reflecting the lag time pertaining to the catabolic mechanism and the response time of the ion chamber in detecting $^{14}CO_2$ evolved from the incubation flask. The slope of the rate curve should soon display a plateau which reflects that the metabolism of the substrate is at essentially the metabolic steady state. Since data needed for calculation of catabolic rates can be collected within a few minutes at the plateau phase, the experiment can be terminated at the time when the steady state is observed for a duration of 5 to 10 min. On the other hand, if one is interested in the effect of an external factor upon catabolic rate, a longer duration of experiment is warranted.

If the conversion of the labelled carbon atom of the substrate is a slow process; i.e., involving a rather complex mechanism (such as the conversion of C-6 of glucose to CO_2 via the EMP–TCA Cycle pathway), one may not be able to observe a plateau relative to the rate of $^{14}CO_2$ evolution. For this reason, in a given series of experiments using a given substrate, it is highly desirable that at least one of the ^{14}CO-specifically labelled carbon atoms be one of the types that can be promptly converted to respiratory $^{14}CO_2$ via known catabolic pathways. Some typical examples are glucose-3-^{14}C, glucose-3(4)-^{14}C, gluconate-1-^{14}C, glucose-1-^{14}C, DL-glutamate-1-^{14}C, etc.

C. A typical experiment—glucose catabolism in bakers' yeast†

1. Determination of the detection efficiency for $^{14}CO_2$ by means of a flow ion chamber-electrometer assembly

The gas inlet to the micro-Fernbach flask containing 10 ml of incubation medium without micro-organism is connected to the air pump (Fig. 3). A stream of air is then introduced into the micro-Fernbach flask at the rate of 95 ml/min. Meanwhile, the flow rate of argon gas, derived from an argon tank, is set at 205 per min and directed by way of the 3-way stopcock to mix with the air derived from the incubation flask. The signal output from

† Jacobsen and Wang, unpublished work.

the electrometer is then monitored for a period of 10 min by taking readings from the scaler in digital form at 1 min intervals. The data so obtained represent the background counting rate of the detection system and are generally in the order of magnitude of 1120 digits/min. The air pump is then replaced by a tank of air-$^{14}CO_2$ mixture. The optimal composition of the mixture is generally set at 0.03% of $^{14}CO_2$ in air with the specific activity of the $^{14}CO_2$ being 0.0025 μc/ml. Air flow through the incubation flask is resumed at the same rate; i.e., 95 ml/min. The flow rate of argon remains to be the same as previously stated. A period of 5 min is allowed for the sweeping process to continue to ensure equilibrium of incubation atmosphere with respect to the air-$^{14}CO_2$ mixture. The signal from the ion chamber-electrometer assembly is then measured in digital form for a period of 10 min with readings printed out at 1-min intervals. By subtracting the data of the background radiation in digits/min from the data obtained with calibrated gas, digits/min, one is provided with the detection efficiency of the ion chamber-electrometer system expressed in digits/min/μc of $^{14}CO_2$ radioactivity. The procedure should be repeated with each of the radiorespirometer assemblies if multiple flask systems are employed. Once the detection efficiency of each assembly is known, the information can be used for future experiments unless the situation calls for recalibration of the entire assembly. With the assembly depicted in Fig. 3, 1.13×10^7 digits are equivalent to 1 μc of radioactivity as $^{14}CO_2$ in air.

For fast catabolic reactions, data collection can be made at intervals of seconds. However, one should be aware of the limitations derived from the response time of the electrometer, the turnover time of chamber volume, etc.

2. Incubation experiment

To carry out a multiple flask experiment; i.e., for concurrent experiments with a substrate labelled with ^{14}C at specific carbon atoms, it is advisable to grow the yeast cells in a sizeable micro-Fernbach flask (e.g., 100 ml flask for four concurrent experments). The composition of the growth medium is 2.5 g $(NH_4)_2SO_4$, 2.0 g NaCl, 2.0 g KH_2PO_4, 0.25 g $MgSO_4$.$7H_2O$, 0.25 g $CaCl_2.2H_2O$, 1.0 mg H_3BO_3, 1.0 mg $ZnSO_4$, 1.0 mg $MnSO_4.4H_2O$, 1.0 mg $FeCl_3$, 0.1 mg $CuSO_4.5H_2O$, 0.1 mg KI, 18 g glucose, and 0.1 g Difco yeast extract all dissolved in 1 litre of distilled water. The pH of the medium was adjusted to 4.5 with HCl.

The concentration of glucose is set at 1.80 g/100 ml (0.1M) on the basis of results obtained in preliminary experiments. At this concentration there will be an ample supply of glucose for cell proliferation but there would not be an excessive amount of unlabelled glucose in the medium, when yeast cells are grown to the middle logarithmic phase, to dilute the labelled glucose. An optimal amount of inoculum of yeast cells is then introduced into 50 ml of incubation medium in the flask aseptically; the flask is placed in the waterbath and the incubation is permitted to proceed with shaking while a stream of sterile air is introduced into the flask at the rate of 95 ml/min. The duration of the incubation is dependent on the desired growth phase of the yeast cells for the experiment. The rate of growth of yeast cells can be readily determined by a set of preliminary experiments using the same procedures and sampling the suspension periodically for cell counting.

At the end of the prescribed incubation period, 10 ml aliquots of the cell suspension are pipetted into each of the four 25 ml micro-Fernbach incubation flasks. Another 5 ml aliquot are pipetted into a test tube for the measurement of cell population and glucose content. From a series of preliminary studies, it is known that the simple transfer process described

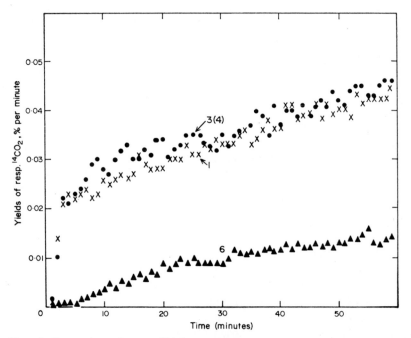

FIG. 9. Rate of respiratory $^{14}CO_2$ production from *Saccharomyces cerevisiae* (OSU Strain 2), in middle log phase, metabolizing ^{14}C-specifically labelled glucose substrates. Continuous substrate feeding experiment. Numerals refer to the labelled position of glucose. The yield of $^{14}CO_2$ is expressed as per cent of substrate radioactivity detected in respiratory CO_2/min. (D. W. Jacobsen and C. H Wang, 1967).

here does not inflict significant perturbation of the physiological state of the yeast cells.

Each of the 25 ml micro-Fernbach flasks are then connected to the respective radiorespirometer assemblies. Aeration is initiated at a stated rate and the shaking mechanism is turned on. Five minutes are allowed to elapse to restore the normal incubation environment and the labelled substrate; i.e., ^{14}C-specifically labelled glucose substrates are introduced individually into each of the four flasks. The radiochemical levels are: glucose-3(4)-^{14}C (sp. act. 5·6 μc/mg) 3·04 μc; glucose-1-^{14}C (sp. act. 10·7 μc/mg) 5·04 μc and glucose-6-^{14}C (sp. act. 11·5 μc/mg) 5·69 μc. Incubation of the yeast cells with the labelled substrate is allowed to proceed for a period of 60 min while the radioactivity of the respiratory $^{14}CO_2$ is measured continuously with the data registered in digital form at 1 min intervals, or if desirable at even shorter time intervals. A small

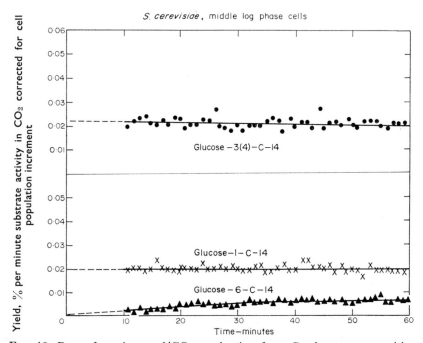

FIG. 10. Rate of respiratory $^{14}CO_2$ production from *Saccharomyces cerevisiae* (OSU Strain 2), in middle log phase, metabolizing ^{14}C-specifically labelled glucose substrates and corrected for cell population increment. Continuous substrate feeding experiment. Numerals refer to the labelled position of glucose. The yield of $^{14}CO_2$ is expressed as per cent of substrate radioactivity detected in respiratory CO_2/min. (D. W. Jacobsen and C. H. Wang, 1967).

aliquot; e.g., 0·2 ml is removed from each of the flasks periodically (e.g., at 15 min intervals) for glucose determination and cell countings.

At the end of a prescribed incubation period, the micro-Fernbach flasks are removed from the waterbath and 0·2 ml aliquots are taken from each flask and transferred into an ice-chilled test tube for the purpose of measurement of cell population. The remaining portion of the cell suspension is centrifuged to separate the cell from the incubation medium. The cells are resuspended in 10 ml of growth medium without carbon source and harvested by centrifugation. The radioactivity in the incubation medium (along with washings) and in the cells can then be determined by the conventional method.

A typical set of radiorespirometric data obtained by this method is given in Fig. 9 and the same data corrected for increments of cell population are given in Fig. 10. These data are presented as time course plots of interval yields of $^{14}CO_2$ expressed as per cent of labelled substrate radioactivity in respiratory CO_2/min.

V. GENERAL APPLICATIONS

A. Scope

Up to the present moment, radiorespirometry has been advantageously used in the following type of studies:

1. *Utilizability of carbonaceous compounds by micro-organisms*

The use of the radiorespirometric technique permits one to learn whether a given carbonaceous compound can be utilized by a given organism incubated under normal conditions. Thus, in the case of *Penicillium digitatum*, TCA cycle acids such as succinate and fumarate cannot be utilized by the mold in a medium containing only inorganic nutrients. Yet when glucose is present in the medium, one finds that these acids can be utilized at respectable rates (Jacobsen and Wang, 1968). It is also noteworthy that the radiorespirometric technique is one of the best ways to study the diauxie effect. Thus, when yeast cells are incubated in a proliferating medium containing ^{14}C-labelled mannose and glucose in one case and ^{14}C-labelled glucose and unlabelled mannose in another case, one learns that glucose is preferentially utilized by the yeast cells and that only when the glucose is completely exhausted from the medium before mannose can be utilized by this organism (Forbusch and Wang, unpublished work).

2. *Identification of catabolic pathways in micro-organisms*

Whereas conclusive evidence demonstrating the operation of a given catabolic pathway in micro-organisms relies on the detection of all enzyme systems associated with the catabolic pathway, the use of ^{14}C-specifically labelled substrates in a set of single-dose radiorespirometric experiments often provides one with sufficient evidence for the operation of a certain catabolic pathway. Data interpretation may be difficult in some cases, particularly where several catabolic pathways are operating concurrently in the organism. Another problem one may encounter is that certain substrates are not permeable to an organism despite the fact that other evidence points to the involvement of the substrate in one of the demonstrated pathways. An example in this regard is the compound gluconate. It is a well-known fact that gluconate is a key intermediate in the pentose phosphate pathway and the Entner-Douordoff pathway; yet many micro-organisms equipped with these pathways would not assimilate gluconate present in the incubation medium (Zagallo and Wang, 1967).

3. Estimation of relative participation of concurrent pathways

In studying the carbohydrate metabolism of micro-organisms, particularly with such important carbon sources as glucose and fructose, it is of great interest to learn the relative roles played by catabolic pathways operating concurrently. Such information can provide one with insight pertaining to the function of each of the catabolic pathways in overall microbial metabolism. During the past decade, a number of methods have been developed in this regard. Two of the methods rely on the data collected in radiorespirometric experiments; i.e., the $^{14}CO_2$ yield method and the catabolic rate method. Details of these methods will be presented in a later section.

4. Studies on the alteration of catabolic pathways

It is well recognized that catabolic pathways operative in a micro-organism can be altered by external factors such as inhibitors, growth regulators, temperature, composition of the incubation medium, etc. The radiorespirometric method offers a rapid means to evaluate qualitatively and even quantitatively the effect of these external factors. Information in this regard is of importance in studies on mode of action, toxicology, metabolic control and regulation, substrate permeability, and microbial physiology in general.

5. Biochemical taxonomy of micro-organisms

In recent years much of the biochemical behaviour of micro-organisms has been included as important criteria for microbial taxonomy. Information on the operation and the relative participation of catabolic pathways in micro-organisms has provided much information in recognizing bio-types of a well-defined genus and in providing ground for the need of reclassification of certain species in a given genus. Information in this regard is not only of importance to biochemical taxonomy but also the understanding of phyllogenetic relationships among different genera.

B. Identification of catabolic pathways in micro-organisms

The catabolic mechanism for the assimilation of carbon sources in micro-organisms is, in some aspects, more complex in comparison to other biological systems. It may be desirable to first review briefly the known catabolic pathways functioning in micro-organisms. In essence, the catabolic mechanism for the utilization of glucose, presumably the most important carbon source for biological systems, can be classified in two major categories; namely, the primary pathway, which breaks down glucose into small intermediates of which pyruvate is generally recognized as the key one; and the secondary pathway, which is responsible for the catabolism of pyruvate and acetate derived therefrom, giving rise to carbon skeletons of various sizes and eventually to respiratory CO_2.

The known primary glucose pathways are the Embden-Meyerhof-Parnas (EMP) pathway; the Entner-Douordoff (ED) pathway; the pentose phosphate (PP) pathway, the affiliated pentose cycle (PC) pathway and the glucuronic acid (GA) pathway. In micro-organisms one finds that either the EMP pathway or the ED pathway are operating concurrently with the PP pathway. It is not known that the EMP pathway and the ED pathway can function concurrently for glucose utilization. Another unique situation is the fact that the ED pathway is found only to be operative in the micro-organism but not in any other biological system. The glucuronic pathway is not an important route for glucose catabolism in most micro-organisms.

The secondary pathway; i.e., the catabolic routes responsible for the degradation of C_3 units such as triose phosphate and pyruvate derived from glucose, include the TCA Cycle pathway and the glyoxylic acid Cycle pathway. A schematic diagram showing the basic reactions involved in each of these pathways as well as the relative order (with respect to both rate and extent) of formation of CO_2 from individual carbon atoms of glucose, is given in Fig. 11. In this scheme, one can visualize the relative time sequence as one traces the conversion of carbon atoms of glucose on the right to CO_2 stepwise toward the left side of the scheme.

The scheme given in Fig. 11 provides a basis for analysing the radio-respirometric data on utilization of glucose by micro-organisms. Three cases are presented here as illustrative examples.

The use of the radiorespirometric method to identify the operation of the TCA Cycle pathway in micro-organisms can be illustrated by the case of *Brevibacterium stationes* (ATCC 14403). As shown in Fig. 6, it appears

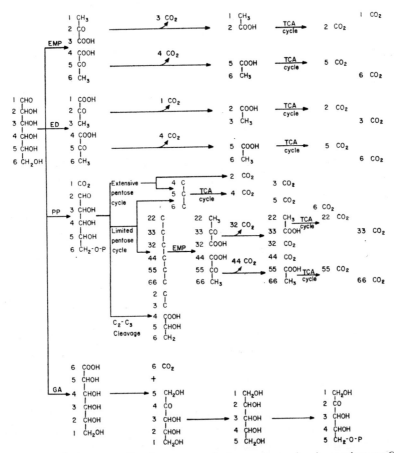

FIG. 11. Relative rates of carbon atoms of glucose appearing in respiratory CO_2 via known catabolic pathways. EMP: The Embden-Meyerhof-Parnas pathway; ED: The Entner-Douordoff pathway; PP: The Pentose Phosphate pathway; GA: The Glucuronic Acid pathway; TCA: The Tricarboxylic Acid Cycle pathway.

that only L-isomers of glutamic acid can be utilized by this micro-organism. The rate and extent for the conversion of glutamate carbon atoms to respiratory CO_2 follows the order of C-1 > C-2 = C-5 ≫ C-3 (Wang and Krackov, 1962). It is reasonable to assume that the utilization of L-glutamate by this organism includes the intermediary formation of α-ketoglutarate which is then routed into the TCA Cycle pathway as shown in Fig. 12. The observed radiorespirometric pattern provides one with reasonably good proof that the TCA Cycle pathway is indeed operative in this micro-organism.

The radiorespirometric data for the utilization of ^{14}C-specifically labelled

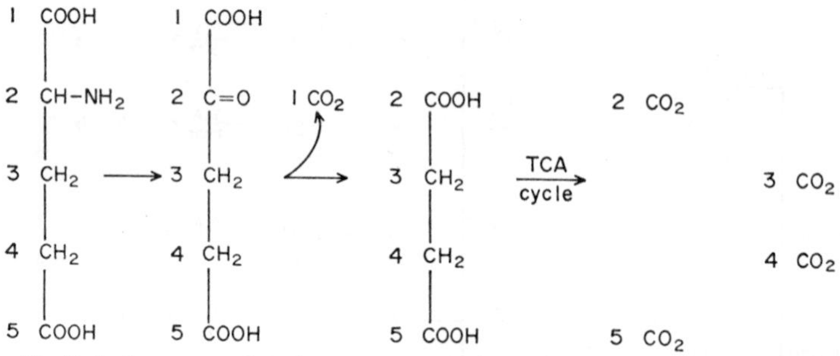

```
 1  COOH        1  COOH                    
    |              |                        
 2  CH-NH2     2  C=O      1 CO2    2  COOH              2  CO2
    |              |                 |                    
 3  CH2    ---> 3  CH2              3  CH2    --TCA-->    3  CO2
    |              |                 |         cycle
 4  CH2        4  CH2              4  CH2                 4  CO2
    |              |                 |
 5  COOH       5  COOH             5  COOH                5  CO2
```

Fig. 12. Relative rates of carbon atoms of glutamic acid appearing in respiratory CO_2 via the intermediary formation of α-ketoglutarate and the TCA cycle pathway.

glucose by yeast (*Saccharomyces cerevisiae*, (OSU Strain 1)), shown in Fig. 5, provides clear evidence pointing to the important role played by the EMP glycolytic pathway in yeast catabolism. This is true since one finds that C-3 and C-4 of glucose are converted to respiratory CO_2 promptly and extensively. Since the rate and extent for the conversion of C-1 to resporatory CO_2 is significantly higher than that of C-6 of glucose during the first 2 h of the experiment, one is also led to believe that the PP pathway is also operative, although to a much lesser extent, in this organism. From the data given in Fig. 5, one can also conclude that the administered glucose in the form of a single dose is exhausted from the medium in approximately 2 h. From there on the yeast cells are going through a depletion phase. It is known (Wang *et al.*, 1953) that during the active assimilation of substrate glucose by yeast, a sizeable amount of glutamic acid is synthesized from substrate glucose and stored in the cells. It is reasonable to believe that during the depletion phase, a portion of endogenous reserve, accumulated freshly from the administered substrate, is channelled into the catabolic processes.

In accordance with the mechanism of the EMP–TCA pathway, the endogenous glutamic acid derived from labelled glucose will have a labelling pattern as follows:

$$\overset{2,5}{HOOC}-\overset{1,6}{CH_2}-\overset{1,6}{CH_2}-\overset{1,6}{CH}-\overset{2,5}{COOH}$$
$$|$$
$$NH_2$$

The numerals refer to the position of the carbon atoms in substrate glucose. The conversion of carbon atoms of glutamic acid to respiratory CO_2 by way of the intermediary formation of α-ketoglutarate and the operation of the TCA Cycle pathway has been described in Fig. 12.

In Fig. 13 are given the radiorespirometric data for the utilization of

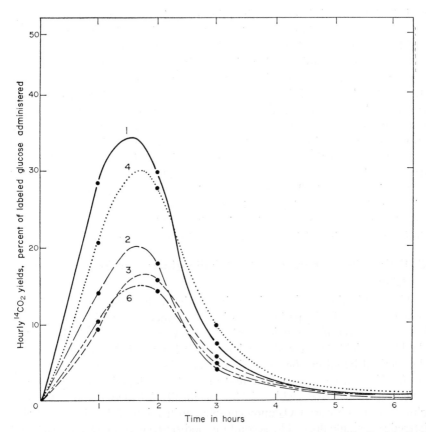

FIG. 13. Radiorespirometric pattern for the utilization of specifically labelled glucose-^{14}C substrates by *Xanthomonas phaseoli*. Single-dose experiment. The data represent the average values for four replica experiments. Numerals associated with each curve designate the position of ^{14}C labelling of the glucose substrate. Data pertaining to the substrate glucose-4-^{14}C are calculated by difference, making use of the findings in the glucose-3-^{14}C and glucose-3,4-^{14}C experiments.

^{14}C-specifically labelled glucose by *Xanthomonas phaseoli*. In this case, one finds that the rate and extent for the conversion of carbon atoms of glucose to respiratory CO_2 follows the order of C-1 > C-4 ≫ C-2 > C-3 ≈ C-6. As indicated in the scheme given in Fig. 11, the operation of the ED pathway for glucose catabolism will give rise to an equivalence in catabolic behaviour of C-1 to C-4 and C-3 to C-6, and it is therefore justifiable to state that in *X. phaseoli*, glucose is catabolized to a large extent by way of the ED pathway and to a much lesser extent via the PP pathway. The latter conclusion is derived from the consideration that the radiochemical yield of

C-1 in CO_2 is slightly greater than that of C-4 of glucose, not in line with the exclusive operation of the ED pathway which will give rise to equal yields in CO_2 from either C-1 or C-4 of substrate glucose.

It should be emphasized again at this point that radiorespirometric experiments for studies on the utilization of a given substrate should be so designed and executed that a time course for complete substrate utilization is followed. In order to analyse a set of radiorespirometric data, one needs not only to know the rate for the conversion of carbon atoms of the substrate to CO_2 but also of more importance is the cumulative radiochemical yields for each of the labelled carbon atoms in respiratory CO_2. The yield data would not be meaningful unless such data were collected at the end of the time course. Thus, with the radiorespirometric patterns shown in Figs 5 and 6, if respective experiments were terminated prematurely, such as 1 h after substrate administration, it would be indeed impossible to draw any meaningful information from these findings.

C. Estimation of concurrent catabolic glucose pathways in micro-organisms

The application of the radiorespirometric method for the estimation of concurrent catabolic pathways, primarily concerned with glucose catabolism, consists of two major methods. They are (1) the method based on the $^{14}CO_2$ yield (Wang and Krackov, 1962; Katz and Wood, 1963) and (2) the method based on the catabolic rate (Jacobsen and Wang, 1967; Wang et al., VII Int. Congress). The first method, developed several years ago, relies on cumulative yields of ^{14}C-specifically labelled carbon atoms of glucose in respiratory CO_2 upon complete utilization of the glucose administered as a single dose. The second method represents a new approach and is applicable only to the experiments involving continuous substrate feeding. The rate method is not subject to some of the limiting factors inherent in the yield method and thus provide more precise information on glucose catabolism and related facets.

Prior to a brief description of each of these two methods for pathway estimation, it is desirable to establish the basic concept with respect to the issue of relative participation of "concurrent glucose pathways". These pathways are shown in Fig. 11. In recent years, much attention has been focused on the extent of participation of the PC pathway in biological systems. Interest in this regard is derived from the consideration that the PC pathway is one of the major mechanisms in supplying NADPH for various biosynthetic functions. However, in reality, information on the exact extent of participation of the PC pathway in micro-organisms is not meaningful since a number of arbitrary assumptions will have to be made before one can even attempt a crude estimation. For this reason it is better to consider glucose catabolism in micro-organisms primarily in light of the immediate catabolic fate of substrate glucose which consists of the following three sequences.

The EMP pathway is defined as:

$$1 \text{ Glucose-6-P} \rightarrow \text{fructose-1,6-di-P} \rightarrow 2 \text{ triose-3-P} \rightarrow x \text{ pyruvate}$$

in which x is the actual yield of the pyruvate and the value of x has a limiting magnitude of two.

The ED pathway is defined as:

$$1 \text{ Glucose-6-P} \rightarrow 1 \text{ pyruvate} + 1 \text{ glyceraldehyde-3-P}$$

The PP pathway is defined as:

$$3 \text{ Glucose-6-P} \begin{cases} \rightarrow 3 \text{ CO}_2 \\ \rightarrow 3 \text{ pentose-P} \rightarrow z \text{ fructose-6-P} \\ \qquad + q \text{ glyceraldehyde-3-P} \end{cases}$$

in which z and q represent the actual yields of fructose-6-P and glyceraldehyde-3-P, respectively. In the uppermost limiting case, $z = 2$ and $q = 1$. On the other hand, if pentose-P is used completely for biosynthetic purposes (an unlikely case), $z = 0$ and $q = 0$. The fate of fructose-6-P derived from substrate glucose via the PP pathway is variable. Thus, fructose-6-P can be converted to glucose-6-P thereby completing a full cycle of the pentose cycle pathway. Further catabolism of the glucose-6-P so formed via the PP and the PC pathways constitutes the operation of the extensive PC pathway (Fig. 11). On the other hand, fructose-6-P can be readily converted to fructose-1,6-di-P and degraded further to triose phosphates if the EMP pathway is operative in the biological system in question. This would constitute the operation of a limited pentose cycle pathway (Fig. 11). In the case that the EMP pathway is the predominant route for glucose catabolism of a given micro-organism, while the PP pathway is playing only a minor role, one would expect that the fructose-6-P derived via the PP pathway would be converted extensively to fructose-1,6-di-P and then to triose phosphates. In other words, if one assumes that a glucose-6-P is equilibrated promptly with fructose-6-P, one would expect that the fate of the fructose-6-P derived from the PP pathway follows the same pattern as the glucose-6-P derived from the substrate glucose.

1. The $^{14}CO_2$ yield method

A set of equations have been derived on the basis of the following assumptions:

(a) Glucose is catabolized in a given micro-organism primarily by way of two sets of catabolic sequences; namely, either the concurrent operation of the EMP pathway and the PP pathway or the concurrent operation of the ED pathway and the PP pathway, for respiratory and biosynthetic functions.

(b) The preferential conversion of C-1 of glucose to CO_2 via the PP pathway is a virtually irreversible process.

(c) The C_3 units formed in the glucolytic pathway are virtually equivalent to each other with respect to further metabolic reactions.

(d) The formation of hexose by way of recombination of trioses is virtually insignificant in magnitude.

(e) The randomization of hexose skeleton via the transketolase or transaldolase exchange reaction or other similar processes does not occur to any significant extent.

(f) The substrate gluconate is utilized by the biological system in a manner virtually identical with the phosphogluconate derived from glucose *in vivo*.

Justifications (Wang and Krackov, 1962) of these assumptions are derived from the current understanding of glucose catabolism in biological systems. On the basis of the foregoing assumptions, the derivation of the necessary equations for the estimation of pathway participation in glucose catabolism follows.

Let G_T = amount of each labelled glucose administered, expressed on the percentage basis as unity; i.e., $G_T = 1 \cdot 00$, and $G_{T'}$ = fraction of the labelled glucose administered that was engaged in anabolic processes, expressed as a fraction of unity. It is understood that equal amounts of ^{14}C-specifically labelled glucose substrate are used in a given set of radio-respirometric experiments.

G_1, G_6 or G_4 = $^{14}CO_2$ yields observed at time t, where a microbial system is permitted to metabolize equal amounts of glucose labelled with ^{14}C at C-1, C-6 or C-4 carbon atoms, respectively. The yields are expressed as fractions of unity. Since glucose-4-^{14}C is not commercially available, data for the CO_2 yield derived from C-4 of glucose is calculated from findings in separate experiments with glucose-3-^{14}C and glucose-3,4-^{14}C as substrates.

A_6 = $^{14}CO_2$ yield observed at time t while a biological system is permitted to metabolize a given amount of gluconate-6-^{14}C. The yield is expressed as fraction of unity.

It should be noted that when the end of the time course for complete utilization of the substrate glucose is realized, the $^{14}CO_2$ yields observed can be considered as the "specific yield" as defined by Katz and Wood (1963).

G_p = fraction of administered glucose, engaged in catabolism, that has been routed into the PP pathway, expressed as a fraction of unity.

G_e = fraction of the administered glucose, engaged in catabolism, that has been routed into the EMP pathway, expressed as a fraction of unity.

G_{ed} = fraction of the administered glucose engaged in catabolism that has been routed into the ED pathway expressed as a fraction of unity.

During the early phase of the incubation experiment, the amount of substrate actually metabolized by the biological system cannot be readily ascertained. Consequently, only the cumulative $^{14}CO_2$ yield data collected at the time of substrate exhaustion or thereafter are those useful for the estimation of pathway participations. The term t is therefore confined to a time interval covering the entire course of complete utilization of substrate.

To estimate relative participation of concurrent operation of the EMP and the PP pathway, if one assumes that the pentose phosphate, as derived from glucose via the PP pathway, was not further catabolized, one would reach the conclusion expressed in equation A.

$$G_p = \frac{G_1 - G_6}{G_T - G_{T'}} \tag{A}$$

With most micro-organisms, the magnitude of the term $G_{T'}$ is generally small, despite the fact that certain carbon atoms of substrate glucose are converted to CO_2 to the extent of only 30 to 60%. This is true since the substrate radioactivity found in either cells or fermentation products in the incubation media represents, by the large, the catabolic products of glucose rather than the intact glucose molecules. When $G_{T'}$ is small, $G_T - G_{T'} = 1$ and equation A becomes equation B.

$$G_p = G_1 - G_6 \tag{B}$$

However, when the catabolism of the pentose phosphate is taken into consideration, a portion of the C-6 of substrate glucose can also be converted to the respiratory CO_2 via the PP pathway along with the portion of C-6 of glucose converted to CO_2 via the EMP-TCA Cycle pathway. The amount of CO_2 derived from C-6 of glucose via the PP pathway can be estimated, on the basis of the scheme shown in Fig. 11, as equal to $G_p \cdot G_6$, i.e., the amount of substrate glucose that traversed the PP pathway × the CO_2 yield from C-6 of glucose. This is theoretically correct since C-6 of glucose is converted to C-3 of glyceraldehyde-3-P via either the EMP of the PP pathway in the same yield. However, if one recognizes the biosynthetic functions of the respective pathways, the conversion of C-6 of glucose to C-3 of glyceraldehyde-3-P by the EMP and the PP pathways respectively, may differ slightly in extents. Bearing this consideration in mind, the amount of CO_2 derived from C-6 of glucose via the PP pathway may be, therefore, more realistically estimated as equal to $G_p \cdot A_6$; i.e., the amount of substrate glucose that traversed the HMP pathway × the CO_2 yield of C-6 of gluconate.

In accordance with the derivation underlying equation A, the term G_p should be represented by the following expression:

$$G_p = \frac{G_1 - (G_6 - G_p \cdot A_6)}{G_T - G_{T'}} \tag{C}$$

and when the magnitude of $G_{T'}$ is small, equation C becomes equation D:

$$G_p = G_1 - G_6 + G_p A_6 \tag{D}$$

Simplification of equation D gives equation E:

$$G_p = \frac{G_1 - G_6}{1 - A_6} \tag{E}$$

If one assumes that the troise phosphate derived from glucose via the PP pathway behaves catabolically identical to that derived from the administered gluconate via the PP pathway, equation E can then be expressed as:

$$G_p = \frac{G_1 - G_6}{1 - G_6} \tag{F}$$

Equation F is useful particularly when one is concerned with microorganisms that cannot utilize gluconate as the external carbon source in radiorespirometric experiments.

Since it has been assumed that the EMP and PP pathways constitute the major routes for glucose catabolism, the participation of the EMP pathway can be estimated by difference, thus:

$$G_e = 1 - G_p \tag{G}$$

In applying the foregoing described equations for pathway estimation, one is assuming that the bulk of the assimilated glucose has been engaged in catabolic functions; i.e., $G_{T'} = 0$. Whereas such an assumption is justifiable in many cases, in some micro-organisms, particularly fungi or any other micro-organisms that are known to store a considerable amount of substrate glucose as an endogenous reserve, it would be necessary to assess the value of $G_{T'}$ by some means. This is indeed a difficult task and hence, this aspect constitutes one of the drawbacks in the application of the $^{14}CO_2$ yield method for pathway estimation.

2. The catabolic rate method (continuous substrate feeding experiments)

Considerable efforts have been devoted in several laboratories recently in applying the radiorespirometric method to gain information on the rate of catabolic pathways (Wang et al., VII Int. Congress; Williams, 1965). This is feasible in view of recent developments of techniques for measurement of the rate of production of respiratory $^{14}CO_2$ with high resolution.

The use of information on the catabolic rates associated with individual pathways to estimate relative participation of concurrent glucose pathways is derived from several basic considerations. First, by examining the EMP-TCA Cycle sequence depicted in Fig. 11, one notes that C-3 and C-4 of glucose are *promptly* converted to respiratory CO_2 leading to the formation of acetate which is the key entry into the TCA Cycle pathway. If one assumes that C_3 intermediates derived from glucose via the EMP pathway, such as triose phosphate and pyruvate, are not engaged as intact units in metabolic processes, for each mole of glucose catabolized by way of the EMP-TCA pathway, one should expect to yield 1 mole each of CO_2 from C-3 and C-4 of glucose. Such an assumption is justifiable in view of the fact that triose phosphates generally do not participate extensively in biosynthetic functions. Pyruvate is known to be involved in CO_2 fixation processes; however, the extent of the operation of such processes in micro-organisms is limited in reference to the overall amount of pyruvate produced. Such an understanding leads one to conclude that the rate for the production of respiratory CO_2 from C-3 and C-4 of glucose reflect directly the catabolic rate of the EMP pathway. It is further noted that the CO_2 pool in micro-organisms is very small and hence there should be no significant time lag in the evolution of CO_2 from the cells once it is formed catabolically.

Second, on similar premises, the net rate of formation of respiratory CO_2 from C-1 of glucose should represent directly the catabolic rate of the PP pathway. However, since C-1 of glucose can be converted to CO_2 via either the EMP-TCA pathway or the PP pathway, the information on the net rate of CO_2 formation of C-1 of glucose via the PP pathway can be obtained by taking advantage of the understanding that the catabolic rate for the conversion of C-1 to CO_2 via the PP pathway is prompt and the conversion of C-1 or C-6 of glucose via the EMP-TCA pathway is relatively slow. Consequently, the rate of CO_2 formation from C-1 of glucose extrapolated to the time for the administration of the labelled substrate is the same as the rate of the PP pathway.

The advantages of the catabolic rate method are two-fold. First, the relative participation of concurrent pathways such as the EMP-TCA and the PP pathways are measured independently and directly from the information on the catabolic rate rate of the respective pathways. This is in contrast to the $^{14}CO_2$ yield method in which the extent of operation of the PP pathway is measured directly and the extent of the operation of the EMP pathway is measured by difference. Second, since the total rate of assimilation of glucose can be readily determined, the information on the amount of substrate glucose routed into each of the two catabolic pathways makes it possible to ascertain the amount of substrate glucose engaged in anabolic functions. Such information cannot be obtained by the $^{14}CO_2$ yield method. In fact, with the yield method one has either to assume that the amount of glucose engaged in anabolic functions is negligible or find means to determine the amount of substrate glucose that has been routed into anabooic processes as intact units.

The data for the utilization of ^{14}C-specifically labelled glucose by *Saccharomyces cerevisiae* in a radiorespirometric experiment involving continuous substrate feeding can be cited to illustrate the essential features of the catabolic rate methods. The estimation of the concurrent operation of the EMP and the PP pathways by means of this method can be described to include the following steps:

(a) Correction of rate data depicted in Fig. 9 to account for the increment of cell population. As indicated by the raw data given in Fig. 9, with cells at the middle logarithmic phase, the rate for the production of respiratory CO_2 from various carbon atoms of glucose assume an ascending slope due to the fact that the net amount of glucose assimilated by yeast cells per unit time is increasing with the time as a result of increments in cell population. Thus, it was found that, at the time of substrate administration, the cell population in each of the radiorespirometric flasks was 0.50×10^9 cells and increased to 0.80×10^9 cells after 30 min of incubation, to 1.10×10^9 cells after 52 min of incubation.

Using data on cell population increment during the incubation period, one obtains the rate curve as shown in Fig. 10. It should be noted that the corrected curves for the rates of [14]CO_2 production in the glucose-3,4-^{14}C and glucose-1-^{14}C experiments is essentially flat and hence provide evidence that the cells are metabolizing the administered glucose under essentially metabolic steady state conditions. With the data obtained in the glucose-6-^{14}C experiment, the corrected rate curve for [14]CO_2 production displays a slight ascending slope presumably reflecting the time lag in converting C-6 of glucose to CO_2 via the lenthy EMP-TCA sequence.

(b) Extrapolation of the rate curve to the time of administration of the labelled substrate. When each of the rate curves is extrapolated to T_0 (time of administration of labelled glucose substrates), one obtains more reliable information on the rate of [14]CO_2 production from the respective labelled carbon atoms. This is true since randomization of substrate labelling would not occur to any significant extent during the time interval shortly after administration of the specifically labelled glucose substrate. The extrapolations are represented by the broken lines for each of the rate curves. It is noted that the corrected rate curve for [14]CO_2 production from C-6 of glucose, when extrapolated to $T_{0'}$ intercepts with the origin. This fact implies that at $T_{0'}$ C-6 of glucose and presumably C-1 of glucose were not converted to respiratory CO_2 by way of the EMP-TCA sequence to any noticeable extent. It further implies that the rate data in the glucose-1-^{14}C experiment extrapolated to T_0 represents only the rate of conversion of C-1 of glucose to respiratory CO_2 via the PP pathway.

(c) Estimation of concurrent glucose pathways (the EMP and the PP pathways in *S. cerevisiae*). The essential data used for the estimation are given in the following:

Cell population at $T_0 = 0.50 \times 10^9$ cells

Amount of glucose present at T_0 : 747 μmoles

Radiochemical level of substrate glucose:

Glucose-1-^{14}C: 5.04 μc; specific activity =
    5.04/747 = 0.00675 μc/μmole.

Glucose-3,4-^{14}C : 3.04 μc; specific activity =
    3.04/747 = 0.00407 μc/μmole.

Glucose-6-^{14}C : 4.85 μc; specific activity =
    4.85/747 = 0.00649 μc/μmole.

Assimilation rate of glucose (G_{ar}) as determined by periodic chemical assay of glucose contents in the incubation medium. In the case of *S. cerevisiae* cells at mid-log phase, the rate of glucose assimilation is found to be a linear function, at least during the brief period soon after substrate administration. One finds in the present case:

$G_{ar} = 0.540$ μmole/min.

Rate of $^{14}CO_2$ production from carbon atoms of glucose at T_0 (G_{r-1}, G_{r-6}, $G_{r-3(4)}$, etc.) as obtained from data shown in Fig. 10:

G_{r-1} = 0.020% of total substrate radioactivity/min or
    0.00020×5.04 μc = 0.00101 μc/min

$G_{r-6} = 0$

$G_{r-3(4)}$ = 0.022% of total substrate radioactivity/min or
    0.00022×3.04 μc = 0.00067 μc/min.

From the above foregoing given data, the relative participation of glucose pathways can be calcuated in accordance with the following set of equations:

Let, G_{pr} represent the catabolic rate of the PP pathway;

G_{er} represent the catabolic rate of the EMP-pyruvate decarboxylation pathway;

G_{cat} represent the rate of glucose catabolism;

G_{ana} represent the rate of glucose anabolism.

The overall rate of glucose metabolism is therefore:

$$G_{ar} = G_{cat} + G_{ana} \tag{J}$$

Under the assumption that there are only two catabolic pathways; i.e., the EMP and the PP pathways operative in this organism:

$$G_{cat} = G_{er} + G_{pr} \tag{K}$$

The catabolic rate of individual catabolic pathways can be calculated on the basis of the following equations:

$$G_{er} = \frac{G_{r-3(4)}}{\text{sp. act. of glucose-3(4)-}^{14}\text{C}} \qquad \text{(L)}$$

$$G_{pr} = \frac{G_{r-1}}{\text{sp. act. of glucose-1-}^{14}\text{C}} \qquad \text{(M)}$$

In the present case,

$$G_{er} = \frac{0{\cdot}00067 \ \mu c/\text{min}}{0{\cdot}00407 \ \mu c/\mu\text{mole}}$$

$$= 0{\cdot}165 \ \mu\text{moles/min}$$

$$G_{pr} = \frac{0{\cdot}00101 \ \mu c/\text{min}}{0{\cdot}00675}$$

$$= 0{\cdot}150 \ \mu\text{moles/min}$$

$$C_{cat} = G_{er} + G_{pr}$$

$$= 0{\cdot}165 + 0{\cdot}150$$

$$= 0{\cdot}315 \ \mu\text{moles/min}.$$

According to equation J:

$$G_{ana} = G_{ar} - G_{cat}$$

$$= 0{\cdot}540 - 0{\cdot}315$$

$$= 0{\cdot}225 \ \mu\text{moles/min}.$$

From the foregoing rate values, one can then calculate relative participation of various glucose pathways, expressed on the basis of rate of glucose assimilation, i.e., G_{ar}, in the following manner:

$$\text{Anabolic pathways} = \frac{0{\cdot}225 \times 100}{0{\cdot}540} = 42\%$$

$$\text{Catabolic pathways} = \frac{0{\cdot}315 \times 100}{0{\cdot}540} = 58\%$$

$$\text{The EMP pathway} = \frac{0{\cdot}165 = 100}{0{\cdot}540} = 30\%$$

$$\text{The PP pathway} = \frac{0{\cdot}150 \times 100}{0{\cdot}540} = 28\%$$

The relative participation of individual catabolic pathways expressed on the basis of net amount of substrate glucose routed into catabolic meachanisms is therefore:

$$\text{The EMP} = \frac{30 \times 100}{58} = 52\%$$

$$\text{The PP pathway} \quad = \frac{28 \times 100}{58} = 48\%$$

The foregoing given examples illustrate well the advantage of using the catabolic rate method for estimation of concurrent glucose pathways. In the case cited, under the conditions of continuous substrate feeding a significant amount of substrate glucose has been routed into the anabolic pathways. This fact invalidates one of the key assumptions underlying the $^{14}CO_2$ yield method and consequently, the pathway information gained by the catabolic rate method is more reliable. Moreover, using the catabolic rate method one needs the radiorespirometric data collected over a period of only a few minutes in contrast to the average duration of several hours for the single-dose experiment associated with the $^{14}CO_2$ yield method. These facets make it possible to use the catabolic rate method to estimate pathway participations in micro-organisms at different development stages. There is ample evidence demonstrating that relative participation of glucose pathways is not a constant manifestation when the micro-organisms are studied at different growth stages. Better understandings in this regard would enable one to evaluate more precisely the function of individual metabolic pathways in cell proliferation.

D. Studies on the alternation of catabolic pathways

The radiorespirometric method can be readily used to study alternation of catabolic pathways due to external or internal factors. The scope of this type of study encompasses the examination of mode of action of inhibitors and growth regulators; effect of cultural conditions (such as medium composition, temperature, etc.) and many other similar tasks.

Single-dose radiorespirometric experiments have been commonly used for this type of study. Thus, in the case of *Bacillus subtilis* (Wang and Krackov, 1962), one finds that when cells were grown on glucose–salts–ammonium medium, glucose is catabolized 65% and 35%, respectively via the EMP and PP pathways. With cells grown on glucose–tryptone–salts medium, glucose is catabolized 80% and 20%, respectively via the EMP and PP pathways. These findings lead one to believe that the PP pathway is playing an important role in biosynthetic functions in this organism since when tryptone is present in the medium, a considerably less amount of substrate glucose is routed into the PP pathway.

The use of radiorespirometry to study the effect of growth inhibitors can be illustrated by a recent study on the effect of 2-deoxy-glucose upon yeast metabolism (Conrad and Wang, unpublished work). The results obtained from a series of single-dose radiorespirometric experiments are given in Table I. From these data one learns that when the concentration of 2-deoxyglucose is 1·64 mg in 10 ml of incubation medium, substrate

TABLE I

Fate of substrate glucose and fructose metabolized by *Saccharomyces cerevisiae* **cells in the presence or absence of 2-deoxyglucose (2-DG)**

Substrate	CO_2		Medium		Cells		Total	
	2-DG	control	2-DG	control	2-DG	control	2-DG	control
Glucose-1	44	35	16	14	34	44	94	93
Glucose-2	37	30	15	12	39	50	91	92
Glucose-3(4)	54	47	7	5	26	35	87	87
Glucose-6	27	18	14	10	43	56	84	84
Fructose-1	43	37	16	9	30	46	89	92
Fructose-6	37	25	14	7	40	64	91	96

Experimental conditions: cell weight, 10 mg; volume of medium, 10 ml; substrate, 15 mg glucose or fructose labelled with ^{14}C at carbon position indicated; 2-DG, 1·64 mg in 2-DG experiments, none in control experiments. Values expressed as per cent of administered substrate.

glucose or fructose is routed to a relatively greater extent into catabolic pathways in comparison to the case of normal yeast cells. Meanwhile, from the data on the incorporation of substrate radioactivity in cells, it appears that 2-deoxyglucose reduces the net assimilation of glucose or fructose via anabolic pathways.

Radiorespirometric experiments involving the continuous feeding of substrates can also be advantageously used to study the kinetics pertaining to the effect of inhibitors. In studying the effect of 2-deoxyglucose upon yeast catabolism, the findings obtained in an experiment using glucose-3(4)-^{14}C as labelled substrate can be cited as an illustrative example. As shown in Fig. 14, upon administration of 164 mg of 2-deoxyglucose to 10 ml of a yeast culture fed continuously with glucose-3(4)-^{14}C, the interval yield of respiratory $^{14}CO_2$ is immediately reduced to a practically insignificant level. With lower concentrations of 2-deoxyglucose; e.g., 1·64 mg in 10 ml, one finds that the rate of glucose utilization is only slightly reduced, as reflected by the lower interval yield of $^{14}CO_2$ from C-3(4) of glucose (Curve C). However, for a given amount of substrate, the cumulative yield of CO_2 from C-3(4) of glucose is greater when 2-deoxyglucose is present at this concentration.

E. Comparative studies relative to biochemical taxonomy of micro-organisms

In recent years much effort has been devoted by various workers to the classification of micro-organisms on the basis of biochemical behaviours.

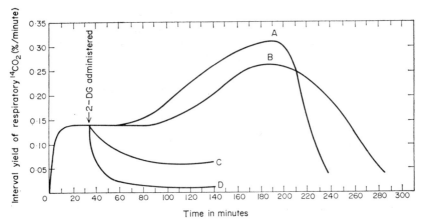

FIG. 14. Radiorespirometric patterns for utilization of glucose by *Saccharomyces cerevisiae* cells in the presence of various amounts of 2-DG, continuous feeding experiment. Experimental conditions: cell weight, 13 mg; volume of medium, 10 ml; substrate, 60 mg (0·33 mmole) glucose; tracer amount of glucose-3(4)-^{14}C added at time 0. The following amounts of 2-DG were added at time indicated: A, 0·00 mg; B, 1·64 mg (0·01 mmoles); C, 16·4 mg (0·10); D, 164 mg (100 mmole).

The nature and the relative participation of glucose pathways in micro-organisms has been used as one of the critera. However, detailed study on glucose pathways involves identification of enzymes present in the micro-organism, total inventory of fermentation products and similar tasks which are time consuming and thereby prevent one from carrying out extensive surveys on many species of a given genus.

In contrast, radiorespirometric experiments of the single-dose type are easy to carry out and can provide valuable information on glucose catabolism of a great number of micro-organisms. The use of radiorespirometry on the studies on microbial taxonomy can be illustrated by the results given in Table II. In this regard, previous studies also include such micro-organisms as *Bacillus subtilis* (Wang and Krackov, 1962), *Acetobacter* species (Kitos *et al.*, 1958; Wang and Bjerre, 1961), *Zymomonas mobilis* (Stern *et al.*, 1960), *Pseudomonas* species (Stern *et al.*, 1960; Wang *et al.*, 1959), *Streptomyces* species (Wang, *et al.*, 1958), *Penicillium* species (Wang *et al.*, 1958; Reed and Wang, 1959), *Escherichia coli* (Wang, *et al.*, 1958), *Micrococcus radiodurans* (Raj *et al.*, 1960; Duryee *et al.*, 1961), and *Azotobacter vinelandii* (Still and Wang, 1964). It is evident that all *Xanthomonas* species (Zagallo and Wang, 1967) studied display a striking resemblance to each other with regard to the nature and relative participation of glucose pathways, thereby justifying the classification of all the species under the genus. In contrast, one finds that the five species of *Arthrobacter*

TABLE II

Relative participation of concurrent glucose pathways in *Xanthomonas* species, *Arthrobacter* species and *Corynebacteria* species

Micro-organisms	Relative participation of primary glucose pathways (% of administered glucose)		
	EMP	ED	PP(PC)
*Xanthomonas species**			
X. hyacinthi		84	16
X. translucens		90	10
X. juglandis		87	13
X. pruni		81	19
X. malvacearum		92	8
X. carotae		90	10
X. pelargonii		85	15
X. phaseoli		93	7
*Arthrobacter species**			
A. ureafaciens	93		7
A. globiformis	68		32
A. simplex		65	35
A. pascens		94	6
A. atrocyaneus		77	23
*Corynebacterium species**			
C. hoagii	78		22
C. tritici	70		30
C. equi	62		38
C. sepedonicum	44		56
C. xerosis	17		85

* EMP: The Embden-Meyerhof-Parnas pathway; ED: The Entner-Douordoff pathway; PP: The Pentose Phosphate pathway; PC: The Pentose Cycle pathway.

(Zagallo and Wang, 1962) studied should really be classified into two different categories on the basis of their respective catabolic behaviour. Similarly, there exists an extensive difference in the nature and relative participation of pathways in the *Corynebacterium* (Zagallo and Wang, 1967) species studied. These findings point out the need for re-examination of taxonomical classification of a great number of micro-organisms.

VI. FUTURE OUTLOOK

It is believed that radiorespirometry will become a more common laboratory method for studies in the area of microbial physiology. As stated previously, single-dose experiments are easy to carry out and findings in experiments of this type can provide valuable clues leading to more detailed studies by other means.

The radiorespirometric experiments involving continuous substrate feeding provide one with much more refined data pertaining to the kinetics of catabolic mechanisms. Further improvement of methodology and techniques in this regard will soon provide one with kinetic data with even finer resolution. It is anticipated that this type of experiment will be used more extensively in the future in studies on cell catabolism of various carbonaceous substrates; regulation of catabolic mechanisms; developmental physiology; and numerous other areas.

The kinetic data obtained in a radiorespirometric experiment are potentially useful in estimating the rate of sequential reactions such as the TCA Cycle pathway (Williams, 1965), etc. However, detailed methodology in this regard has yet to be worked out.

ACKNOWLEDGMENT

The contents presented in this chapter represent the work of a great number of investigators with many of whom I have had the privilege of having close association in our laboratory.

I would like to specifically acknowledge the efforts of Dr. Donald W. Jacobsen who was instrumental in developing the catabolic rate method for estimation of glucose pathways. My thanks also go to the National Institutes of Health, the Air Force Medical Command and the Atomic Energy Commission. These agencies provided generous support for the major portion of the work described in this chapter.

REFERENCES

Conrad, C., and Wang, C. H. Unpublished work.
Duryee, F. L., Raj, H. D., Wang, C. H., Anderson, A. W., and Elliker, P. R. (1961). *Can. J. Microbiol.* 7 : 799.
Forbusch, I., and Wang, C. H. Unpublished work.
Jacobsen, D. W., and Wang, C. H. (1968). *Plant Physiol.*, 43 : 1959–1966.
Jacobsen, D. W., and Wang, C. H. (1967). *Fed. Proc.* 26(2).
Jacobsen, D. W., and Wang, C. H. Unpublished work.
Kalberer, F., and Rutschmann, J. (1961). *Helv. Chim. Acta*, 44 : 1956–1966.
Katz, Joseph and Wood, Harland G. (1963). *J. Biol. Chem.*, 238(2) : 517–523.
Kitos, P. A., Wang, C. H., Mohler, B. A., King, T. E., and Cheldelin, V. H. (1958). *J. Biol. Chem.*, 233, 1295–1298.
Raj, H. D., Duryee, F. L., Deeney, A. M., Wang, C. H., Anderson, A. W., and Elliker, P. R. (1960). *Can. J. Microbiol.*, 6 : 289–298.
Reed, D. J., and Wang, C. H. (1959). *Can. J. Microbiol.*, 5 : 59–66.
Schöniger, W. (1955). *Mikrochim. Acta* (1) : 123–129.
Stern, I. J., Wang, C. H., and Gilmour, C. M. (1960). *J. Bact.*, 79 (4): 601–611.
Still, G. G., and Wang, C. H. (1964). *Arch. Biochem. and Biophys.*, 105.
Umbreit, W. W., Burris, R. H., and Stauffer, J. F. (1964). "Manometric Techniques", Burgess, Minneapolis.

Wang, C. H. (1967). "Radiorespirometry". A chapter in Vol. XV, Methods of Biochemical Analysis. (Ed. David Glick), John Wiley and Sons, New York.

Wang, C. H., and Bjerre, S. H. (1961). *Fed. Proc.* **20(1)**.

Wang, C. H., Christensen, B. E., and Cheldelin, V. H. (1953). *J. Biol. Chem.*, **201(2)** : 683–688.

Wang, C. H., Jacobsen, D. W., and Ikeda, G. (1967). VII International Congress of Biochem. Proceedings, p. 1052.

Wang, C. H., Krackov, J. K. (1962). *J. Biol. Chem.*, **237**, 3614.

Wang, C. H., Stern, I. J., Gilmour, C. M., Klungsoyr, S., Reed, D. J., Bialy, J. J., Christensen, B. E., and Cheldelin, V. H. (1958). *J. Bacteriol.*, **76** : 207–216.

Wang, C. H., Stern, I. J., and Gilmour, C. M. (1959). *Arch. Biochem. and Biophys*, **81(2)** : 489–492.

Wang, C. H., and Willis, D. L. (1965). "Radiotracer Methodology in Biological Science", Prentice Hall, Englewood Cliffs, New Jersey.

Warburg, O. (1923). *Biochem. Z.*, **142**, 317.

White, C. G., and Helf, S. (1956). *Nucleonics*, **14**, 46.

Williams, G. R., (1965). *Can. J. of Biochem.*, **48** : 603–615.

Zagallo, A. C., and Wang, C. H. (1962). *J. Gen. Microbiol.*, **29** : 389–401.

Zagallo, A. C., and Wang, C. H. (1967). *J. Bact.*, **93(3)** : 970.

Zagallo, Z. C., and Wang, C. H. (1967). *J. Gen. Microbiol.*, **47** : 347.

CHAPTER VIII

Pulse Labelling of Micro-organisms

NORMAN R. EATON

*Department of Biology, Brooklyn College of the City University of New York,
Brooklyn, New York, U.S.A.*

I. INTRODUCTION

Pulse-labelling techniques have been of considerable importance in studies on macromolecular syntheses in micro-organisms. These procedures allow one to distinguish rapidly formed or rapidly turned-over minor components from the bulk of similar classes of compounds in the cell. The kinds of macromolecules labelled by the pulse can, to some extent, be predetermined by controlling the nature of the radioactively labelled precursor that is used and by attention to the previous history of the culture or suspension of organisms. For example, one can "pre-condition" the cells to synthesize preferentially, over the brief span of the pulse, mRNA, rRNA or specific protein. The "pulse" may vary from a few seconds to minutes or hours, depending upon the organism and conditions, and incorporation of the labelled compound may be terminated simply by harvesting-the organisms, by application of a "chase" of unlabelled precursor or by addition of an appropriate inhibitor. Because of the wide variation possible in experimental design, the discussion below will necessarily be somewhat limited. Detailed examples will therefore be drawn only from studies of protein and RNA synthesis using *Escherichia coli* as a representative bacterium, or yeast as an example of application to eucaryotic cells. These techniques are sufficiently general, however, that extrapolation to other systems may easily be made.

II. PREPARATION OF CELLS

Although cultures growing logarithmically in either a rich or a chemically defined medium can be used simply by adding the radioactive compound for a brief period before harvesting, a greater measure of control may be exercised with respect to the component labelled by restricting the biosynthetic capability of the cell. Several procedures by which this can be accomplished are detailed below.

A. Step-down cultures

Addition of a labelled RNA precursor to cells that have been transferred from a rich growth medium to a poor one ("step-down" culture) results in preferential incorporation of the precursor into mRNA (Hayashi and Spiegelman, 1961). *E. coli* is grown to late logarithmic phase in a modified penassay medium—

Modified penassay medium (Nomura et. al., 1960)

Beef extract	$1 \cdot 75$ g
Yeast extract	$1 \cdot 5$ g
Peptone	$5 \cdot 0$ g
NaCl	$3 \cdot 5$ g
Distilled water	1 litre

The cells are washed twice with a minimal medium, such as medium C—

Medium C (Roberts et al., 1957)

NH_4Cl	2 g
Na_2HPO_4	6 g
NaCl	3 g
$MgCl_2$	$0 \cdot 04$ g
Na_2SO_4	$0 \cdot 142$ g
Glucose	2 g
Distilled water	1 litre

and are re-suspended in the minimal medium. The culture is aerated at 37°C and the labelled precursor is applied for 3–15 min. The procedure is also applicable to other bacteria, an example of which is given in Fig. 1.

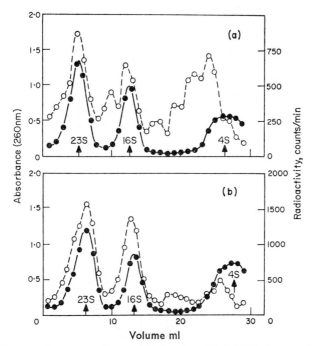

Fig. 1. Sucrose density-gradient analysis of purified RNA from pulse-labelled "step-down" (a), and control (b), cultures: broken curve, radioactivity; continuous curve, absorbance. (From Hayashi and Spiegelman, 1961.)

B. Shift-up cultures

In contrast to step-down cultures, cells that are transferred from a poor to a rich medium synthesize r and tRNA in preference to mRNA (Mitsui et al., 1963; Osawa, 1965). E. coli is grown overnight in a Tris–glucose medium—

Tris–glucose medium (*Ishihama* et al., *1962*)

NaCl	4·676 g
KCl	1·491 g
NH_4Cl	1·070 mg
$FeCl_3$	54·1 μg
KH_2PO_4	0·87 g
Glucose	0·2 g
0·1M Tris, pH 7·8	1 litre

The cells are harvested, re-suspended in fresh medium to a cell density of 5×10^7/ml and grown under aeration at 37°C to a cell density of 4×10^8/ml. The culture is centrifuged and the cells resuspended in the same medium less glucose to a density of 8×10^{10} cells/ml and starved with aeration at

10

37°C for 50 min. The culture is diluted 200-fold with peptone broth, which, for studies on ^{32}P incorporation, is treated to reduce the inorganic phosphate content in the following way: 2g of peptone in 100 ml of water are passed through a 15 ml column of Amberlite 1RA–400 (OH form), neutralized with HCl and diluted with an equal volume of Tris–glucose medium plus 0·01% Difco Casamino Acids. Pulsing these cells for 1–10 min with labelled RNA precursors results in appearance of the label in 23S, 16S and sRNA species and a virtual absence of label in mRNA (Fig. 2).

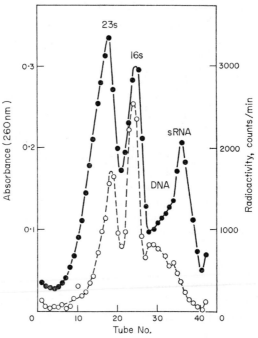

FIG. 2. Sucrose density-gradient analysis of purified RNA from a "shift-up" culture exposed for 20 sec to 0·6 μC/ml[^{3}H]uridine: broken curve, radioactivity; continuous curve, absorbance. (From Mitsui *et al.*, 1963.)

C. Derepressed cultures

An excess of a metabolite in the growth medium, will, in many cases, specifically repress formation of enzymes of the biosynthetic pathway leading to the synthesis of the metabolite. Removal of the specifically inhibiting end product of the biosynthetic sequence (i.e., derepression) allows the synthesis of mRNA specific for the enzymes of the pathway. It has been possible, for example, to identify with this technique multi-cistronic messengers of entire biosynthetic sequences. The technique is especially useful when carried out as a double-labelling experiment (see Section IIIA).

The procedure is described for cultures that have been derepressed with respect to tryptophan synthesis (Imamoto *et al.*, 1965), although it is equally applicable to other repressible systems. *E. coli* is grown to a density of $1 \cdot 5 \times 10^9$ cells/ml in a minimal medium plus 100 μg/ml of tryptophan—

Minimal medium

$(NH_4)_2SO_4$	1 g
Sodium citrate	0·5 g
$Mg_2SO_4 \cdot 7H_2O$	1 g
Glucose	10 g
0·05M Tris, pH 7·3	1 litre

The cells are washed twice in cold medium and re-suspended in the same medium, without tryptophan, to which has been added the other 19 amino-acids at concentrations of 0·005M. The suspension is incubated at 37°C with aeration.

D. Non-growing suspensions of yeast

Because of the presence of relatively large metabolic pools in yeast, it is possible to induce restricted metabolic processes, such as the formation of specific enzymes, in non-growing suspensions. Although the kinds of protein and RNA that are pulse labelled under these conditions are not uniquely limited, some selective synthesis does occur. Two examples will be given: respiratory adaptation in anaerobically grown yeast and induction of resting yeast suspensions to maltase formation.

1. *Respiratory adaptation*

A respiratory sufficient ("grande") strain of yeast (*Saccharomyces*) is grown to early stationary phase (20–24 h) in the following medium—

Medium

Yeast extract	10 g
Glucose	50 g
$(NH_4)_2SO_4$	1·2 g
†Ergosterol–Tween solution	5 ml
Distilled water	1 litre

† 250 mg ergosterol + 25 ml Tween 80 diluted to 100 ml with ethanol.

The medium is inoculated with the equivalent of 15 mg dry wt of yeast/litre and incubated at 25°C under an atmosphere of N_2 to ensure anaerobic conditions. The culture is harvested by pouring it onto an equal volume of crushed ice and centrifuging, and the cells are washed with cold distilled water. For adaptation, the cells are suspended to a density of 3·2 mg dry wt/ ml in a solution containing 0·05M phthalate buffer (pH 4·5), 0·2M glucose and 10^{-5}M KH_2PO_4, and are pre-incubated at [28°C while flushing with N_2 for 2 h. Adaptation is started by replacing the N_2 with air (Shortman and Fukuhara, 1963; Fukuhara, 1967). An example of protein synthesis under these conditions is shown in Fig. 3.

2. *Maltase induction*

The induction of maltase in resting suspensions of yeast is critically dependent upon the cultural conditions. When grown under the conditions described below, efficient production of the enzyme occurs only when the cells are harvested after 18 h of growth (Fig. 4). A 1 ml sample of an overnight culture of a haploid strain of *Saccharomyces*, carrying a single dominant maltase gene (MA_3), is inoculated into 1 litre of the following medium—

Medium

Yeast extract	10 g
Peptone	20 g
Glucose	20 g
Distilled water	1 litre

The culture is shaken at 30°C for 18 h, harvested by centrifugation and washed twice with cold distilled water. For maltase induction, cells from 1 litre of culture (approximately 12 g wet wt) are re-suspended in water or 0·1M phosphate (pH 5·4). Maltose is added to a final concentration of 50 μmoles/ml, and the suspension is aerated at 30°C. Radioactive precursors are added after 2 h, when increasing amounts of maltase can be detected in extracts of the cells. The results of this procedure seem to be analogous to step-down cultures of bacteria. Virtually no rRNA is formed during the pulse (Fig. 5).

III. SELECTION AND APPLICATION OF THE LABELLED COMPOUND AND TERMINATION OF THE REACTION

A. Choice of isotope

RNA may be pulse labelled with ^{32}P or more specifically with [^3H]- or [^{14}C]uracil or uridine. In general ^{32}P is used as the neutralized phosphate, carrier-free, in amounts of 10–200 μC/ml. Tritiated or ^{14}C-labelled amino-acids, either single or as an amino-acid mixture, (0·5–10 μC/ml) may be used to pulse label proteins. A convenient and readily available source of the latter are the commercial preparations of hydrolysed ^{14}C-labelled alga or yeast protein. ^{35}S may also be used to label proteins and is most conveniently added, carrier-free, as the neutralized sulphate.

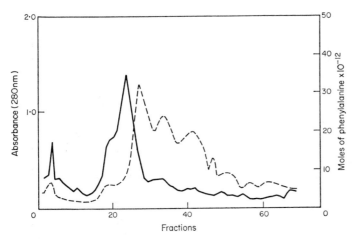

FIG. 3. DEAE-cellulose chromatography of an extract of respiratory adapted yeast exposed to $3·5 \times 10^{-5}$M (10 μC/μmole) [^{14}C] phenylalanine for 10 min. The cells were broken in a Nossal shaker and after centrifugation at 3000 g, the supernatant containing about 150 mg of protein, was added to the top of a 1×20 cm column of DEAE-cellulose. The protein was eluted with an exponential gradient of NaCl (0–0·6M) in 0·01M Tris buffer, pH 7·3. Fractions of 3 ml were collected for determination of absorbance and radioactivity. (From Fukuhara, 1967.)

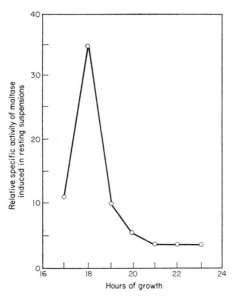

FIG. 4. Maltase induction in non-growing suspensions of yeast as a function of growth time.

10§

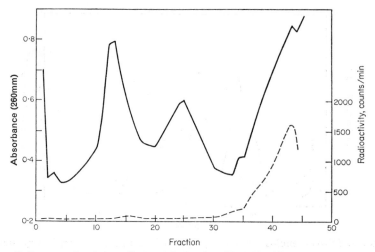

FIG. 5. Sucrose-density gradient analysis of purified RNA from a maltase-induced non-growing suspension of yeast exposed to 0·5 μC/ml ^{32}P for 15 min.

Identification of specific mRNA has been possible by using a double-labelling technique, which, in the case of β-galactosidase mRNA, is carried out as follows (Hayashi *et al.*, 1963; Guttman and Novick, 1963). A culture of *E. coli*, growing logarithmically in a lactate medium, is divided into two equal portions. To one is added a gratuitous inducer (isopropyl-β-D-thiogalactopyranoside) and [^{14}C]uridine, and to the other is added ^{3}H-uridine. After 2–3 min of continued incubation, the cultures are mixed, the cells are harvested and extracts are prepared and analysed. The two isotopes, in fractions separated, for example, by density-gradient centrifugation, are determined by liquid scintillation spectrometry. A plot of the differences between the two isotopes reveals fractions containing material uniquely formed during induction of the enzyme (Fig. 6). Pre-mixing of the cultures avoids errors that might otherwise result from slight variations in the analytical procedure.

B. Terminating the reaction

Incorporation of the labelled precursor is rapidly halted by pouring or pipetting aliquots of the reaction mixture onto crushed ice or frozen crushed medium containing 0·01M sodium azide or by rapidly cooling the suspension in a dry ice–acetone mixture. The cells are then removed by centrifugation and are subjected to an appropriate analytical procedure. If turnover of the rapidly labelled cell component is to be examined, the pulse is followed by addition of unlabelled precursor in a concentration 100–1000 times greater than the concentration of the labelled compound used for the pulse. An

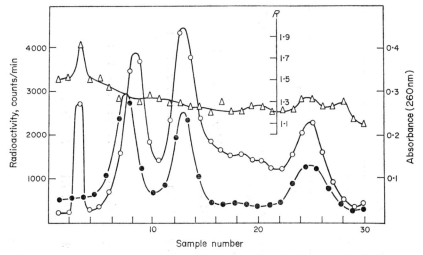

FIG. 6. Sucrose density-gradient analysis of purified RNA from β-galactosidase-induced cultures. *E. coli* was pulsed for 4% of a generation with [^{14}C]uridine in the induced culture and [^{3}H] uridine in the un-induced culture: $\triangle$, R ($= ^{14}$C/^{3}); $\bigcirc$, radioactivity; $\bullet$, absorbance. (From Guttman and Novick, 1963.)

example of such a "chasing" experiment is shown in Fig. 7. This approach has met with considerable success in studies on turnover of RNA and protein in bacteria using any of the precursors mentioned above (Section IIIA), and in yeast, using uracil or [^{35}S]sulphate as the labelled precursor. However, because of the large internal phosphate pool in yeast, less satisfactory results are obtained in attempts to "chase" ^{32}P-labelled RNA.

Turnover of RNA in bacteria may also be studied by stopping further synthesis of RNA with actinomycin D at concentrations of 10–50 μg/ml (Leventhal *et al.*, 1962, 1963).

Table I presents a selected list of precursors used for pulse labelling specific cell components and the conditions for their application.

IV. ANALYSIS OF RESULTS

Obviously, the method of analysis will depend upon the compounds of interest. If only data relating to total incorporation of the labelled precursor are desired, aliquots of the cell suspension are pipetted into an equal volume of cold (0–5°C) 10% trichloroacetic acid. The suspension is filtered onto cellulose acetate or cellulose nitrate filters (e.g. Millipore, Type HA, 0·45 μm pore size), washed three times with cold trichloroacetic acid and once with ethanol, dried and counted. Alternatively, the substances of interest can be isolated in bulk, and the component species can be separated by ion-

TABLE 1

Conditions for pulse-labelling selected micro-organisms

Organism	Cultural conditions	Cell concentration	Labelled compound	Pulse time, min	Macro-molecule labelled	Reference
Escherichia coli	Synthetic medium	(log phase)	$1 \mu C$ (2·7 mg)/ml [^{14}C]adenine	2	RNA†	Moore & McCarthy (1967)
E. coli	Step-down	(log phase)	20–200 μC/ml ^{32}P or 3–10 μC (0·5–2 mg) [^{3}H]uridine	3–15	mRNA (pre-ferentially)	Hayashi & Spiegelman (1961)
E. coli	Shift-up	4×10^8/ml	15–300 μC/ml ^{32}P or 0·1–0·6 μC/ml [^{3}H] or [^{14}C]uridine	1–10	r and s (t) RNA	Mitsui *et al.* (1963)
Bacillus subtilis	Synthetic medium	log phase; absorbance at 540 nm = 0·3–0·35	0·08 μC (5 mg)/ml [^{14}C]uracil	0·5–3	RNA†	Leventhal *et al.* (1962)
E. coli	Tryptophan depressed	$1·8 \times 10^9$/ml	50–300 μC/ml ^{32}P or 20–50 μC/ml [^{3}H]uridine	1	mRNA‡	lmamoto *et al.* (1965)
Salmonella typhimurium	Histidine derepressed	6×10^8/nl	7·3 μC (1 μmole)/ml [^{14}C]uridine or 100 μC(1 μmole)/ml [^{3}H]uridine	2	mRNA‡	Martin (1963)

E. coli	β-Galactosidase induced	9×10^8/ml	[14C]uridine or [3H]uridine	1·5	mRNA[‡]	Guttman & Novick (1963)
E. coli	Synthetic medium	(log growth)	1 μC/ml [35S]SO_4 (carrier-free)	0·25	Protein	McQuillen et al. (1959)
Yeast (Saccharomyces)	Resting suspension (Respiratory adapting)	2–3 mg dry wt/ml	0·05–3 μC/ml [14C]uracil	10	RNA[§]	Shortman & Fukuhara (1963)
Yeast (Saccharomyces)	Resting suspension (Respiratory adapting)	2·3 mg dry wt/ml	0·1–0·5 μC/ml [14C]phenylalanine (4×10^{-5} moles) or 4 μC/ml [35S]$SO_4 =$ (carrier-free)	1–5	Protein	Fukuhara (1967)
Yeast (Saccharomyces)	Maltase induced	120 mg (wet wt)/ml	0·5–1 μC/ml 32P (carrier-free)	15	mRNA	Eaton (1963)

† Both m and r RNA precursors are labelled under these conditions (Midgley and MaCarthy, 1962; Bolton and McCarthy, 1962).
‡ The identification of specific m RNA depends upon a double-labelling technique (See Section IIIA).
§ Results of chase experiments suggest that both m and r RNA are labelled.

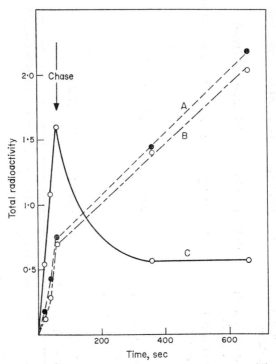

FIG. 7. Total radioactivity in the three major fractions of ribosomal RNA after a "chase" with unlabelled percursors. *E. coli* was exposed to [^{14}C]uracil (0·5 μg/ml) for 1 min followed by a 10 min period in [^{12}C]uridine and cytidine (100 μg/ml each): A, 18 S; B, 28 S; C, 4–8 S. (From McCarthy and Aronson, 1961.)

exchange chromotography, chromatography on methylated serum albumin columns, density-gradient centrifugation or other appropriate method, and the separated fractions can be assayed for radioactivity. Sucrose density-gradient centrifugation has perhaps most often been used in conjunction with pulse-labelling experiments. This technique has the advantage of giving an overall view of the pattern of incorporation into sub-cellular fractions, and will be described in some detail below.

A. Breaking the cells

The harvested cells may be broken by grinding with abrasives, such as Al$_2$O$_3$ or powdered glass, shaking with glass beads, by passage of the suspension through a French press or Hughes press or by digesting off the cell wall with specific enzymes. If the major interest is in fragile structures, such as polyribosomes, particular care should be given to selection of a method that is as gentle as is consistent with reasonable cell disruption (see Hughes *et al.*, this Series, Vol. 5). Although digestion of the cell wall and osmotic lysis would seem to be the method of choice, the time and conditions required allow metabolic processes to resume, and the method is therefore normally not well suited to pulse-labelling experiments. A cell press based on a modification of the Hughes press has been found to give satisfactory results with both bacteria and fungi (Eaton, 1962).

It is also important to select carefully the buffer used for extracting the cells. the integrity of the ribosomes is dependent on the maintenance of a magnesium ion concentration of 5×10^{-3}–10^{-2}M. Tris or cacodylate buffer should be used in preference to phosphate because of the instability of ribosomes in phosphate buffer (Eaton, 1966).

Bentonite (Brownhill *et al.*, 1959) or Macaloid (Stanley and Bock, 1965) is often added to the crude extract, or preferably to the cell suspension before breaking, to inhibit ribonuclease. Yeast ribonuclease can be inhibited by 10^{-5}M zinc (Otaka and Uchida, 1963).

B. Sucrose-gradient centrifugation

Most commercially available sucrose is contaminated with ribonuclease and material that absorbs at 260 nm, and must therefore be purified before use; four volumes of ethanol are added to a hot, autoclaved, saturated solution of sucrose. The mixture is slowly shaken until it reaches room temperature, and the precipitated sucrose is filtered, washed with ethanol and dried under vacuum at 50°C. The purified sucrose is dissolved in the same buffer as that in which the sample to be analysed is dissolved or suspended. Concentrations of 5 and 20% are used for separating the various RNA classes, 15 and 30% for separating polyribosomes, ribosomes and ribosomal sub-units.

Linear sucrose gradients are prepared with the apparatus described by Britten and Roberts (1960), using either 5 ml or 30 ml tubes for the Spinco model L swinging-bucket rotors (SW–39 and SW–25, respectively; Spinco Ltd, Palo Alto, California, U.S.A.). A 0·2 ml "cushion" of 60% sucrose is placed in the bottom of the 5 ml tube (0·5 ml for the larger tube) and the gradient is formed on top of this cushion (4·8 ml for the smaller, 25 ml for the larger tube). The sample (0·2 or 1·0 ml) is layered on top of the gradient and the tubes are carefully placed in the buckets which are then attached to the centrifuge rotor. For separating purified RNA samples, the smaller tubes are centrifuged for 4·5 h at 35,000 rev/min and the larger tubes at 25,000 rev/min for 12–18 h. Polyribosomes, ribosomes and ribosomal sub-units are separated by centrifugation of the SW–39 rotor for 2·5 h at 30,000 rev/min and the SW–25 rotor for 5–6 h at 24,000 rev/min. The rotor is allowed to coast to a stop without braking, and the tubes are removed for fractionation.

The tubes may be placed in a holder consisting of a closely fitting glass test tube having a small hole blown in the bottom. The bottom of the centrifuge tube is pierced with a small gauge hypodermic needle, and fractions of 5–6 drops (about 0·1 ml) from the 5 ml tube or 0·5–1·0 ml from the 30 ml tube are collected in small screw-capped vials. The fractions are transferred to microcuvettes for absorption measurements, and measured samples of each are then removed for determination of radioactivity. Because of differences in viscosity, some variation occurs in the size of the fractions collected in this manner. A more even distribution of material is obtained with the fractionating device described by Heckly (1960) or by one of the several fractionating devices now available commercially.

C. Methylated serum ablumin column chromatography

Mixtures of nucleic acids isolated from pulse-labelled cells may be efficiently fractionated by chromatography on columns composed of methylated serum albumin and diatomaceous earth (kieselguhr). The procedure described below for the preparation and use of such columns is essentially that of Mandell and Hershey (1960).

1. *Preparation of methylated serum albumin*

Suspend 5 g of Fraction V bovine serum albumin in 500 ml of absolute methanol and dissolve it by adding 4·2 ml of 12M HCl. Allow the mixture to stand at room temperature in the dark for at least 3 days with occasional shaking. Collect the precipitate that forms by centrifugation and wash it twice with absolute methanol and twice with anhydrous ether. Allow most of the ether to evaporate in air, and then place the material *in vacuo* over KOH. Store the resultant dry powder over KOH to ensure complete removal of residual acid.

The methylated protein is used for preparing the column as a 1% (w/v) aqueous solution and as a suspension of protein-coated kieselguhr. The latter is prepared as follows. Suspend 20 g of kieselguhr (Hyflo SuperCel, Johns-Manville Corp., New York) in 100 ml of 0·1M buffered saline (0·1M NaCl in 0·05M phosphate, pH 6·7), boil and cool to expell dissolved air and mix with 5 ml of 1% methylated serum albumin. Add 20 ml of 0·1M buffered saline, and transfer the suspension in 10 ml portions to a 2 cm diameter chromatography column, in the bottom of which a pad of cellulose powder has been formed. After each addition to the column, remove the excess of saline, either under air pressure (3 lb/sq. in.) or, more conveniently, by attaching a 1–2 mm i.d. plastic tubing to the bottom of the column and pumping the saline through with a peristaltic pump. Then wash the packed material by passing through the column 300 ml of 0·4M buffered saline,

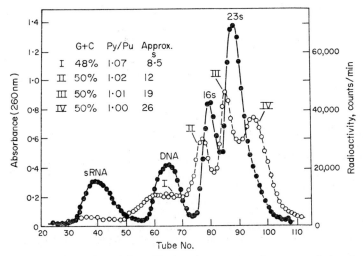

FIG. 8. Separation of nucleic acids by chromatography on methylated serum albumin. The mixture of nucleic acids was isolated from a growing culture of *E. coli* pulse labelled for 30 sec with ³²P. (From Otaka *et al.*, 1962)

remove the entire contents of the chromatography tube and re-suspend them in 125 ml of 0·4M buffered saline.

Both the 1% aqueous solution of methylated albumin and the suspension of washed, protein-coated kieselguhr may be stored in the refrigerator (4°–5°C) for several weeks.

2. *Preparation of the column*

The analytical column is prepared in three layers in a 2 cm diameter tube containing a supporting pad of cellulose powder. Mix 8g of kieselguhr in 40 ml of 0·1M buffered saline with 2 ml of a 1% aqueous solution of methylated serum albumin. Add 15 ml of 0·1M saline and use the suspension to form the first layer of the column. Wash sides of the tube down with 0·1M saline, and remove the excess of saline as described above. Form the second layer from a mixture of 6 g of kieselguhr in 40 ml of 0·4M buffered saline (boiled and cooled) to which is added 10 ml of protein-coated kieselguhr prepared as described above. The top layer consists of 1 g of kieselguhr in 10 ml of 0·4M buffered saline. After packing, wash the column with 150 ml of 0·4M buffered saline.

3. *Operation of the column*

The mixture of nucleic acids (approximately 0·4 mg in 50 ml of 0·4 M buffered saline) is added to the top of the column. Elution of the nucleic acids is effected with a linear NaCl gradient (0·4–1·5M) in 0·05M phosphate, pH6·7. The air pressure or pump speed should be adjusted to achieve a flow rate of approximately 25 ml/h. Fractions of 4–5 ml are collected for determination of absorbance at 260 mμ and of radioactivity. An example of the kind of separation achieved by this technique is shown in Fig. 8.

REFERENCES

Bolton, E. T., and McCarthy, B. J. (1962). *Proc. Natn. Acad. Sci. U.S.A.*, **48**, 1390–1397.

Britten, R. J., and Roberts, R. B. (1960). *Science, N.Y.*, **131**, 32–33.

Brownhill, T. J., Jones, A. S., and Stacey, M. (1959). *Biochem. J.*, **73**, 434–438.

Eaton, N. R. (1962). *J. Bact.*, **83**, 1359–1360.

Eaton, N. R. (1963). *Ann. N.Y., Acad. Sci.*, **102**, 678–687.

Eaton, N. R. (1966). *Biochim Biophys. Acta*, **129**, 511–518.

Fukuhara, H. (1967). *Biochim. Biophys. Acta*, **134**, 143–164.

Guttman, B. S., and Novik, A. (1963). *Cold Spring Harb. Symp. Quant. Biol.*, **28**, 373–374.

Hayashi, M., and Spiegelman, S. (1961). *Proc. Natn. Acad. Sci. U.S.A.*, **47**, 1564–1580.

Hayashi, M., Spiegelman, S., Franklin, N. C., and Laria, S. E. (1963). *Proc. Natn. Acad. Sci. U.S.A.*, **49**, 729–736.

Heckly, R. J. (1960). *Analyt. Biochem.*, **1**, 97–102.

Imamoto, F., Morikawa, N., Sato, K., Mishima, S., and Nishimura, T. (1965). *J. Molec. Biol.*, **13**, 157–168.

Ishihama, A., Mizuno, N., Takai, M., Otaka, E., and Osawa, S. (1962). *J. Molec. Biol.*, **5**, 251–264.

Leventhal, C., Keynan, A., and Higa, A. (1962). *Proc. Natn. Acad. Sci. U.S.A.*, **48**, 1631–1638.

Leventhal, C., Fan, D. P., Higa, A., and Zimmermann, R. A. (1963). *Cold Spring Harb. Symp. Quant. Biol.*, **28**, 183–190.

Mandell, J. D., and Hershey, A. D. (1960). *Analyt. Biochem.*, **1**, 66–77.

Martin, R. G. (1963). *Cold Spring Harb. Symp. Quant. Biol.*, **28**, 357–361.

McCarthy, B. J., and Aronson, A. T. (1961). *Biophys. J.*, **1**, 227–245.

McQuillen, K., Roberts, R. B., and Britten, R. J. (1959). *Proc. Natn. Acad. Sci. U.S.A.*, **45**, 1437–1447.

Midgley, J. E. M., and McCarthy, B. J. (1962). *Biochim. Biophys. Acta*, **61**, 696–717.

Mitsui, H., Ishihama, A., and Osawa, S. (1963). *Biochem. Biophys. Acta*, **76**, 401–409.

More, R. L., and McCarthy, B. J. (1967). *J. Bact.*, **94**, 1066–1074.

Nomura, M., Hall, B., and Spiegelman, S. (1960). *J. Molec. Biol.*, **2**, 306–326.

Osawa, S. (1965). *Prog. Nucleic Acid Res. Molec. Biol.*, **4**, 161–188.

Otaka, Y., and Uchida, K. (1963). *Biochim. Biophys. Acta.*, **76**, 94–104.

Otaka, E., Mitsui, H., and Osawa, S. (1962). *Proc. Natn. Acad. Sci. U.S.A.*, **48**, 425–430.

Roberts, R. B., Abelson, P. H., Cowie, D. B., Bolton, E. T., and Britten, R. J. (1957). "Studies of Biosynthesis in Escherichia coli," p. 5. Publication 607 of the Carnegie Institute of Washington, D.C.

Shortman, K., and Fukuhara, H. (1963). *Biochem Biophys. Acta*, **76**, 501–524.

Stanley, W. M., Jr., and Bock, R. M. (1965). *Biochemistry*, **4**, 1302–1311.

CHAPTER IX

Cellular Electrophysiology

M. J. ALLEN

Shell Research Ltd. Borden Microbiological Laboratory, Sittingbourne, Kent, England

> We may walk the same path
> many a time, but each time we see
> more of the beauty that abounds

I. INTRODUCTION

Where did it start? How did it begin? These questions which are sometimes difficult to answer can actually be answered with a simple comment.

* Former Address : Department of Physiology and Biophysics, Georgetown University Medical School, Washington, D.C.

With the first spark of life upon this planet, metabolic processes began. As these processes involve anabolic as well as catabolic functions which of necessity require the addition or loss of electrons, we have in essence an electrochemical system related to a life-function which can be found in the lowest form of life—the bacteria.

The recognition of the relationship of electrochemistry to biological function did not occur on the "first day". Many, many lifetimes intervened until that "second day" when Galvani's extremely intelligent wife observed that a scalpel in contact with an electric machine produced muscular contractions when touched to the body of a skinned frog. This finding caused Galvani in 1786 to initiate a series of experiments using a devic made of copper and iron in which muscular contractions were induced by bringing one metal into contact with the frog's nerve and the other with a muscle. In 1791 Galvani published a report on his studies, "De viribus electricitatis in motu musculari commentarius", in which he ascribed his results as being due to electricity. He however erroneously assumed that the electricity had been generated by the frog's tissue. This assumption no doubt can be attributed to his observations of the electric fish which does generate an electric current.

As a result of Galvani's publication, Volta deduced that the current observed by Galvani was due to two dissimilar metals in contact with the cellular fluid of the frog's tissues. This led to investigations which resulted in the discovery of the production of the electrochemical reactions between two dissimilar metals in an electrolyte. This was the forerunner of our modern dry battery.

An insight into electron transfer processes in biological systems came much later than the knowledge of the effects of electricity on living systems. The credit for these pioneer efforts falls upon Paul Ehrlich who in 1885 published reports describing his studies relating to the different abilities of animal organs to reduce dyes as correlated with the organs' oxygen requirements (Ehrlich, 1885a, 1885b). This was the beginning of an era in which tremendous progress was made in relation to Ehrlich's initial findings which led ultimately to the development of staining techniques for micro-organisms. This too, led to the period in which numerous investigators studied the redox potentials of various biological and biochemical systems by use of indicator dyes or by direct measurement with electrodes on metabolizing animal and microbial cell systems.

It is the author's belief that Potter should receive credit for the "third day" for it was he who in 1911 first observed that the electrode potential of culture medium containing viable organisms demonstrated a more negative potential than a comparable sterile medium. These findings were confirmed by other investigators. They were also extended to demonstrate the fact that the potential of the medium decreases or becomes more strongly reducing as bacterial growth proceeds toward the stationary phase of the growth cycle (Gillespie, 1920; Cannan, Cohen, and Clark, 1926). Thereafter there were a large number of investigations performed on the potentials developed by numerous types of growing micro-organisms as well as by pure biochemical systems. This was splendidly reviewed by Hewitt in 1950.

Although there are still a considerable number of electrochemical studies being done on pure biochemical systems, effort being devoted to investigations related to whole microbial systems has diminished to a considerable extent. The reason for this may very well be the appreciation, finally, of the fact that potential measurements yield only an indication of the oxygen tension of the solution surrounding the cell systems. Therefore, such data cannot be construed as being related to the metabolic behaviour of the cell itself. It does, however, indicate that one bacterial system may have a greater reducing power than another system. The fact that potential measurements cannot be considered as a direct indication of the metabolic behaviour of the cell is not a recent or an original proposition by the author. Yudkin in 1935 demonstrated with microbial systems that the observed potentials were strictly fortuitous and not directly related to the activity of the bacterium. Rather, they represented the potentials developed by the secretion products of microbial metabolism.

In view of the demonstrated inadequacy of these potential measurements, the author embarked upon studies related to the determination of another electrochemical parameter, namely, the capacity factor of the system to do work, which appeared to offer a distinct advantage over potential measurements.

Whether the study of capacity factors as well as the kinetic data obtained using the so-called "coulokinetic" technique will be construed as the beginning of the "fourth day" can only be decided in the future. One thing is certain, however, more information is obtained using this electrochemical approach; and what is being measured is directly related to the metabolic activity of the living cell.

II. FUNDAMENTAL CONSIDERATIONS

A. Thermodynamics

A biological system is not thermodynamically reversible, nor does it achieve a state of thermodynamic equilibrium except upon its death. Instead one must think of living systems as being an open-ended system, rather than a closed vessel, in a steady-state condition. These steady-states of course are not fixed, but will be dependent on the surrounding medium and endogenous changes in the cell itself. Regardless of the fact that we are not dealing with thermodynamic reversibility, there should be an awareness of the thermodynamic implications of the various electrochemical parameters to be used in subsequent discussions.

The electrochemical parameters to be discussed are related to oxidation-reduction reactions (see Jacob, this Series, Vol. 2)

It would be advisable at this point to review the standard measures used in electrochemistry to insure a better understanding of these measurements when applied to biological systems.

The **joule** is the standard unit of electrical work and is equal to 10^7 ergs. An **erg** is the work done by the force of 1 dyne in moving a particle a distance of 1 cm and a **dyne** is the force required to accelerate 1 gm of mass 1 cm sec^{-2}. The **calorie** is defined as being equal to 4·184 joules. A **Faraday** (F) is approximately 96,500 coulombs with the **coulomb** being equivalent to the passage of an electric current of 1 ampere for 1 second. The coulomb is the capacity factor for electrical work. Its potential or intensity factor counterpart is the **volt** (E). Electrical work can now be expressed as the product of the capacity factor times a potential, or as nFE, where n is the number of electrons transferred per mole of reactant utilized.

In an electrochemical reaction any electrical work done is at the expense of free energy $(-\Delta G)$. Therefore the net electrical work done at constant temperature and pressure, exclusive of any pressure-volume work is expressed as,

$$\Delta G = -nFE \qquad (1)$$

where ΔG is given in joules and nFE are in units of amperes.seconds. volts. From this equation it is obvious that if $E > 0$ then $\Delta G < 0$ and a spontaneous reaction occurs. Conversely, if $E < 0$ then $\Delta G > 0$ and the reaction will require energy from an external source in order that it occur.

If two half-cells, each containing a different metal, are connected by a salt bridge or a wire, an electric or galvanic cell will have been created. The established convention for describing such a cell is that the electrons will flow from left to right. One of the simplest electric cells is the Daniell cell which consists of a zinc electrode immersed in zinc sulphate and a copper electrode immersed in copper sulphate, the two solutions being separated from each other by a porous membrane. This cell can be described according to convention in the following manner,

$$Zn^0; Zn^{2+}//Cu^{2+}; Cu^0$$

The electromotive force or potential of this cell is 1·100 volt at 25°, with the zinc electrode being negative and the copper positive. As each electrode is bathed in a solution of its ions and as there is a state of equilibrium, the reactions can be indicated by

$$Zn^0 = Zn^{2+} + 2e$$

$$Cu^0 = Cu^{2+} + 2e$$

To compute the free energy change as the cell consumes 1 mole of metallic zinc the equation used is

$$\Delta G^0 = -nFE^0 \tag{2}$$

The superscript zero is used in this instance, as 1 mole is, in standard states, the amount required for a change in free energy, ΔG^0, and is a special case of equation 1. E is designated E^0 as it is the standard electrode potential and represents the potential of a half-cell in which all ions are at unit activity. To determine ΔG^0 of the electrical cell just described substitute in equation 2

$$\Delta G^0 = -2 \times 96,500 \times 1 \cdot 100 = -212,300 \text{ joules mole}^{-1}$$

$$\Delta G^0 = -212,300/4 \cdot 184 = -50,740 \text{ cal mole}^{-1}$$

The equation for the free energy change in a chemical reaction is given as

$$\Delta G = RT \ln Q - RT \ln K \tag{3}$$

where Q represents the concentrations of products divided by reactants when the system is not in a state of equilibrium. When Q becomes unity ($Q = 1$) $\ln 1$ will equal 0 and ΔG will become as symbolized for the standard state

$$\Delta G^0 = -RT \ln K \tag{4}$$

Thus the free energy relationship between the equilibrium constant (K) and that of an electrochemical cell can be seen.

Combining equations 1 and 3 gives

$$E = \frac{RT}{nF} \ln K - \frac{RT}{nF} \ln Q \tag{5}$$

The Q term is eliminated at standard states and equation 5 becomes

$$E^0 = \frac{RT}{nF} \ln K \tag{6}$$

Substitution of (6) in equation (5) gives the Nernst equation

$$E = E^0 - \frac{RT}{nF} \ln Q \tag{7}$$

where the gas constant, R (joules) $= 8 \cdot 314$ and T represents the absolute temperature.

The following simple example illustrates the use of the Nernst equation.

In the cell, Sn^0; $Sn^{2+}//Pb^{2+}$; Pb^0, where $E^0 = 0.0140$ (25°) compute the cell voltage when the activity ratio at 25° of the oxidized to reduced ions $(aSn^{2+}/aPb^{2+}) = 2$.

$$E = E^0 - \frac{RT}{nF} \ln (aSn^{2+}/aPb^{2+})$$

$$E = 0.0140 - (8.314 \times 298.1/2 \times 96,500) \, 2.303 \log 2$$

$$E = 0.0140 - 0.0089 = 0.0051 \text{ volt}$$

$$\Delta G = -nFE = 2 \times 96,500 \times 0.0051/4.184 = -235 \text{ cal}$$

This cell will operate spontaneously as E is positive. As a result the free energy, ΔG, will therefore be negative.

B. Reference electrodes

The voltage of an electrochemical cell is equal to the sum of the potentials of the two half-cells if one assumes the absence of a junction potential. The potential of an electrode is the difference between this electrode and the solution which surrounds it. As a result, it is impossible to measure this difference in potential unless another electrode is used as a reference. Therefore, the potential of a half-cell reaction cannot be measured directly. However, if a potential is arbitrarily assigned to one electrode, it is possible to determine the potentials of other electrodes with respect to this standard electrode.

The hydrogen electrode has been universally adopted as the primary standard reference electrode. This electrode has been assigned a value of zero when the pressure of hydrogen is 1 atm and the activity of hydrogen ions is unity. The distinct advantage of this reference electrode unlike the other types to be discussed, is that its potential is independent of temperature. The one condition which makes this electrode totally unsuited for biological systems is the high hydrogen ion concentrations required to create this half-cell. Aside from this disadvantage, the hydrogen electrode has many other problems associated with its preparation which makes it generally unsuited for routine use. As a result, other types, often referred to as secondary reference electrodes, are used routinely.

The most important criterion of all reference electrodes is that they be reversible systems. There are three such systems known:

(1) A metal or non-metal in contact with a solution of its own ions, e.g., the hydrogen electrode, $H_2 = 2H^+ + 2e$.

(2) A metal and a sparingly soluble salt of this metal in contact with a solution of a soluble salt of the same anion. The two reference electrodes

most commonly used for biological studies fall in this category. One of these being the silver/silver chloride electrode whose reaction may be written as

$$Ag(s) + Cl^- = AgCl(s) + e^-$$

whose potential is $+0.197$ volt vs. the normal hydrogen electrode (N.H.E.) at $25°$. The other electrode which has probably been used more extensively is the calomel electrode,

$$1/2\ Hg_2Cl_2(s) + e^- = Hg(s) + Cl^-.$$

The potential of the saturated calomel electrode is $+0.246$ volt vs. N.H.E. at $25°$.

(3) An inert metal immersed in a solution containing both oxidized and reduced states of an oxidation reduction system, e.g., platinum immersed in a solution containing Fe^{3+} and Fe^{2+}.

C. Working electrodes

The one most important characteristic which must be inherent in all electrodes used for biological studies is that they be chemically inert under the experimental conditions used. Its only function is to serve as an inert transporter of electrons either from or to the system being investigated. Electrodes having the characteristics described above are:

(1) Platinum—Shiny platinum foil or wire has been the electrode of choice by most investigators. However, although extremely inert under most conditions it is attacked to some extent if used in a halogen medium. Under such conditions the incorporation of a small amount of iridium, i.e. 1%, into the platinum will alleviate this difficulty.

(2) Gold—Electrodes of this type have been used by some investigators (Dixon and Quastel, 1923). In the author's laboratory, electrodes prepared with this metal have been found unsatisfactory. It was extremely difficult to obtain the reproducible results so readily available when platinum was used for electrode material.

(3) Iridium—This metal has been found satisfactory (Lepper and Martin, 1930) but offers no advantage over platinum.

Other electrode materials such as mercury, graphite, tungsten, and palladium have been used but none of these have demonstrated the desirable characteristics of platinum.

In the foregoing discussions there has been presented a minimal amount of the information necessary for an understanding of the material to be presented in subsequent sections. For those interested in delving deeper into the various fundamentals discussed, the author recommends the numerous excellent treatises available on electrochemistry and thermodynamics (e.g. Potter, 1956).

III. EXPERIMENTAL DESIGN OF MEASURING SYSTEMS

The design of the system used for measurement of the electrochemical parameters desired is most important if reproducible results are to be obtained. Therefore, each separate entity of this system will be discussed.

A. Electrochemical cells

The type of electrochemical cell used for determining the potentials of microbial systems during growth or as a suspension of washed cells can be as varied as one's imagination will permit.

For the measurement of potentials or changes in potentials any glass container, e.g., test tube or spoutless beaker, with an adequate closure through which is inserted the working and reference electrodes, can be

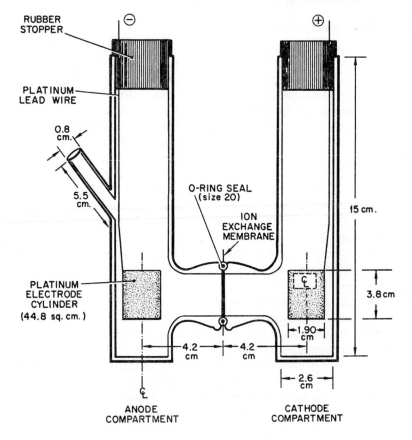

FIG. 1.

used. Also, an adequate opening, either as a side-arm addition to the glass vessel or as an additional opening in the closure, should be provided for the introduction of substrates or any other materials, whose effects are to be investigated. Another consideration in designing the electrochemical cell is that it be convenient to immerse the unit in a constant temperature bath.

When considering the measurement of currents produced by metabolizing microbial systems, it is then necessary to design an electrochemical cell consisting of two half-cells, each containing a working electrode. The designs found most satisfactory in our laboratory are shown in Figs 1 and 2. The first of these has been designed to accommodate from 40 to 50 ml of liquid in the anode compartment and 40 to 80 ml of liquid in the cathode compartment. Into the anode compartment is placed the

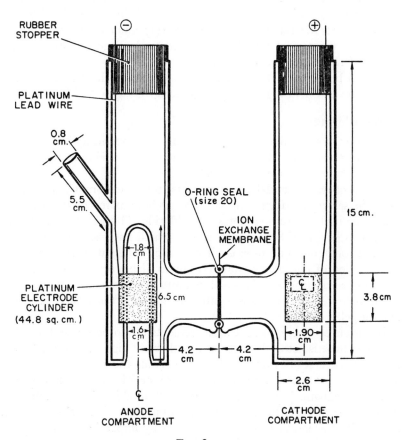

Fig. 2.

bacterial suspension or the inoculated culture medium and the substrate under investigation, and in the cathode compartment a solution of a reducible species, e.g., potassium ferricyanide, so as to establish the cathode as a nonpolarizable counter-electrode. The side arm of the anode half-cell is used for introduction of substrate solutions, anti-metabolites, etc., after the electrochemical cell has been assembled and equilibrated to bath temperature.

The only differences between the cells illustrated, is that the anode compartment of the mini-electrochemical cell (Fig. 2) can be used with quantities of liquid from 25 to 30 ml, and because of the design, the electrochemically active species has a shorter path to travel from the bulk of the solution to the electrode surface (the electron sink). As a result of the latter, a greater efficiency is obtained from the system.

Whereas in potential measurements it is not necessary to completely immerse the working electrode in the liquid being studied, with current measurements this is a necessity in order to (1) obtain the maximum current output for the size of the electrode used, and (2) achieve the maximum degree of reproducibility of results.

As will be noted in Figs 1 and 2, the two half-cells are separated by a membrane and held together by a standard "U" type ball joint clamp.

B. Membranes

The purpose of a membrane is to attempt to chemically isolate one half-cell from the other. Ideally a membrane separator should be chemically inert and have a low electrical resistance.

For electrical potential measurements, the "membrane" of choice has been the salt-agar bridge. The salt-agar gel is prepared by dissolving 2·5 g agar in 55 ml hot saturated potassium chloride. This gel is then drawn into a warmed length of 8 to 14 mm tubing which has been tapered to about 1 mm at one end. The tube is filled to such a height so as to permit the introduction of one of the commercially available or "home-made" types of reference electrodes and a small quantity of saturated potassium chloride solution to cement electrical continuity between the reference electrode and the gel.

In instances where current measurements are to be made, the salt-agar bridge is unsatisfactory because of its relatively high resistance. However, after extensive studies on membrane materials the author found that the anionic or cationic membranes (MA 3148 or MC 3142, Ionic Chemical Co., Birmingham, N.J., U.S.A.) were most suitable with the cationic type being in recent years the preferred membrane material. These membranes are excellent separators as they are essentially impervious to the transport of water or other uncharged particles.

C. Electrodes

As indicated earlier, platinum either in foil or wire form is the electrode material of choice. Its size and shape depend on the configuration of the glass half-cell with which it is to be used. For current measurements, the electrode should occupy as much of the liquid space as possible as shown in Figs 1 and 2.

The platinum electrode can readily be cleaned after each use by immersing it in hot nitric acid for 10 min followed by a thorough rinse in distilled water.

D. Voltage detectors

The most important criterion of all voltage detector instruments is that they do not draw current from the electrode system being used to study the electrochemical characteristics of a biological phenomena. Were this to occur, the steady state condition of the system under investigation might be changed depending on the amount of current drawn, and more important, the voltage measured would be inaccurate. Therefore, in order to satisfy this condition a voltage measuring device of at least a resistance of 1·0 megohm/volt or higher is required. With the instrumentation available now, it is no problem to obtain the necessary high resistance measuring devices.

A voltage detector most commonly found in the laboratory is the pH meter. This instrument has the desired high resistance measuring circuit and therefore can be used without difficulty. Another voltage measuring instrument is the readily available and relatively inexpensive vacuum tube voltmeter. This device, although extremely reliable and accurate if properly calibrated, cannot be generally used to detect small changes in potential in the millivolt region. Of course, for the ultimate in accuracy in all voltage ranges one cannot find a measuring device to surpass that of the electrometer.

If potential or voltage changes are to be measured over long time intervals, and especially if the increments of change are non-uniform, then it would be advisable to consider the use of a recorder to obtain data. In addition to the resistance requirements mentioned earlier, the recording pen should have a full scale response of about 1 sec in order to present transient phenomena which are so abundant at times with microbial systems. In a recorder it is also desirable to have available recording speeds from 1 in/hr to 2 in/min for the study of both slow and relatively fast reactions. As there are so many types of recorders with the desired characteristics available at this time, it would be unwise to recommend any one unit in particular to the reader.

11

E. Background electrolytes and catholytes

An item of importance in the measurements of the potential of a half-cell vs. a reference electrode or between two working half-cells, is that the background solvent, which in all cases is water, should be made as highly conducting as possible so that the potential developed by the metabolizing bacterial suspension is not distorted by the electrical resistance of the medium. In studying growing bacteria the media used, whether natural or synthetic, generally contains an adequate quantity of highly conducting ionic species, e.g., inorganic salts, so as to reduce the electrical resistance to a minimum. However, as is the situation when harvested micro-organisms are suspended in an aqueous medium containing a non-ionic carbon source such as glucose, the potentials observed would be so far from their true values that the voltage measurements, if any, would be meaningless. It is for this reason that a large excess of an indifferent electrolyte is added to the bacterial suspending medium. Of further importance too is the fact that a change in pH will contribute to a change in the measured potentials. Therefore, to approach more closely the potentials attributable to the microbial system itself, as a result of its metabolism of a particular substrate, the indifferent electrolyte should assume the composition of a buffer. This buffer should be of such a concentration as to be compatible with the electrical as well as the bacterial systems. 0·05 to 0·30 M buffer solutions serve the above conditions quite satisfactorily. It is essential also that all substrates added to the suspension of bacteria be dissolved in the same background electrolyte solution.

It is only necessary to consider the catholyte when current is to be drawn from two connected half-cells, as for example when a resistance is placed in parallel with the combined units. If a metabolizing microbial system is contained in the anode compartment of the electrochemical cell (Figs 1 and 2), as the substrate is utilized and oxidized by the bacteria, electrons will be contributed to the electrode which as a result will assume a negative charge. In order to have a completed circuit, as in a battery, it is necessary to have in the cathode portion of the electrochemical cell a solution of a species which can readily accept electrons or be reduced. The electron acceptor of choice in our laboratory has been potassium ferricyanide dissolved in the same background electrolyte solution as used in the anolyte. The concentration of ferricyanide should be such that it be present in excess of the quantity which will be reduced by the electrons transferred from the anode through the external circuit to the cathode as a result of the microbial substrate oxidation. For our studies a 0·01 to 0·02 M solution of the ferricyanide has been found quite adequate. This half-cell electrode is not considered a true reference electrode, but it does maintain a reasonably constant potential throughout the course of the reaction and therefore it is referred to as a nonpolarizable counter-electrode.

F. Preparation of micro-organisms

The bacteria to be studied are grown to the desired stage of their growth cycle, e.g., mid-log phase, stationary phase, etc., and then collected by centrifugation. After two washings the bacteria are suspended in the desired electrolyte and made up to a volume so that there are present the requisite number of cells/ml.

The above can be illustrated by the method used for the preparation of *Escherichia coli* (Strain W, ATCC 9637) grown to the stationary phase of their cycle.

A sterile medium containing 2·7% Trypticase soy broth (Baltimore Biological Laboratories) and 1·0% glucose in 400 ml of 0·1 M pH 6·7 buffer consisting of mono- and di-basic potassium phosphates is inoculated with the organism and incubated for 16 h at 37°C. The bacterial suspension is centrifuged at $27,300 \times g$ for 15 min (Sorvall RC-2B). After decantation the bacterial residue is washed with 50 ml of 0·2 M pH 6·7 phosphate buffer and centrifuged. The washing and centrifugation process is repeated a second time and finally the bacteria resuspended in a volume of the buffer so as to give a concentration of 10^9 cells/ml.

In the investigation of growing bacteria, it is merely necessary to inoculate sterile media already in the half-cell from which potential measurements will be obtained or in the anode compartment of the electro-chemical cell (Figs 1 and 2) from which current will be drawn.

IV. CORRELATION OF POTENTIALS WITH THE METABOLIC BEHAVIOUR OF BACTERIAL SYSTEMS

For an efficient and normal sequence of events to occur during microbial metabolism, the following conditions must be adhered to:

1. Compatible pH, ionic concentrations and temperature conditions.
2. At suitable times the production of specific enzymes and coenzymes.
3. The production of reactants by a previous step in the metabolic pathway.
4. Product removal by subsequent reactions.
5. The necessary transfer of free energy by coupled reactions.
6. The absence of antimetabolites and poisons.

One of the results of bacterial growth in a culture medium is the development of reducing conditions. This condition is the consequence of the dynamics of the system whose steady states are continuously changing as growth progresses. Initially when bacteria are inoculated into a broth the potential of the medium will be positive when compared to a reference electrode (saturated calomel electrode), but as metabolism commences and growth ensues, the electrode potential begins to decrease or becomes more negative as the bacteria go into the log-phase of their growth cycle reaching its most negative potential when the organisms attain the stationary phase of growth. The rate of change of potential with time depends to a great extent on the bacteria, the composition of the medium and whether aerobic or anaerobic conditions are being used in the study. Of course if conditions are maintained aerobic, the potentials will be less negative than under anaerobic conditions as oxygen competes with the other hydrogen acceptors present in the system. As more and more of the hydrogen acceptors are reduced the potential will become more negative.

Therefore, we may look upon the electrode potential as being an indication of the dynamic state between the constituents of the medium and the activity of the enzyme systems present in the organisms. In fact it was demonstrated by Yudkin (1935) that these observed potentials were found to develop even if the bacteria were prevented from coming in contact with the electrode surface. This investigator also found these potentials not to be significantly different from those observed using an unprotected electrode. Therefore the natural conclusion based on his findings, is that the potentials observed are due to the products secreted by the bacteria and not to the organisms themselves. On this basis then, it might be extremely difficult, as we are not dealing directly with the bacteria, to arrive at some sort of correlation between the different species of bacteria and the potentials developed by the respective systems. It should also be noted that the same bacteria may give the same potential profile even though the carbon source in the medium of necessity would have to be metabolized in different metabolic pathways, as for example with glucose and gluconolactone. The former being metabolized to a major extent by the Embden-Meyerhof pathway and the latter by the pentose phosphate shunt or Entner-Doudoroff pathway, or both. Therefore, the only legitimate correlation which can be made when discussing the potentials developed by metabolizing bacterial systems is that one is more strongly reducing than another as can be seen from the extensive studies presented by Hewitt (1950).

V. THE COULOKINETIC TECHNIQUE

In view of the obvious inadequacies in describing the metabolic behaviour of bacterial systems using the electrical potential parameter, it was felt that perhaps if the capacity factor of the system to do work were correlated with the metabolic activity of bacterial systems, more specific information relative to the systems' behaviour would be obtained. Let us examine this capacity factor in a very elementary fashion. If one wished to use a 12 V battery to start a motor car, could eight 1·5 V flashlight batteries connected in series serve the purpose? The answer is obvious for if these batteries were connected to the starter, and the button depressed, the starter would not respond. What then is the difference between this 12 V system and a standard 12 V motor-car battery? It cannot be the intensity factor, for they are both identical, 12 V, and therefore it must be the capacity factor of the battery to perform electrical work.

This important capacity factor can be better understood if we examine an electrochemical system as exemplified by a hydrogen-oxygen cell. In a cell of this type the following reactions occur.

Overall anodic reaction (doubled):

$$2H_2 + 4OH^- - 4e^- \rightarrow 4H_2O$$

Overall cathodic reaction:

$$O_2 + 2H_2O + 4e^- \rightarrow 4OH^-$$

Overall cell reaction (4 Faradays):

$$2H_2 + O_2 \rightarrow 2H_2O$$

The capacity of the above system is dependent on the number of electrons transferred in the course of the total reaction. In this particular instance four electrons are transferred, which is equivalent to 4 Faradays or a total of 386,000 coulombs. If instead of reacting 2 moles of hydrogen with 1 mole of oxygen, the quantities of reactants were doubled, an equivalent capacity of 8 Faradays, or twice that of the electro-chemical system under previous conditions, would be obtained. The potential of the system just described (with a silver anode and a nickel cathode, and an aqueous potassium hydroxide electrolyte) would be 1·3 V, regardless of the quantities of reactants used. However, the larger the quantity of these reactants, the greater the electrical capacity of the system.

Therefore, the potential or the voltage developed by an electrochemical system, though important, is in itself inadequate to describe this system, unless its capacity is known. This is more apparent in biological systems where the total reactants and products formed as a result of metabolism are not readily ascertained.

Thus, it can be seen why a greater understanding of an organism's metabolic behaviour toward particular substrates would be gained through a knowledge of its capacity to perform this function. This capacity factor can, under suitable experimental conditions, manifest itself as the organism's ability to produce an electric current for whatever period of time it can do so.

From the outset it was realized that the capacity factor or coulombic output would be indicative of the amount of electron transfer occurring within the system. This would represent only the net electron processes taking place within the biological system. Furthermore, were it possible to obtain a coulombic output representing all electron transfer processes which occurred, one would surely disturb the normal biological functions by diverting the electrons from the synthetic processes required for the maintenance of life. On the other hand, electron transfer reactions occur for which there are no critical, life-sustaining receptors. It was felt that these electrons could be captured at an electrode (anode) surface. Therefore, in an electrochemical cell containing a smooth platinum anode and cathode separated by a membrane and with a reducible species in the cathode compartment serving as the counter-electrode it is possible to obtain under "loaded" conditions, i.e., a resistance in parallel with the electrochemical cell, a current output. This, when plotted against time, would yield, upon integration of the area under the curve, the capacity of the system to do work or the coulombic output.

The problem, in retrospect, of using metabolizing bacteria to obtain this capacity factor was readily solved. It was decided to utilize *E. coli* for the studies as it would then be possible to correlate its known metabolic behaviour with the electrochemical data. As two half cells are required to construct an electrochemical cell, the apparatus shown in Fig. 1 was developed and used in the initial studies.

In a typical experiment the anode compartment of the electrochemical cell contains 20 ml of the *E. coli* suspension prepared as described under III-F diluted with 20 ml of the pH 6·7 phosphate buffer. To the cathode chamber is added 50 ml of 0·01 M potassium ferricyanide in the same buffer. The cathode serves as a nonpolarizable counter-electrode. The potential of this electrode when compared to a saturated calomel reference electrode remains essentially constant throughout the course of an experiment. The cell is immersed in a bath (37°C) and equilibrated for 10 min. A 1000 ohm resistor is then inserted in parallel with the cell and the background current (5–10 μA) recorded for a few minutes after which 5 ml of 0·252 M-glucose in the phosphate buffer is added to the anolyte. This is the optimum concentration of substrate to be used in conjunction with this concentration of bacterial and electrochemical cell. The criteria used for optimization are: a reasonable reaction period (period of current production), i.e., 8 h or less, and a relatively sharp end-point on the current/time curve. The choice of resistance to be used in the circuit is based on the fact that the current/time curve of the system under "load" should be parallel to the open cell potential curve.

After introduction of the substrate the recording of current output is continued until it decreases and plateaus at a low level. The current/time curve obtained from the above described experiment is shown in Fig. 3. The shaded region, whose boundary is established from the intersection of tangents, represents that area from which the coulombic output is obtained. This is accomplished in the following manner. Let A represent the area bounded by 200 μA on the vertical axis and 1 h on the horizontal

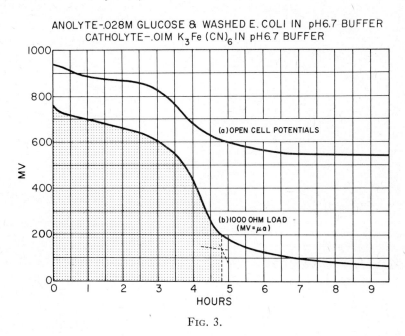

FIG. 3.

axis. As 1 coulomb is equivalent to a current of 1 amp flowing for 1 sec, the coulombic output for area A can be obtained by multiplying the current in amperes by time in seconds, or $200 \times 10^{-6} \times 3600$, which equals 0·72 coulomb. By using a planimeter, the total area under the curve is obtained, and is divided by the numerical value for A. This, when multiplied by 0·72, will give the total coulombic output.

It might have been possible, with the system described to use resistances slightly lower than 1000 ohms and still obtain a current/time curve which would parallel the open cell potential/time curve. However, the 1000 ohm value was chosen because it made conversion of the recorder chart scale (1 V, full scale) from millivolts to microamperes more convenient.

The net electrochemical picture visualized as a result of the microbial metabolism after addition of the substrate, then, was that the electrons released to the anode from substrate oxidation were transferred through the external circuit to the cathode, where they served to reduce the ferri-cyanide. The circuit was then completed in solution by ionic conductance of phosphate ions through the anionic membrane or by potassium ions through the cationic membrane. An overall view of the total apparatus used for coulokinetic studies at the present time is shown in Fig. 4.

Fig. 4.

VI. MECHANISM OF CURRENT GENERATION

It was realized quite early in the coulokinetic studies that the currents developed by metabolizing bacterial systems might be due to one of several factors. The generated current could be in part the result of the oxidation of a microbial secretion product or products or due to the direct transfer of electrons from the micro-organisms to the electrode surface. It was also possible that a combination of both of the above mentioned factors resulted in the observed current. The substrate itself cannot be considered to be responsible for current production, for in the absence of the bacteria no current is produced. In order to define the source of the electrons available to the electrode, experiments were performed in which the bacteria were prevented from coming in contact with the electrode (Allen, 1966b). This was accomplished by enclosing the anode in a dialysis membrane. Glucose and formate were used as substrates for this study.

The data obtained from the experiments performed with membraned, as compared with non-membraned, anodes are shown in Fig. 5. It can be

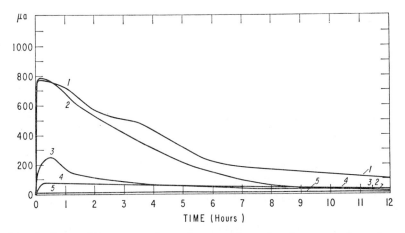

FIG. 5. Current/time curves for various membraned and non-membraned anode systems with 1000 ohm loads across the electrochemical cells. Anolyte 1 : 20 ml of buffer, 20 ml of a suspension of *Escherichia coli*, 5 ml of 0·252 M-glucose. Anolyte 2: same, but with 0·252 M-formate instead of glucose. Anolyte 3: (inside membrane) 15 ml of buffer, 5 ml of formate; (outside) 20 ml of *E. coli*, 5 ml of formate. Anolyte 4: (inside) 15 ml buffer, 5 ml of glucose; (outside) 20 ml of *E. coli*, 5 ml of glucose. Anolyte 5: 25 ml of buffer, 20 ml of *E. coli*.

seen from the current/time recordings obtained with membraned and non-membraned anode systems that the current and resultant coulombic outputs are a result of electron transfer through contact of the micro-organism with the electrode surface. Therefore, it appears that the coulo-kinetic technique permits the direct measure of some biological activities of the micro-organisms. It can be assumed that there are electrons present on the microbial cell wall surface. During the course of active metabolism, there is a continuous transfer of electrons from the cytoplasm to the cytoplasmic membrane and the cell wall surface. It is also probable that some of the terminal oxidative processes occur predominantly at the cytoplasmic membrane surface. In either case those electrons not captured by the electrode serve to reduce the hydrogen ions, formed at the same time as electron release, to hydrogen gas. This aspect will be further discussed in some detail below. In all probability, the micro-organism makes contact with the electrode by the combined process of electrophoretic migration and the motility of the organism itself. Of interest is the fact (curve 5, Fig. 5) that the organisms themselves do not produce a significant current. Therefore, the coulombic outputs obtained with a useable substrate are due completely to exogenous metabolism.

The data also show that there was low conversion efficiency obtained with formate, the last product to be oxidized in the dissimiliation of

12

glucose. According to the electrochemical studies performed on the oxidation of formate (Gottlieb, 1964), we would anticipate the following processes:

$$(1) \ HCOO^- \rightarrow CO_2 + H^+ + e^-$$
$$(2) \ H^+ + e^- \rightarrow 1/2 \ H_2$$

This series of reactions has a biochemical counterpart in that the enzyme
system, formic hydrogenlyase which catalyses the overall oxidation of
formate to carbon dioxide and hydrogen is found in the *coli-aerogenes*
group of bacteria. Evidence has been obtained which indicates that this
hydrogenlyase is a multienzyme system consisting of formic dehydrogenase
and hydrogenase which catalyse reactions (1) and (2) respectively (Strecker,
1961).

In view of the profuse amounts of hydrogen liberated by *E. coli* during
glucose dissimilation, as well as formate metabolism in an electrochemical
cell under "load", it is apparent that reaction 1, which is the predominant
electrode or current contributing reaction while the organism is in contact
with the electrode, is quickly supplemented by reaction 2. It is not beyond
reason to expect that both of these reactions occur at the cytoplasmic
membrane. As a result there might be a competitive reaction taking place
between the passage of hydrogen ions and transfer of electrons through the
cell wall, and the reduction of these ions to hydrogen gas. If these assumptions are valid, it might be anticipated that reaction 2, as well as reaction 1,
would be slowed to some extent at a lower temperature, with the possibility that reaction 2 would be the slower of the two reactions. On this
basis then, a greater coulombic output might be obtained at the lower
temperature, than at 37°C. This, in fact, was the case when the metabolic
process was allowed to proceed at 24°C. At this lower temperature, an
increase from approximately 11 to 20 coulombs was obtained.

As the electron transfer appeared to occur via micro-organism-electrode
contact, it was suspected that greater transfer potentiality could be achieved
if the number of cells in the solution of substrate was increased. Use of
twice the number of cells resulted in approximately a two-fold increase in
coulombic output. On this basis, should the anolyte be agitated, the micro-
organisms might be expected to bombard the electrode surface at a greater
rate, and possibly increase the current output. The reverse effect was
observed, even under relatively mild conditions. Accordingly, it was concluded that agitation removes the cells or prevents them from coming into
intimate contact with the electrode. This finding is of great importance,
for it indicates that the micro-organism must not only make contact with
the electrode, as it certainly must as a result of agitation, but also the cells
must remain at the electrode for some period in order to adhere to its

surface. This assumption was supported by the fact that the electrode surface was found to be coated with cells of the bacterium.

A current decrease, as a result of agitation, also eliminated the possibility of the generated current being due to an oxidizable nondialysable polymeric metabolite. If this were the case, by analogy to the behaviour of organic and inorganic depolarizers when stirred, an increase in current would be observed (Allen, 1958).

In summary, it can be stated that the current produced by the metabolizing micro-organisms is a result of their making intimate contact with, and transferring potentially available electrons to the electrode surface. Therefore, the observed parameters, i.e., current and coulombic output, are a direct indication of the activity of the biological cell.

VII. COULOKINETIC BEHAVIOUR OF NORMAL METABOLIC SYSTEMS

Early metabolic studies involved investigations related to the coulombic outputs obtained from various prime and intermediate substrates common to the glycolytic and monophosphate pathways, i.e., glucose, fructose, gluconolactone, pyruvate and formate (Allen *et al.*, 1963). Based on available information, glucose is metabolized by *E. coli* predominantly via the glycolytic pathway (Wang *et al.*, 1958). On this basis then, one would expect to obtain the equivalent of 2 pyruvates for every one glucose molecule. However, if a portion of the glucose formed dihydroxyacetone phosphate from fructose-1,6-diphosphate, which in turn formed glycerol, only that portion of the phosphorylated fructose which formed glyceraldehyde-3-phosphate could be further converted to pyruvate. Furthermore, pyruvate can be reduced to lactate. Lactate as well as glycerol were found to be electrochemically inert under the experimental conditions used. These factors would contribute to the possibility of observing electrochemically, somewhat less than 2 pyruvates. It was expected that fructose could enter the glycolytic pathway via fructose-6-phosphate, and that it would then be treated by the micro-organisms in a manner similar to that of glucose. Gluconolactone, on the other hand, by the nature of the shunt pathways could yield the equivalent of 2 pyruvates, or a greater coulombic output than obtained with glucose.

The results indicated that the original premise was reasonable in that the coulombic outputs for glucose and fructose were essentially the same as that resulting when pyruvate or formate were used as substrates. Of further interest was the observed coulombic output for gluconolactone, which was approximately twice that of pyruvate.

Since the terminal steps in the oxidation of fructose by *E. coli* is the oxidation of formate to carbon dioxide and hydrogen, it was thought that the coulombic output obtained could be attributed to the formation of hydrogen. This would give the equivalent of a hydrogen-oxygen cell. The contribution of hydrogen itself to the coulombic output was found to be negligible. Furthermore, a smooth platinum anode is quite inefficient for the oxidation of hydrogen. Therefore, the possibility is remote that the hydrogen liberated as a result of the bacterial cells' metabolic processes is the major contributing factor to the observed coulombic outputs.

It was apparent from the earlier studies that the electron transfer of the terminal oxidation steps, i.e., formate via reactions 1 and 2 to carbon dioxide and hydrogen, was being measured. A gradation of energy outputs was not obtained during the degradation of glucose to formate, probably because naturally occurring receptors capture electrons released by the intermediate reactions and transfer them to reducible substances.

As investigations progressed in this area, and in view of the effects of oxygen noted on the electro-chemical system (Allen and Januszeski, 1964), the coulokinetic technique was improved, yielding a more definite picture of metabolic behaviour. It was felt that if, in fact, *E. coli* metabolized glucose by both the glycolytic and to a considerably smaller extent, the monophosphate pathways (Wang *et al.*, 1958), then under mutually aerobic conditions mono-phosphate shunt might be completely missed by imposing the resistance across the electrochemical cell approximately 10 min after the addition of the substrate, as was done in the early studies. By imposing the "load" prior to the addition of the substrate, glucose gave a coulombic output of 13·4 coulombs as compared to the 10·6 coulombs with the former technique. Extrapolation back to zero time (addition of substrate) on the current/time curve obtained by the former technique gives a value of approximately 0·5 coulomb. The difference of 2·8 coulombs between the two methods of observation is attributed to some other metabolic process or processes in which oxygen participates either directly or indirectly. Therefore, it was decided to investigate the coulokinetic behaviour of various substrates under initially aerobic and anaerobic conditions (Allen, 1964). As shown in Table I, the values were different for glucose and fructose under initially aerobic and anaerobic conditions. This difference for glucose would indicate, for the strain of *E. coli* used in this study, that 23% of the glucose was metabolized via the monophosphate pathway and 77% via the glycolytic path. These values are in good agreement with those obtained by other methods (Wang *et al.*, 1958). The results for fructose indicated that 17% of the oxidation proceeded via the monophosphate pathway and 83% via the glycolytic path. With fructose, a smaller percentage of the oxidative process went through the monophosphate pathway.

TABLE I

Comparative coulombic outputs for various substrates under initially aerobic and anaerobic conditions

Substrate	Initially aerobic	Anaerobic
Glucose	13·4	10·3
Fructose	17·6	14·6
Gluconate	28·7	28·5
Pyruvate	13·0	12·9
Formate	12·6	12·8

This could be due to the fact that fructose, in order to pass through this cycle, was transformed to fructose-6-phosphate and then to glucose-6-phosphate which was oxidized to 6-phosphogluconolactone. Glucose, however, requires two less intermediates.

If the oxidation of glucose via glucose-6-phosphate to the phosphorylated gluconolactone is the essential aerobic step in the monophosphate pathway, it is not too surprising to find that the coulombic values, under initially aerobic and anaerobic conditions, are essentially the same. This finding, of course may be inconsistent with the fact that nicotinamide adenine dinucleotide phosphate participates in the conversion of glucose-6-phosphate to 6-phosphogluconate, and 6-phosphogluconic acid to ribulose 5-phosphate (Kornberg, 1961b). However, as the above is based on *in vitro* experiments, it may not be completely valid under *in vivo* conditions such as those used in the electrochemical studies.

No apparent difference has been observed between the initially aerobic and anaerobic coulombic outputs for pyruvate and formate. This is ascribed to the fact that the degradation of pyruvate via formate to carbon dioxide and hydrogen is essentially an anaerobic process.

At this point in the studies, it was felt that it would be of interest to apply the coulokinetic technique to growing *E. coli* cells (Allen, 1966c). Since the glycolytic pathway supplies the "high-energy" mixed phosphoric-acyl anhydride and thiol ester bonds transferable to the nucleotide carrier systems so necessary for growth and maintenance of living systems (Lipmann, 1941), it is the major, if not the sole, route of fermentation for growing *E. coli* cells (Endo, 1938). The substrates glucose, glucose-6-phosphate, fructose, and pyruvate were chosen because they are involved either directly or indirectly in the glycolytic pathway; fructose is present in the phosphorylated state (Kornberg, 1961a).

The anolytes in these experiments consisted of 20 ml of a buffered solu-

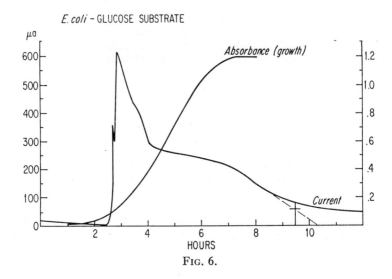

E. coli – GLUCOSE SUBSTRATE

Absorbance (growth)

Current

HOURS

FIG. 6.

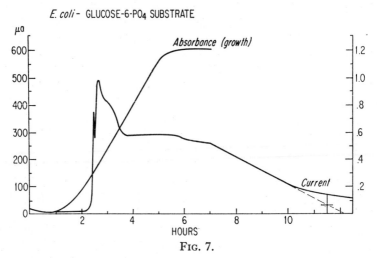

E. coli – GLUCOSE-6-PO_4 SUBSTRATE

Absorbance (growth)

Current

HOURS

FIG. 7.

tion (pH 6·7) of Trypticase Soy Broth and 20 ml of a buffer solution containing 1·10 mmoles of substrate, to which was added 0·04 ml of a freshly grown 8-h *E. coli* culture. The coulokinetic behaviour of each system was correlated with the rate of microbial growth.

The data obtained for the various substrates are shown in Figs 6–9. The growth curves shown in these figures were obtained from cells grown in the "loaded" electrochemical cells. No significant difference was noted between these growth curves and those obtained under normal conditions.

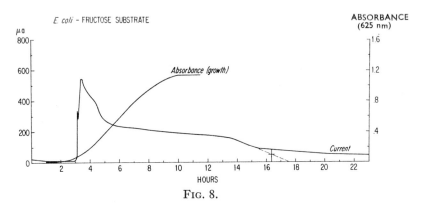

FIG. 8.

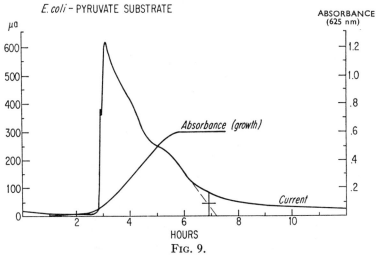

FIG. 9.

This suggests that the manner by which coulombic outputs were obtained did not apparently interfere with the normal metabolism of the microorganisms. This is important, for it indicates that by drawing these small currents no apparent artifacts are introduced into the system.

The following data (Table II) were derived from the curves: the total coulombic output for each substrate (by integration of the area under the current/time curve); the maximal absorbance at the stationary phase of growth, which reflects the cell density; and the rate of growth (change in absorbance) from the log phase of the growth curve, which is related to the metabolic rate of the cells. The fact that, in the presence of the trypticase soy broth alone, only 0·8 coulombs was obtained, may be indicative of the organisms' endogenous metabolism or its ability to adapt to a small degree and to utilize the carbon sources present in the broth.

TABLE II

Comparison of coulombic outputs with growth characteristics of *Escherichia coli* with various substrates

Substrate	Output (coul)	Maximal absorbance (A_{max})	Change in absorbance with time (dA/dt)	C_1*	C_2**
Glucose	6·26	1·19	$5·5 \times 10^{-3}$	$6·26 \times 1 = 6·26$	$6·26 \times 1 = 6·26$
Glucose-6-phosphate	7·39	1·23	$5·4 \times 10^{-3}$	$7·39 \times 0·96 = 7·09$	$7·09 \times 0·98 = 6·94$
Fructose	10·11	1·14	$3·3 \times 10^{-3}$	$10·11 \times 1·04 = 10·51$	$10·51 \times 0·60 = 6·30$
Pyruvate	4·16	0·60	$3·8 \times 10^{-3}$	$4·16 \times 1·98 = 8·23$	$8·23 \times 0·69 = 5·67$

* C_1 (first correction) = output (A_{max} with glucose)/(A_{max} with intermediate substrate).

** C_2 (second correction) = $C_1(dA/dt$ intermediate substrate)/(dA/dt glucose).

It was shown previously that, under initially aerobic conditions with equal concentrations of stationary-phase cells of *E. coli*, essentially the same coulombic outputs were obtained for glucose and pyruvate. Also, as mentioned earlier, a doubling of concentration of cells yielded approximately a two-fold increase in coulombic output. On this basis, then, it might be assumed that, were the maximal absorbance for growing *E. coli* the same for both substrates, the coulombic outputs would be similar. Therefore, as the maximal absorbance is a measure of the final concentration of cells which are the electrochemically active species, it appears logical to normalize the coulombic outputs for the various intermediate substrates to the final concentration of cells obtained with glucose. This correction results in a rather negligible change in coulombic output for all but pyruvate, which is doubled (C_1, Table II).

It was stated previously that the coulombic output was greater at 24 than at 37°C, which was interpreted as an indication that decrease in the metabolic rate resulted in increase in the coulombic output for the same concentration of substrate. Accordingly, since the slope (dA/dt) of the log phase of the growth curve is an indication of metabolic rate, it is not unreasonable to suspect the coulombic outputs for fructose and pyruvate would be similar were their dA/dt values similar to that of glucose. Therefore, the coulombic outputs were also normalized to the dA/dt obtained from the glucose growth curve. This correction results in essentially the same coulombic outputs (C_2, Table II) obtained for the various substrates. The trend of these results is in conformity with those obtained for the stationary-phase micro-organisms under initially aerobic conditions.

It appears, upon examination of the curves for each of the substrates, that the rapid current increase occurred at approximately the same time as the onset of the most active growth of the microbial system. That a current was observed for a period of time after the stationary-phase was reached was to be expected from earlier studies with stationary-phase *E. coli* systems. These cells continued to metabolize a useable substrate until it was completely depleted or until the waste products of metabolism accumulated and the conditions necessary for development were no longer present.

An explanation for the charge-discharge phenomen (spur) observed in the ascending portion of the current/time curve is ascribed to a transient steady state which manifests itself again as the second plateau in the descending section of the curve.

Because of the need to use smaller quantities of substrates and micro-organisms the cell shown in Fig. 2 was constructed. In designing this electro-chemical cell another objective was also taken into consideration, that is, increased electrochemical efficiency by reducing the distance the

274   M. J. ALLEN

bacteria had to travel to reach the electrode surface from the bulk of the
solution. With this cell it was found that the anolyte could consist of 10 ml
of the bacterial suspension (section III-E) diluted with 10 ml of the pH 6·7
phosphate buffer. To the anolyte is then added 5 ml of 0·0473 M of an
active substrate and coulombic measurements made as previously described.

The performance of this cell was checked using glucose and a number of
its metabolic intermediates as substrates (Allen, 1967c). The data obtained
is described in Table III.

TABLE III

**Coulombic output for various substrates
using the mini-macro electrochemical
cell**

Substrate	Coulombic output
Glucose	12·63
Fructose	14·44
Gluconolactone	22·00
Pyruvate	11·46
Formate	11·49

In studies in which 1260 μmoles (5 ml 0·252 M) of substrate was used,
a theoretical output of 121·6 coulombs per electron should have been
obtained assuming a 100% conversion efficiency. The maximum efficiency
attained was 12·3% (Allen, 1966b). Using the present electrochemical
system 236·5 μmoles of substrate should yield 22·8 coulombs per electron.
Based on the coulombic output obtained for glucose the efficiency of
conversion has been significantly increased to 55·3%.

From the earliest days of the coulokinetic study of metabolic phenomena,
it was thought that it would be extremely desirable to have available another
intermediate in the monophosphate shunt pathway to use as a substrate.
Unfortunately, these intermediates are not readily available. Although
L-arabinose is not a normal intermediate in this pathway, it can be isomerized by the bacteria to ribulose, which is then phosphorylated to yield
ribulose-5-phosphate (Lim and Cohen, 1966). This being the acknowledged
sequence of events, then a coulombic output slightly less than that obtained
for gluconolactone would be anticipated. On this basis it was not unex-
pected to obtain a coulombic output of 20·83 coulombs for arabinose
as compared to 22·00 coulombs for gluconolactone (Allen, 1967c).

At this point in the discussion it may be advisable to introduce two additional parameters obtained from coulokinetic measurements. The first is
the rate of current rise with time (dI/dt) in μA/min, after introduction of
the substrate into the anolyte, and the second is the maximum current,

in μA, which is the maximum current obtained after the initial current rise. The dI/dt may be considered as being related to the rate of transport of the substrate to the site of enzymatic activity. As current is dependent on the rate of electron transfer, the maximum current, I_{max}, is the maximum rate of electron transfer from the micro-organisms to the electrode. The further implications of the initial current rise with time will be referred to again when enzyme induction is discussed.

For the present, however, in reference to the discussion of the electro-chemical observations made using arabinose, it should be noted that the initial rate of increase of current with time for arabinose was 3·4 with a maximum current output of 580 μA as compared to values of 7·2 and 730 respectively for gluconolactone. This slower response with arabinose might possibly be an indication of the rate controlling step in the reaction, i.e., the isomerization of arabinose to ribulose, or as will be discussed later, the induction of the enzyme required for the rate determining reaction.

In previous investigations using *E. coli* harvested in the stationary phase of their growth cycle, a pH 6·7 buffered medium was used as the background electrolyte. At this pH under normal conditions, that is, in the absence of agents affecting normal metabolic functions, a 1 : 1 relationship, as indicated by coulombic outputs, was obtained for glucose and pyruvate. The reasons that the anticipated 2 : 1 relationship was not obtained were discussed earlier in this section.

It has been shown that under alkaline conditions only 2·7 % of the glucose metabolized is converted to lactate as compared to a 43% conversion in an acidic medium (Thimann, 1963). In an alkaline system the quantities of glycerol, another electrochemically inert product, is also formed to a lesser extent when glucose is metabolized by *E. coli* (Wood, 1961). On this basis, if the coulokinetic studies were performed in an alkaline medium using glucose and various of its intermediates formed in the glycolytic pathway as substrates, then it might be possible to obtain the 1 : 2 glucose-pyruvate relationship.

The results of the study (Allen, 1967c) using the mini-macro cell and a pH 7·8 buffered medium are presented in Table IV.

Apparently the fact that a considerably smaller quantity of glycerol and lactate is produced in an alkaline system results in approximately a 2 : 1 glucose-pyruvate coulombic output ratio. The glucose-fructose and gluconolactone-pyruvate relationships at pH 7·8 are essentially the same as obtained in the pH 6·7 medium.

It might have been expected that the coulombic outputs obtained with gluconolactone, pyruvate and formate at pH 7·8 would have remained essentially the same as those values obtained at pH 6·7. As a result in order to obtain the 2 : 1 glucose-pyruvate ratio it would have been necessary for

TABLE IV

**Coulombic outputs obtained for various
substrates at pH 7·8**

Substrate	Coulombic output
Glucose	13·25
Fructose	15·31
Gluconolactone	14·74
Pyruvate	7·91
Formate	6·44

glucose and fructose to yield approximately twice the coulombic output obtained in the acidic medium. One possible explanation why the results were not as anticipated is the sub-optimal pH conditions under which the enzyme systems for the conversion of pyruvate to acetate and formate and formic hydrogenlyase which catalyses the oxidation of formate to carbon dioxide and hydrogen are required to operate. These enzymes demonstrate optimum catalytic behaviour at pH 6·8 and 6·0 respectively. Therefore, with these enzyme systems operating under non-ideal pH conditions lower coulombic outputs might be anticipated. For this reason the substrates glucose, fructose and gluconolactone, which when metabolized pass through a pyruvate intermediate, would be expected to give a lower coulombic output than would have been obtained had the above-mentioned enzyme systems been operating under ideal conditions. It is not implied by these comments that the micro-organisms do not utilize all the substrate in the medium, but rather that it is possible once the substrate has been taken up by the bacteria, that they are unable to metabolize it as efficiently as they might have at pH 6·7. This in no way distracts from the validity of the 2 : 1 relationship for glucose, fructose and gluconolactone to pyruvate for it appears that the enzymatic inefficiency for conversion is in the terminal steps of the metabolic pathway.

VIII. COULOKINETIC BEHAVIOUR OF MICROBIAL SYSTEMS UNDER ABNORMAL CONDITIONS

The effects of chlorpromazine on the coulokinetic behaviour of *E. coli* will be described to illustrate the kind of results that may be obtained by studying microbial systems under carefully selected abnormal conditions.

Chlorpromazine (CPZ) has been reported to be a general depressant of cellular metabolism (Decourt, 1955). In view of this effect, the action of CPZ on the coulokinetic behaviour of *E. coli* was investigated (Allen, 1966a). The coulombic outputs obtained with various concentrations of

TABLE V

Coulombic outputs obtained from the metabolism of 1·26 mmoles glucose by *E. coli* in the presence of various concentrations of chlorpromazine hydrochloride

Chlorpromazine conc.*	Coulombic output
0	13·8
0·5 (1·407)	12·4
1·0 (2·814)	9·1
2·0 (5·628)	23·6
4·0 (11·257)	36·4
8·0 (22·514)	8·7
10·0 (28·142)	3·2

* Amount (milligrams) per 45 ml of anolyte (micromolar equivalents in parentheses).

CPZ when the micro-organisms metabolize glucose (macro cell, Fig. 1) are described in Table V.

Although the coulombic values differed from the control in the CPZ concentration range from 0·5 to 4·0 mg, the time required for a current response and the rate of current increase (dI/dt) after addition of the glucose were essentially the same as for the control, i.e., 4 min and 210 μA/min, respectively. With the 8·0- and 10·0-mg CPZ concentrations, 27 min elapsed before a current response was noted. The dI/dt was 70 μA/min. The maximal current (I) in all cases was 760 to 780 μA.

The second phase of the investigation involved a study of the effects of

TABLE VI

Coulombic outputs obtained in the metabolism of various substrates (1·26 mmoles) in the presence of chlorpromazine hydrochloride (11·257 μmoles/45 ml anolyte)

Substrate	Coulombic output
Glucose	36·4
Fructose	39·4
Gluconolactone	7·8
Pyruvate	27·8
Formate	16·2

the maximal potentiating dose of CPZ (4 mg/45 ml) on glucose, fructose, and some of their major metabolic intermediates (Table VI).

The period required for current response with the substrates listed was virtually unaffected by CPZ. However, a marked difference was observed in the rate of current increase after the addition of the gluconolactone. The dI/dt in this instance was $5 \cdot 1$ μA/min, as compared to 218 μA/min for this substrate in the absence of CPZ. Of interest also is the fact that without CPZ all of the substrates gave a maximal current output of 760 to 780 μA. With the exception of gluconolactone, which yielded a maximal current of only 530 μA, the other substrates, in the presence of $4 \cdot 0$ mg of CPZ/45 ml, also developed a maximal current of 760 to 780 μA.

Although the CPZ concentration-coulombic output data obtained in the metabolism of glucose may appear erratic, this behaviour has been noted in many cases with drug action. At one dose level there is an inhibitory pharmacological effect, whereas at another dose level there is a potentiating effect on some metabolic processes. As CPZ is known to inhibit phosphorylation at low concentrations (Abood, 1955), the decreased coulombic outputs obtained with $0 \cdot 5$ and $1 \cdot 0$ mg CPZ may be possibly due to inhibition of the reaction which is necessary for formation of glucose-6-phosphate. At the higher dose levels ($2 \cdot 0$ and $4 \cdot 0$ mg/45 ml), the effect may be the result of inhibition of the cytochrome system (Moraczewski and Du Bois, 1959). In the $8 \cdot 0$ and $10 \cdot 0$ mg range, the cells appear to be in a hypometabolic state.

It has been noted earlier that the difference in coulombic outputs from glucose and formate was negligible, whereas a greater value might have been expected from glucose. In an earlier report it was stated that this might have been due to the fact that the platinum anode was able to capture only the electrons released in the oxidation of the formate. As CPZ will inhibit the cytochrome system, it may very well be that this characteristic of CPZ explains, at least in part, the coulombic output gradient in its movement from glucose to formate.

Perhaps one of the more interesting aspects of the findings is the rather large inhibitive effect of CPZ on the coulombic output for gluconolactone. This would tend to indicate that CPZ is a blocking agent for the monophosphate pathway. Confirmation of this assumption comes from the lower maximum current and dI/dt obtained for gluconolactone in the presence of CPZ as compared to the other substrates used in this study.

Coulokinetic behaviour in the presence of mixed substrates has been described by Allen (1966a, 1966b) and the effects of cyanide (which inhibits the oxidation of formic acid in $E. coli$) have been reported by Allen (1967b).

IX. THE COULOKINETIC MANIFESTATIONS OF ENZYME INDUCTION *IN VIVO*

As indicated in Section VII, arabinose is in itself not an intermediate in the pentose phosphate shunt. However, this carbohydrate can be considered a precursor to a shunt pathway intermediate as it is isomerized and phosphorylated by the bacteria to yield ribulose-5-phosphate.

When a substrate is added to the bacterial cells in a buffered medium the initial current rise will be essentially a straight line. The slope of this straight line differs with the nature of the substrate and is probably dependent on the rate of transport to the site of enzymatic activity. Arabinose, however, appeared to give a curve for the initial current rise which was concave upwards, indicating that the measured rate of oxidation was increasing with time. This suggested the possibility that induction phenomena related either to the synthesis of arabinoisomerase or D-ribulokinase, or both of these enzymes was being demonstrated.

In order to further elucidate the electrical characteristics of enzyme induction, a system was studied (Allen, 1967d), which had been intensively investigated and was clearly defined, namely the β-galactosidase system. As is well known, the production of β-galactosidase can be induced in *E. coli* by growth in lactose (Monod *et al.*, 1951), and repressed in glucose media (Cohn and Horibata, 1959). A comparison of the initial I/t curves observed for induced and uninduced *E. coli* cells demonstrated a distinct difference with lactose as an oxidizable substrate and essentially no difference towards glucose as substrate since each system will have the requisite enzymes necessary for the metabolism of glucose. The studies were extended to the use of chloramphenicol as an inhibitor of β-galactosidase synthesis in the presence of the inducer, lactose.

A comparison of the I/t responses of glucose- and lactose-grown *E. coli* to glucose and lactose, in the mino-macro cell is shown in Fig. 10. The current (I) is an indication of the rate of electron transfer to the electrode. As the rate determining step in the metabolism of lactose is its transport via a permease, it is logical to assume that the initial increasing portion of the I/t curve up to the steady state metabolic rate (maximum I), is directly related to the transport of lactose to the site of enzymatic hydrolysis. As expected using bacteria in which β-galactosidase and permease had been induced during growth, the rate of increase of current with time using the lactose substrate was considerably faster than that obtained with bacteria grown on glucose.

Current measurements were conducted with enzyme induction in the presence of various concentrations of chloramphenicol as shown in Fig. 11a and correlated with rate of formation of β-galactosidase (11b).

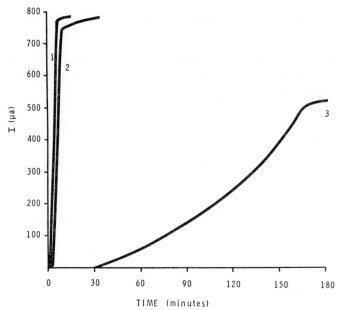

FIG. 10. Behaviour of lactose-grown *Escherichia coli* with glucose and lactose (1), and glucose-grown *E. coli* with glucose (2) and lactose (3).

It was felt that it would be advantageous to reduce the I/t curves (Fig. 11a) to a numerical value. Since the rate of induction is directly related to the increase of dI/dt with time (d^2I/dt^2), a convenient measure of induction was the "induction factor". The "induction factors" were the averaged $\Delta(dI/dt)$ values starting at zero time and continuing up to the end of the initial maximum current rise period. These "induction factors" in $\mu A/min$

TABLE VII

Induction factors obtained using glucose grown *Escherichia coli* with various concentrations of chloramphenicol in the presence of 236·5 μmoles of lactose

chloramphenicol conc (mg/25 ml of anolyte)	"Induction factor"	Av. β-gal. U/min
0	2·77	1·93
0·5	2·58	1·57
1·0	1·76	0·98
1·5	1·10	0·80
2·0	0·77	0·43
2·5	0·51	0·27

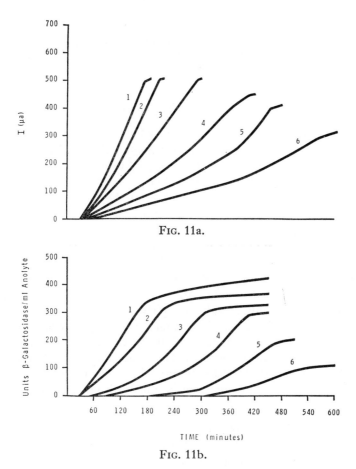

Fig. 11a.

Fig. 11b.

Fig. 11. Correlation of current/time with induction of β-galactosidase/time. Curves obtained with lactose metabolizing *Escherichia coli* (glucose grown) in the presence of various concentrations of chloramphenicol. 1. control; curves 2–6 represent the effect of 0·5, 1·0, 1·5, 2·0, 2·5 mg chloramphenicol, respectively, per 25 ml anolyte.

are given in Table VII. If the averaged rate of increase of β-galactosidase activity with time is correlated with the "induction factors", a value of 0·61 units β-galactosidase/min is obtained which is equivalent to an "induction factor" of 1 μA/min.

The addition of 2·5 mg chloramphenicol to lactose-grown *E. coli* as they metabolized lactose or glucose caused no change in the dI/dt response. The same negative results were noted when the inhibitor was incorporated into the system consisting of glucose and the bacteria grown upon glucose.

Further studies on induced and repressed β-galactosidase systems are described by Allen (1967e), to which report the reader is referred for detailed information concerning the potential value of coulokinetic techniques for the study of such systems.

X. CONCLUSION

The measurement of potentials of metabolizing microbial systems can only suggest that one system is more strongly reducing than another and that this potential is in all probability related to the products secreted by the bacteria. The coulokinetic technique, however, appears to offer a more satisfactory alternative to the study of the metabolic behaviour of micro-organisms, and perhaps in the future to animal cells, because it measures the capacity factor of available free energy at the site of metabolic activity. It has been demonstrated that this electrochemical technique can serve as another tool for the investigation of the pathways taken by a biological system in the metabolism of substrates both under normal and abnormal physiological conditions. More recently its usefulness has been shown in the study of induction phenomena.

There is little doubt that as these studies continue, our knowledge of the meanings of many observations will be better understood and readily correlated with biological functions. The future abounds with many interesting discoveries both as related to normal and disease states.

No more appropriate ending can be put forth other than that contributed by a much admired man. . . .

> "This is not the end. It is not even the beginning of the end. But it is, perhaps, the end of the beginning."
>
> WINSTON CHURCHILL

REFERENCES

Abood, L. G. (1955). *Proc. Soc. Exptl. Biol. Med.*, **88**, 688.
Allen, M. J. (1958). "Organic Electrode Processes", pp. 15–16. Chapman and Hall, London.
Allen, M. J. (1964). *Electrochim. Acta*, **9**, 1429.
Allen, M. J. (1966a). *Electrochim. Acta*, **11**, 1.
Allen, M. J. (1966b). *Electrochim. Acta*, **11**, 7.
Allen, M. J. (1966c). *Electrochim. Acta*, **11**, 15.
Allen, M. J. (1966d). *Electrochim. Acta*, **11**, 1503.
Allen, M. J. (1967a). *Electrochim. Acta*, **12**, 563.
Allen, M. J. (1967b). *Electrochim. Acta*, **12**, 569.
Allen, M. J. (1967c). *Curr. Mod. Biol.*, **1**, 116.
Allen, M. J. (1967d). *Curr. Mod. Biol.*, **1**, 177.

Allen, M. J. (1967e). *Curr. Mod. Biol.*, **1**, 181.
Allen, M. J., and Januszeski, R. L. (1964). *Electrochim. Acta*, **9**, 1423.
Allen, M. J., Bowen, R. J., Nicholson, M., and Vasta, B. M. (1963). *Electrochim. Acta*, **8**, 991.
Cannan, R. K., Cohen, B., and Clark, W. M. (1926). *U.S. Pub. Health Rep.*, Suppl., 55.
Cohn, M., and Horibata, K. (1959). *J. Bacteriol.*, **78**, 624.
Cuatrecasas, P., and Segal, S. (1966). *Science*, **153**, 549.
Dawes, E. A., and Foster, S. M. (1956). *Biochim. biophys. Acta*, **22**, 253.
Decourt, P. (1955). *Anesthesia*, **10**, 221.
Dixon, M., and Quastel, J. H. (1923). *J. Chem. Soc.*, **123**, 2943.
Dixon, M., and Webb, E. C. (1958). "Enzymes", p. 375. Academic Press, New York.
Ehrlich, P. (1885a). *Cent. Wissensch.*, **23**, 113.
Ehrlich, P. (1885b). "Das Sauerstoff-Bederfinis der organismus. Eine farben-analytische Studie". Berlin.
Endo, S. (1938). *Biochem. Z.*, **296**, 56.
Gillespie, L. J. (1920). *Soil Sci.*, **9**, 199.
Gottlieb, M. H. (1964). *J. Electrochem., Soc.*, **111**, 465.
Hewitt, L. F. (1950). "Oxidation-reduction Potentials in Bacteriology and Biochemistry". Williams and Williams and Wilkens Co., Baltimore.
Jordan, E., Yarmolinsky, M. B., and Kalckar, H. M. (1962). *Proc. natl. Acad. Sci. U.S.*, **48**, 32.
Keilin, D., and Hartree, R. (1939). *Proc. Roy. Soc.*, **B 127**, 167.
Kornberg, H. L. (1961a). *In* "Biochemists' Handbook" (Ed. C. Long), pp. 535–538. Van Nostrand Co., Princeton, N.J.
Kornberg, H. L. (1961b). *In* "Biochemists' Handbook" (Ed. C. Long), pp. 538–540. Van Nostrand Co., Princeton, N.J.
Lepper, E., and Martin, C. J. (1930). *Brit. J. exp. Path.*, **11**, 140.
Lim, R., and Cohen, S. (1966). *J. Biol. Chem.*, **241**, 4304.
Lipmann, F. (1941). *Adv. Enzymol.*, **1**, 99.
Lynen, F. (1957). *Proc. Intern. Symposium Enzyme Chem.*, p. 25. Tokyo and Kyoto.
Monod, J., Cohen-Bazire, G., and Cohn, M. (1951). *Biochim. biophys. Acta*, **7**, 585.
Moraczewski, A. S., and Du Bois, K. P. (1959). *Arch. Intern. Pharmacodyn.*, **120**, 201.
Neilands, J. B. (1961). *In* "Biochemists' Handbook" (Ed. C. Long), p. 355. Van Nostrand Co., Princeton, N.J.
Paigen, K. (1966). *J. Bacteriol.*, **92**, 1394.
Potter, M. C. (1911). *Proc. Roy. Soc.*, **B 84**, 260
Potter, E. C. (1956). "Electrochemistry". Cleaver-Hume Press, London.
Stecker, H. J. (1961). *In* "Biochemists' Handbook" (Ed. C. Long), p. 447. Van Nostrand Co., Princeton, N.J.
Stier, T. J. B. (1936). *J. gen. Physiol.*, **19**, 461.
Thimann, K. V. (1963). "The Life of Bacteria", 2nd ed., p. 509. McMillan, New York.
Umbreit, W. M. (1960). "Metabolic Maps", Vol. 2, p. 3. Burgess Publishing Co., Minneapolis.
Wang, C. H., Stern, I., Gilmore, C. M., Klingsoyr, S., Reed, D. J., Bialy, J. J., Christensen, B. E., and Cheldelin, N. H. (1958). *J. Bacteriol.*, **76**, 207.
Wood, W. A. (1961). *In* "The Bacteria" (Ed. I. C. Gunsalus and R. Y. Stanier), Vol. 2, p. 85. Academic Press, New York.
Yudkin, J. (1935). *Biochem. J.*, **29**, 1130.

CHAPTER X

Microcalorimetry

W. W. FORREST

The Australian Wine Research Institute, Glen Osmond, South Australia.

I. INTRODUCTION

When microbiological degradations take place in natural systems, one of the most obvious changes occurring is heat production. Indeed, in thermally insulating materials, such as hay and wool, the temperature increase from such degradations may lead eventually to spontaneous combustion. Such gross microbial thermogenesis is, of course, outside the scope of microcalorimetry, but the strikingly obvious correlation of heat production with metabolic activity led to interest in such measurements at an early stage in the development of microbiology. (Microcalorimetry is the study of small heat changes, not necessarily with small quantities of material.)

However, the earliest measurements were made on a grand scale. Dubrunfaut (1856) studied heat production during alcoholic fermentation by measuring a large temperature increase in a vat containing 21,000 litres of material; the work was repeated on a more modest scale by Bouffard (1895) using a Bertholet calorimeter of 1 litre capacity. Bouffard made careful analyses and applied the necessary corrections in his calculations so that he obtained essentially the correct value for the enthalpy change involved in the fermentation of glucose to alcohol. There followed several microcalorimetric studies that approached the subject mainly from the qualitative point of view. This earlier work has been summarized in a review by Peterson and Wilson (1931).

These earlier workers were handicapped by the limitations of their apparatus and often inadequate definition of experimental conditions. The work that has subsequently been cited most frequently is that of Bayne-Jones and Rhees (1929), which showed that more heat was produced by each bacterial cell in the earlier stages of growth of a culture than during the later stages. However there has been controversy both over the observations themselves and over some of the later interpretations based on these experiments (Rahn, 1932; Stoward, 1962; Forrest and Walker, 1964).

With the development of modern apparatus, it became possible to show that thermogenesis in microbial cultures was systematically reproducible and characteristic of the particular organisms and medium (Prat, 1963). Recent developments have been mainly concerned with placing these studies on a more quantitative basis, and particularly in correlating the observed heat production with thermodynamic data (Battley, 1960; Forrest et al., 1961; Belaich, 1962; Boivinet, 1964; Forrest, 1967a; Belaich, et al., 1968).

From the point of view of energetics, it has long been accepted that calorimetry of living organisms gives an index of the complex processes of metabolic activity (Blaxter, 1962). In addition to this, the factors affecting the microcalorimetric behaviour of micro-organisms have now been defined in some detail and related to thermodynamic quantities; as these factors vary at different phases of the growth cycle it will be necessary to consider these phases individually, together with some thermodynamic background information.

II. THERMODYNAMIC AND KINETIC CONSIDERATIONS

A. Heat changes in biological reactions

Since different substances have different amounts of energy, the total energy of the products of a reaction will be different from the total energy of the reactants, so that the process will be accompanied by an absorption or liberation of energy in the form of heat. The difference in energy depends only on the initial and final states of the system†; it is independent of the pathway of the reaction, no matter how complex the intermediate steps

† The term "system" is used in the thermodynamic sense of a defined amount of matter containing definite quantities of given substances.

may be. Calorimetry is concerned with the measurement of such changes, and this statement of the first law of thermodynamics in its application to calorimetry is frequently called the Law of Hess.

This difference in energy is expressed as different thermodynamic parameters depending on the state of the system; however in biological systems, the reaction can be considered to take place in solution both at constant pressure and constant volume, so that thermodynamic differences of definition between energy and enthalpy can be disregarded and the change in energy content accompanying a reaction considered to be the change in enthalpy or heat of reaction, ΔH. This quantity, ΔH, then corresponds to the experimentally measured heat evolution, Q, during a reaction in an isolated system in which no external work is done, with the convention that an exothermic reaction corresponds to a decrease in energy, so that ΔH is negative. The amount of heat evolved is proportional to n the number of moles of reaction which have taken place—

$$Q = -n\Delta H \tag{1}$$

or where several simultaneous reactions occur the total heat produced is the sum of the individual processes—

$$Q = -\sum_0^k n_j \Delta H_j \tag{2}$$

(subscripts 0 to k characterize the k internal processes occurring, n_j is the number of moles of reaction j that have occurred since time zero and ΔH_j is its heat of reaction/mole).

Since *in vitro* calorimetric experiments are in principle performed in isolated systems, energy cannot be transferred out of the system; coupled reactions within the system enter into the summation above, so that calorimetry gives information directly only about the total energy change within the system, and coupled reactions can be detected only by the way in which they modify the end-products of the reactions occurring and so influence the total energy change.

Living organisms do the work required of them by utilizing the free energy of chemical reactions; the heat produced during metabolism has a component representing that fraction of the free energy change, ΔF, which is unavailable to the organisms for the performance of work. The other component of the heat production is due to entropy change, ΔS, and cannot be employed for useful work. In thermodynamic terms, if the system is not isolated so that it can perform external work, that is, can transfer energy other than heat out of the system, the observed heat production is modified according to the amount of energy transferred. These quantities are simply related—

$$\Delta H = \Delta F + T\Delta S \tag{3}$$

where T is the absolute temperature. A detailed discussion of this aspect of heat production is given by Wilkie (1960).

Determinations of such free-energy changes are not directly obtainable from calorimetric measurements, though calorimetric information is often used in indirect calculations of free-energy values and thermodynamic efficiencies of reactions (Wilkie, 1960). However from equation (3) it is seen that ΔH is correlated with the change in entropy, and the approximation can be made (Prigogine, 1961) that the rate of internal generation of entropy within the system is proportional to the rate of heat production—

$$\frac{\mathrm{d}Si}{\mathrm{d}t} \simeq \frac{1}{T}\left(\frac{\mathrm{d}Q}{\mathrm{d}t}\right)_{pT} \tag{4}$$

where the subscripts pT indicate that the reactions take place at constant pressure and temperature.

For simultaneous reactions, the entropy changes in the individual reactions can be summed as in the case of the heats of simultaneous reactions (equation 2), and coupled reactions can be shown to modify the total entropy production and so the observed value of $\mathrm{d}Q/\mathrm{d}t$. A great deal of calorimetric study of living organisms has been based on this premise (Stoward, 1962; Forrest and Walker, 1964), but interpretation of the results must be made with great care since the approximation involved in equation (4) is often a poor one.

In principle then, calorimetry is a sensitive indicator of the energy changes in biological systems, giving information about the rates and extent of reactions, no matter how complex the processes occurring. Since any chemical or physical process will be accompanied by an enthalpy change, the method is completely general. It might seem that there would be considerable difficulty in interpreting results, since resolution of the processes taking place would become impossibly complex in living organisms. However, the practical situation is not usually so complex as it at first sight appears; although a greatly reduced precision must be accepted when compared with accurately defined physicochemical systems, there is often a predominance of a few simple reactions, so that quite accurate correlations between the observed heat production and the major reaction products can be demonstrated. Even in studies on the higher animals, it has repeatedly proved possible to obtain agreement to about 1% between the experimentally measured heat production and the calculated heats of reaction based on heats of combustion of substrates and analysis of respiratory gases (Blaxter, 1962).

In micro-organisms, evidence is now accumulating that shows that heat production during metabolism may be derived almost entirely from catabolism, and that anabolic processes usually modify this catabolically derived heat by a very small amount (Morowitz, 1960; Boivinet, 1964; Senez and Belaich, 1965).

B. Analysis of data

1. Calculation of heats of reaction

Since calorimetry gives the sum of ΔH for all the reactions taking place, the most satisfactory test for the complete definition of the system is the correlation of a calculated value of ΔH for the proposed metabolic scheme with the observed heat production.

Details of the method of calculation of ΔH for a specified reaction from published thermodynamic data are given by Bichowsky and Rossini (1936). The basic calculation is straightforward; it is necessary to define as accurately as possible the state and concentrations of reactants and products, to determine the heats of formation of all products and to subtract from the total of these the sum of the heats of formation of all reactants. Care is necessary in accurate definition, since the calculated value of ΔH is a small difference between large numbers. It is convenient to sub-divide the categories of reactions.

(a) *Catabolic reactions*. Consider as example the homolactic fermentation of glucose. The basic reaction may be defined as—

$$C_6H_{12}O_6 \quad \rightarrow 2CH_3.CHOH.COOH; \qquad \Delta H - 25 \cdot 8 \text{ kcal/mole} \quad (5)$$
(mutarotated, aqueous)   (aqueous)

All the thermodynamic information necessary for this calculation is available from published data (Forrest *et al.*, 1961). In reactions of this type, ΔH may be assumed not to vary significantly with temperature over the physiological range. In many cases, data may be available from internally self-consistent standard tables of heats of formation (Bichowsky, 1929; Bichowsky and Rossini, 1936; Rossini *et al.*, 1961).

(b) *Anabolic reactions*. In microbial growth, synthetic reactions are very obvious. It is somewhat surprising that in most cases the contribution of anabolism to the observed heat production turns out to be insignificant. Consider the growth of *Streptococcus lactis*, where catabolism proceeds according to equation (5). The catabolism of 1 mole of glucose by the Embden—Meyerhof pathway produces 2 moles of adenosine triphosphate (ATP), which is used to synthesize 20 g of new cellular material (Bauchop and Elsden, 1960). The enthalpy of growth, the heat of reaction associated with this synthesis, has been calculated; even in minimal medium its value is $-0 \cdot 12$ kcal./g of bacterial cells, and in a rich complex medium it approaches zero (Morowitz, 1960). Thus the synthetic reactions taking place during growth would be expected to contribute at most $-2 \cdot 4$ kcal. compared with -26 kcal./mole from the corresponding catabolic reaction.

Several attempts have been made to measure the enthalpy of growth on complex media; these have been unable to detect it, and it has been concluded that the quantity is too small to measure (Boivinet, 1964; Senez and Belaich, 1965). Calculations indicate that production of entropy by the cells is the major thermodynamic flux during growth. (Morowitz, 1968; Forrest, 1970).

(c) *Secondary reactions.* Difficulties have arisen in many cases in analysis of results because of inadequate definition of the experimental conditions, so that very significant secondary effects not directly concerned with the main reaction have been overlooked. Thus Sturtevant (1962) has commented that neglect of definition of ionic states and of suitable buffer corrections detracts from the value of much of the earlier calorimetry of biochemical reactions.

In an actual fermentation, the medium is buffered around neutral pH, so that in addition to the main reaction (equation 5) we have, depending on the buffer, some neutralization such as—

$$CH_3CHOH\ COOH + HPO_4{}^{2-} \rightleftharpoons CH_3CHOH\ COO^- + H_2PO_4{}^- \qquad (6)$$

In such a situation, the heat of ionization, ΔH_i will depend markedly on temperature and ionic strength. ΔH_i for phosphate buffer may vary from -4 to $+3$ kcal./mole over a small range of temperature and ionic strength (Bernhard, 1956), so that small errors in the assumptions made may considerably upset calculated values of ΔH_i. Many other ionization reactions behave similarly (Harned and Owen, 1958). Under these conditions experimental blank determinations would seem more satisfactory.

Other secondary effects may also introduce considerable errors. For example, the passage of gases through the calorimeter is a procedure to be avoided wherever possible. The heats of hydration of CO_2 and ionization of H_2CO_3 are large (Roughton, 1941), and evaporation of water also produces large heat effects. Again the only certain rule regarding such effects is that very careful blank experiments are necessary.

Note, however, that these secondary processes may sometimes be turned to advantage; by choosing the correct buffer it is often possible to augment a small primary heat effect considerably.

A detailed thermodynamic calculation for the enthalpy change in the alcoholic fermentations with a good description of the corrections that should be considered is given by Battley (1960).

2. Kinetic calculations

Microbial metabolism is a rate process, and in general follows straight-forward kinetic laws (Dean and Hinshelwood, 1966). Accordingly, kinetic analyses of heat production records allow the most satisfactory determination of rates and quantities of experimentally measured heat production. Since the amount of heat produced may be taken as equivalent to the extent of reaction, standard kinetic treatments may be applied. In growth experiments, the usual type of semi-logarithmic plot of log Q against time is normally satisfactory. In many situations, extrapolation techniques specifically developed for use in calorimetric studies of rate processes by Sturtevant (1945) are of value. Calorimetric records are subject to various perturbations from trivial effects such as the heat of mixing when reagents are added to the calorimeter vessel. By measuring and characterizing the main course of the unperturbed reaction, it is often possible to extrapolate out these artifacts, so that the kinetic analysis gives values for both rate and total heat for the process. Indeed in certain long-continued processes (see Section IVC) where neither the initial nor final states of the system can be measured, but only a portion of the reaction can be observed, such extrapolation procedures are the only practical method of accurate analysis (Walker and Forrest, 1964).

Kinetic information is probably of most use however in obtaining a great deal of non-thermodynamic data; such questions as inhibition of metabolism (Walker, 1965), Michaelis constants for glucose permeation (Belaich et al., 1968), rates of attack on different substrates (Walker and Forrest, 1964) are all basically dependent on specialized kinetic treatment.

3. Units and calibration

Modern calorimetric technique consists finally in referring the observed heat production back to a standard source of heat production; it is the practice almost invariably to use electrical energy as the standard, since the rate of heat input can be readily varied to be comparable with the process under study, and electrical quantities can be timed and measured with high precision. The primary unit of energy then is the joule (i.e., the product of volts × amperes × seconds). To accord with chemical usage this is converted to calories defined in terms of the primary unit as—

$$1 \text{ calorie} = 4 \cdot 183 \text{ joules} \qquad (7)$$

The use of known reactions to calibrate an instrument may be valuable as a secondary standard, but there is no general agreement on a satisfactory reaction. According to Skinner (1962) few reactions have been sufficiently well defined thermochemically to provide an alternative of certified accuracy comparable with electrical calibration even of moderate precision.

III. APPARATUS

In the past it has been quite common for each experimenter to build a specialized calorimeter for his own particular requirements. As a result, the literature contains a very large number of descriptions of calorimeters. Discussion is therefore necessarily restricted here to a few representative instruments satisfactory for microbial studies. Since microbial metabolism is a rate process, its study lies in the most technically difficult area of microcalorimetry, reaction calorimetry. General principles of design and operation of reaction calorimeters have been discussed by Skinner *et al.* (1962). This is a very full treatment, much of which is directly applicable to microbiological studies.

The biggest single problem in the study of slow reactions is to maintain instrumental stability for long periods; to achieve this stability, calorimeters that have been used for microbial studies operate on the twin calorimeter system introduced by Joule. Basically, such instruments consist of two vessels made as nearly as possible identical contained within the same jacket. Measurements are made by comparison of the temperature or some function of it between the two vessels, so that long-term drifts are largely cancelled since both vessels are equally affected.

In addition to this general requirement for stability, several specialized requirements are necessary to allow microbiological manipulations. There should be provision for stirring the medium at least intermittently; a controlled atmosphere must be maintained in fermentation studies, it should be possible to sterilize the vessels, and provision should be made for addition of reagents during the course of an experiment. For convenience in operation, a system of continuous recording is desirable. Within these basic principles, satisfactory instruments vary widely in design.

A. Adiabatic calorimeters

The classical type of adiabatic microcalorimeter depends on isolating the reaction vessel as completely as possible from its environment so that errors due to heat leakage are minimized and the greatest possible temperature rise is produced in the reaction vessel. Electrical heating is applied to the identical balance vessel so that it maintains the same temperature as the reaction vessel. In a design suitable for microbial studies (Figs. 1–4) (Forrest, 1961; Forrest *et al.*, 1964) heating is arranged to operate continuously through a feedback control circuit so that any heat produced by microbial metabolism in the reaction vessel is continuously balanced by electrical heating. The quantity of electrical energy supplied to maintain balance is continuously recorded, but temperature is not measured directly. The temperature sensors in such apparatus are usually resistance thermometers or thermistors. In such a system the electrical power supplied is the

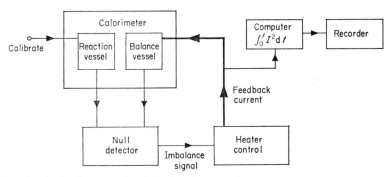

FIG. 1. Block diagram of adiabatic microcalorimeter.

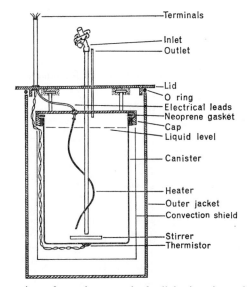

FIG. 2. Cross-section of reaction vessel of adiabatic microcalorimeter.

time integral of the square of the feedback current, where R is the resistance of the calorimeter heater and V is the voltage applied to the heater

$$Q = \int_0^t \frac{V^2}{R} \cdot \mathrm{d}t$$

This is a comparatively difficult electrical measurement to make, and quite elaborate devices have been necessary in the past to evaluate the integral (Buzzell and Sturtevant, 1951). Modern computing techniques have overcome this difficulty in evaluation, but the system has not been generally adopted, and there is no instrument of this type available commercially.

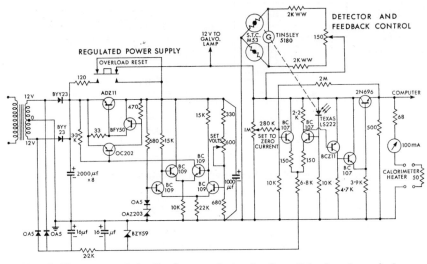

FIG. 3. Detector and feedback control circuits for adiabatic microcalorimeter.

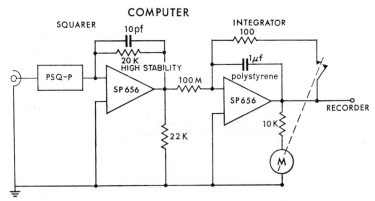

FIG. 4. Computing circuit for adiabatic microcalorimeter. Special components; Philbrick PSQ–P, quadratic transconductor; Philbrick SP656, operational amplifier (both Philbrick Researches, Dedham, Mass, U.S.A.); M—Master controller 0–1 mA with upper limit relay (Master instruments, Sydney, Australia).

A good deal of information is available about methods of handling experimental data obtained with this type of reaction calorimeter (Sturtevant, 1945; Buzzell and Sturtevant, 1951).

B. Thermal fluxmeters

The second main class of instrument is not strictly a calorimeter in the classical sense, but a thermal fluxmeter or "heat-burst" instrument. Such instruments have been exhaustively described by their developers (Calvet, 1962, 1963; Benzinger and Kitzinger, 1963; Benzinger, 1965). Instead of the reaction vessel being isolated, heat is allowed to flow along a controlled path to a heat sink, and its rate of passage detected by monitoring the temperature gradient along the path. The measuring element in such calorimeters is a multi-junction thermocouple (up to 10,000 electrolytically formed junctions have been employed) and the thermopile is also the controlled path through which heat passes (Fig. 5). For maximum stability, the twin-calorimeter principle is used and the measuring element of the reaction vessel compared with that of an identical balance vessel. The record produced is that of the rate of heat flow dQ/dt.

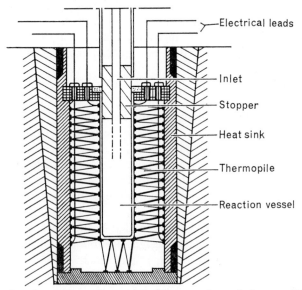

FIG. 5. Section through reaction vessel of Calvet microcalorimeter. (From Calvet and Prat, 1963.)

The Calvet instrument has been widely used in microbiological work. The instrument may be operated isothermally, as there is provision for compensation of the heat evolution in a reaction by the Peltier effect. (When the junctions of the thermopile are maintained at different temperatures, an e.m.f. is produced; conversely when a current is applied to a thermopile, one set of junctions becomes hotter and the other set cooler. The direction and magnitude of this temperature gradient depends on the polarity and magnitude of the impressed current. This is the Peltier effect.) The instrument is designed as a general-purpose microcalorimeter, so that modifications to the standard design have been found necessary for specialized microbiological studies. Thus Belaich *et al.* (1968) made provision for stirring of their calorimeter vessels and Grangetto (1963) incorporated special vessels to allow passage of air without disturbing the thermal equilibrium. For many aerobic experiments passage of air is unnecessary, as the high sensitivity of the instrument will allow measurements of aerobic growth on the O_2 dissolved in the medium. Detailed analyses of its perform-ance under various operating conditions have been published (Calvet, 1963). The instrument is available commercially; the manufacturers are Etablis-sements D.A.M., 6 Avenue Sidoine Apollinaire, Lyon 5e, France.

There is as yet no published data describing the use of the Benzinger instrument in microbiological studies. However, it has been satisfactorily used in studies of synchronous growth (J. Binford, personal communica-tion). This instrument also has a short thermal lag and provision for stirring as required. Calibration of the instrument is by a known reaction. This instrument is manufactured by Beckman Instruments, Palo Alto, California, U.S.A.

A heat-flow instrument of rather different design is that of Monk and Wadsö (1968). The instruments previously described have employed an isolated sample of the reactants, but the instrument of Monk and Wadsö operates on a flow system, so that it can be coupled to a large external reaction vessel, as for example a continuous-culture fermenter, so that addition of reagents or sampling can be performed outside the calorimeter without disturbance of the calorimetric record. Thermal equilibrium is maintained by passage of the reaction mixture through a heat exchanger before its passage through the calorimeter. The heat flow out of the reaction vessel is then measured with a thermopile as in the other heat-flow instru-ments, and dQ/dt is recorded. This design appears very suitable for microbial studies in continuous-culture systems. The sensitivity is comparable with the other instruments described and electrical calibration is employed. The instrument is manufactured by LKB-Produkter AB, Stockholm-Bromma, Sweden. A flow cell for the Benzinger microcalorimeter is also available from Beckman Instruments.

All the instruments described have rather a slow response time; Calvet's (1963) analysis shows the type of response to be expected for a rapid process. All the heat evolved is measured; the thermal lag affects only the time course of the record (Fig. 6). This thermal lag is a limitation inherent in the design of calorimeters; the adiabatic instrument is somewhat better in this respect than the heat-flow type, since measurement does not depend on establishing a thermal flux, but the best that can be achieved with heat-flow apparatus of the types described is a half-time of response, τ, of about 2 min. The kinetic study of more rapid reactions requires different specialized apparatus and has received little attention in microbiological systems, though there is evidence (Section IVB) that important reactions may occur in this time range. An instrument suitable for the study of rapid processes in the time range from a few seconds to a few minutes has been described by Berger *et al.* (1968) but is not at present commercially available.

For comparatively crude measurements, a Dewar flask and thermometer, or its modern equivalent, can still be used (Stoward, 1962). The biggest drawback of such instruments is their large thermal inertia, which makes them unsatisfactory as reaction calorimeters for any precise work.

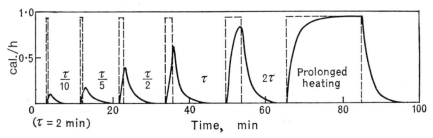

FIG. 6. Response of Calvet microcalorimeter (with response time, τ, 2 min) to pulses of constant thermal power applied for heating periods of $\tau/10$, $\tau/5$, $\tau/2$, τ, 2τ and for a long period. (From Calvet and Prat, 1963.)

C. Sensitivity of calorimetric apparatus

For microbiological work, it is desirable to know the sensitivity in terms of various metabolites as well as in terms of calories.

Consider as an example the Calvet microcalorimeter: at the highest sensitivity standard instruments give an output of about 300 mm deflection of the pen of a strip-chart recorder for a heat flow of 1 cal./h from a 10 ml sample. There is some zero drift at this highest sensitivity, but $0 \cdot 01$ cal./h is very easily detectable. In anaerobic glycolysis (equation 5) this corresponds to a detectable rate of change in glucose concentration of about $0 \cdot 3$ μmoles/ml/h. The most favourable case is the complete oxidation of glucose to CO_2 and water; here the sensitivity to glucose is $0 \cdot 01$ μmoles/ml/h, and towards O_2 $0 \cdot 1$ μmole/ml/h. It is obvious that for a given reaction, the sensitivity depends primarily on the enthalpy change of the reactions taking place.

The absolute sensitivity of the adiabatic calorimeter, which is designed to handle larger volumes, is lower than that of the Calvet instrument, $0 \cdot 5$ cal./h from a 250 ml sample, but its sensitivity expressed as concentration changes is the same as that of the Calvet microcalorimeter.

D. Operation of apparatus

To illustrate the method of operation, representative experiments will be described in some detail.

13

1. *Growth with limited energy source under anaerobic conditions*

Apparatus

Calvet microcalorimeter with glass vessels to contain 10 ml.

Organism

Streptococcus lactis (strain—Institut Mérieux)

Medium

Tryptone	0·5 g
Yeast extract	0·5 g
KH₂PO₄	2·0 g
Na₂HPO₄.12H₂O	7·1 g
Mineral salts solution (described by Bauchop and Elsden 1960)	2·5 ml
Glucose	0·5 g
Distilled water	1 litre

Sterilize the glucose separately from the other ingredients and then add it to the final concentration shown. The temperature of growth should be 30°C.

(a) *Procedure.* The glass vessels were removed from the calorimeter. The balance vessel was filled with 10 ml of water, stoppered and replaced. The reaction vessel was filled with 10 ml of medium and sealed with a stopper through which passed a hypodermic needle; this vessel was then autoclaved for sterilization, together with a tuberculin syringe with needle. After sterilization and addition of glucose, the vessel was held in a water bath at 30°C, the needle in the stopper connected to a vacuum system, the vessel evacuated and flushed three times with argon. Meanwhile, the tuberculin syringe was filled with an inoculum of freshly grown cells of the organism (0·1 ml containing about 30 μg cells). The syringe was connected to the reaction vessel, which was then carefully dried, and the whole assembly was placed in position in the calorimeter.

To obtain a stable base-line for the instrumental record, it was then necessary to wait until thermal equilibrium had been reached. This requires at least 3 h, but it is preferable, if the organisms will tolerate the delay, to allow the equilibration to take place overnight. When thermal stability was reached, the automatic recording system was switched on and the plunger of the syringe was depressed by the operation of a long rod extending outside the constant-temperature jacket of the calorimeter, so that the inoculum was added. This instrument has no provision for stirring so that rapid addition through a fine hypodermic needle assists in the dispersal of the inoculum. For this experiment the lowest sensitivity of the instrument was adequate. This corresponded to a full-scale deflection of the pen of the recorder of about 0·6 cal./h.

(b) *Results.* On addition of the inoculum, a transient pulse of heat evolution arising from mechanical work was observed, then there was essentially no detectable heat evolution till exponential growth began after about 3 h lag. The rate of heat evolution then rose exponentially to a maximum and fell back sharply to zero after all the energy source had been used (Fig. 7).

It is impractical to remove samples from the reaction vessel during the course of an experiment, so that parallel incubation is necessary if sampling is to be carried out. In the present experiment, a growth yield was obtained by measuring the final optical density of the suspension in the reaction vessel.

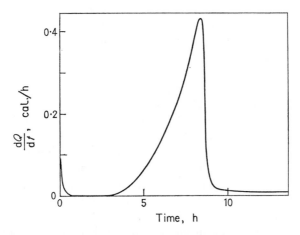

FIG. 7. Rate of heat production from a growing culture of *S. lactis* with growth limited by the energy source, glucose. (From Boivinet, 1964.)

(c) *Analyses.* This instrument gives a plot of the differential rate of heat production $\dfrac{dQ}{dt}$. To obtain growth rate and growth lag, a semi-logarithmic plot of the data was made; to obtain total heat, $\int_0^t Q \,.\, dt$, graphical integration was necessary. The calculated data gave a specific growth rate of 0·030 min⁻¹, a total heat of 0·80 cal., a total yield of 0·54 mg dry wt of cells and a molar growth yield Y_G of 19·5.

2. *Degradation of added energy source by a natural system containing a mixed population of organisms, (ovine rumen contents).*

Apparatus

Adiabatic calorimeter modified to allow the study of semi-solid materials. Modifications consisted of a wide-bore inlet for introduction of samples, and stirring by oscillation of the whole reaction vessel (Forrest *et al.*, 1964). Maintain the temperature at 39°C.

Sample

Rumen contents from a sheep fed 8 hours previously on a daily diet of 500 g each of wheaten hay chaff and lucerne chaff.

(a) *Procedure.* As the sample was in active fermentation at the time of sampling, the procedure was designed to allow its introduction into the calorimeter as rapidly as possible with the minimum of disturbance.

The reaction and balance vessels were each filled with 250 ml of water. The apparatus was allowed to stand overnight to permit the attainment of thermal equilibrium. The following morning, the automatic recording system was switched on and a base-line drift obtained (Forrest, 1961). Meanwhile, a sample of rumen contents had been taken from a sheep fitted with a rumen cannula. A weighed sample of approximately 250 ml was brought to the exact temperature of the calorimeter (39°C) with the aid of a sensitive resistance thermometer (full-scale deflection 0·1°C). The water filling of the reaction vessel was then withdrawn and the rumen contents added in its place. The vessel was briefly gassed with a mixture of nitrogen–40% CO_2 and then sealed.

Fine adjustments to regain thermal balance between the contents of the reaction vessel and the balance vessel were made with the electrical heaters of the reaction or balance vessels as necessary to supply small quantities of heat. After balance was reached, the automatic balancing and recording systems were operated to give a continuous record of the integrated heat production of the sample. The whole procedure from sampling to the beginning of a record took about 30 min. Meanwhile a syringe was filled with the cellobiose solution; this was brought to the temperature of the calorimeter and connected to the inlet of the reaction vessel. After a sufficient length of record of the normal fermentation had been obtained, the cellobiose was injected into the reaction vessel and recording continued till all the cellobiose had been degraded.

A sample of the rumen contents was weighed and dried at 105°C to constant weight. The metabolic activity of the rumen contents was related to this percentage of dry matter.

Low instrumental sensitivity was adequate as the rate of heat evolution was large. The full-scale deflection for the integrated record was 5 cal. in this experiment.

(b) *Results.* The "endogenous" heat production for the degradation of carbohydrates naturally present in the sample followed an exponential decay course. When cellobiose was added, a constant rate of heat production from the degradation of cellobiose was superimposed on the exponential. This additional heat production continued till all the added cellobiose had been catabolized, then the rate of heat production reverted to the "endogenous" rate (Fig. 8).

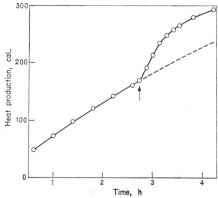

Fig. 8. Rate of heat production from rumen contents, with 2 mmoles of cellobiose added at time indicated by the arrow.

(c) *Analysis.* The calorimeter gives a record of the total heat produced, $\int_0^t Q \cdot dt$. A kinetic analysis was necessary to obtain the rate of heat production; an exponential function was fitted to the recorded data for the period before addition of cellobiose. This was done by computer using a process of successive iteration. Having obtained the best fit exponential function the "endogenous" rate during the period of catabolism of cellobiose could be calculated by extrapolation, so that this could be subtracted from the total heat production to give the rate and heat production contributed to the total by the degradation of cellobiose.

Analysis of the data shown in Fig. 8 gave the rate constant of the normal degradation as $0\cdot331$ h^{-1}, the rate of cellobiose degradation as 156 cal./h and the total heat for degradation of the 2 mmoles of added cellobiose as 56 calories. The total heat for the degradation of 2 mmoles of cellobiose calculated from thermodynamic data is 240 cal. (Forrest, 1967a), and the biochemical implications of this discrepancy are discussed in Section IVC.

IV. CALORIMETRIC BEHAVIOUR OF MICRO-ORGANISMS

A. Growing cells in pure culture

1. *Exponential growth limited by energy source*

In the usual experiments on microbial growth, a small number of cells is used to inoculate a sterilized growth medium in the calorimeter. In most cases there is then no detectable heat evolution during the lag phase. At the end of the lag phase there is a period of transition when the catabolic activity of unit mass of cells and rate of cell division increase until they reach the high rates characteristic of cells undergoing exponential growth and then remain constant at this higher level during growth. The rate of

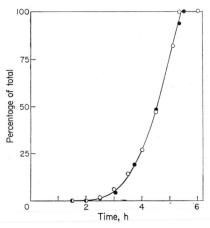

FIG. 9. Relationship between heat production, O, and dry weight of cells, ●, in a growing culture of *Streptococcus faecalis*, with growth limited by the energy source, glucose. Glucose fermented 1·8 mmoles; final bacterial dry wt. 27 mg; total heat produced 49 cal. Reproduced with permission from Forrest *et al.* (1961).

heat evolution also begins to increase exponentially concurrently with the synthesis of new cellular material as the cells divide (Fig. 9). During exponential growth, the rate of heat production per unit cell mass remains constant at the highest level reached by the cells. The rate of synthesis of new cellular material, degradation of energy source, appearance of products of catabolism and heat production are all accurately described by the same exponential function. This relationship has been most fully investigated with *S. faecalis* (Forrest and Walker, 1964), but similar experimental evidence is available with *St. lactis* (Boivinet, 1964) and *Zymomonas mobilis* (Belaich *et al.*, 1968) (Fig. 10). The finding that the rate of degradation of energy source is the same as the rate of heat production would be expected on the basis of equation (2).

As Dean and Hinshelwood (1966) emphasize, some properties of a suspension of growing organisms are best considered as related to the whole mass of the suspension, others are more readily interpreted as concerned with the individual cell or some related quantity. In the present case, in batch culture, most quantities in the culture are varying, but if, as the unit for the thermodynamic system defined earlier (Section IIA) we consider unit mass of cells, then the properties of such a unit mass can be described by time-invariant parameters (Forrest and Walker, 1964); this is the criterion for a steady state. It must be emphasized that this steady state is not directly comparable with the more usually defined steady state related to the proper-

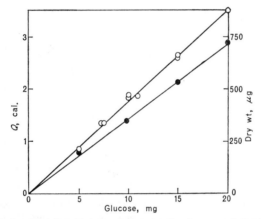

FIG. 10. Relationships between total heat evolved, $\bigcirc$, and final dry weight of organisms, $\bullet$, as a function of glucose consumed in glucose limited cultures of *Z. mobilis*. (After Belaich *et al.*, 1968.)

ties of the whole mass of the suspension observed in microbial growth in continuous culture. It is used in the restricted sense that it applies only to the defined unit mass of cells and not necessarily even to a defined number of cells (Forrest and Walker, 1962). It is concerned primarily with steady states of thermodynamic fluxes, including rate of production of entropy. However the finding that a steady state in batch culture is set up even in this restricted sense is of considerable assistance in analyses of the calorimetric data, as we may then consider microbial metabolism to operate preferentially at one of three well defined but widely different steady-state levels of activity, exponential growth corresponding to the highest level, catabolism by non-proliferating cells to the intermediate level, and endogenous metabolism to the lowest level (Forrest and Walker, 1964).

Heat production is usually undetectable in the lag phase, both because of the small inoculum normally used, and because of the considerable repression of catabolic activity which may be found in lag-phase cells. In *S. faecalis*, this ratio of activities between growing and lag phase cells may be as high as 8 : 1 for glycolysis (Forrest and Walker, 1964). In other organisms, the repression is not so marked; Belaich and Senez (1967) found that *Z. mobilis* doubled its catabolic activity during exponential growth. In this organism, measurable heat evolution may be observed during the lag phase from the time of inoculation (Fig. 11). There are two reasons for this, the high catabolic activity in the lag phase, and the higher absolute level of catabolic activity in *Z. mobilis* compared with other organisms. Comparative measurements (Forrest, 1967b) show that the rate of growth in *S. faecalis* is a little higher than in *Z. mobilis*, but that the

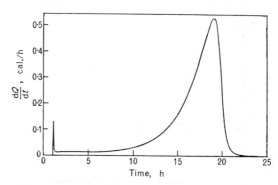

FIG. 11. Rate of heat production from a growing culture of *Z. mobilis* with growth limited by the energy source, glucose. (For Belaich and Senez, 1967.)

reverse is true of the rates of catabolism. This situation is a reflection of the different metabolic pathways and growth yields of the organisms, the Entner–Doudoroff pathway in *Z. mobilis* and the Embden–Meyerhof pathway in *S. faecalis* (Stouthamer, this Series, Vol. 1).

Further obvious differences in the behaviour of these organisms have been detected calorimetrically. If all other nutrients are present in adequate amounts so that the energy source becomes exhausted first, growth ceases completely. In the case of *S. faecalis* (Fig. 9) and *S. lactis* (Fig. 7), the Michaelis constant for the permeation of glucose is very low, so that the enzyme systems responsible for glycolysis remain saturated until the substrate is almost completely exhausted; the ensuing transition from this exponentially increasing rate of heat evolution to no detectable rate of heat production is very rapid. In contrast, with *Z. mobilis* grown with glucose as substrate, the heat evolution at the end of growth decreases quite gradually over a period as the substrate concentration decreases (Fig. 11). Belaich *et al.* (1968) have mathematically analysed this situation in detail. They have shown that the heat of reaction for each mole of glucose degraded and the yield of cells were not affected during this period of retardation; the only variable was in the kinetic description of the heat production, and this observed kinetic change was a function of the residual concentration of glucose (residual glucose was calculated from the proportion of the total enthalpy change that had taken place). From a double reciprocal plot of Lineweaver–Burk type, it was possible to obtain a Michaelis constant and V_{max} for glucose permeation in *Z. mobilis*. The great advantage of this calorimetric procedure over chemical assays was the high sensitivity and the possibility of obtaining a continuous record of catabolism which made calculations more reliable.

Thermograms obtained during the growth of *Saccharomyces cerevisiae* could be analysed similarly, but with *Escherichia coli* the decay to the state of no detectable heat production at the end of growth was extremely rapid, so that with this organism and the streptococci (Figs. 7 and 9) the affinity $(1/K_m)$ for glucose is too great for reliable determination by this method. The value for K_m for *Z. mobilis* calculated by Belaich *et al.* was $3 \cdot 1 \times 10^{-3}$M, compared with values of 10^{-5} to 10^{-6}M reported for other organisms (Horecker *et al.*, 1960; Knowles *et al.*, 1965). It seems then that the metabolism of *Zymomonas* is rather unusual in many details.

When exponential growth is limited by energy source, heat evolution ceases when the exogenous energy source is exhausted; such cells exhibit no calorimetrically detectable endogenous metabolism (Belaich and Senez, 1967; Belaich *et al.*, 1968; Figs. 7, 9 and 11). Under these circumstances, the observed heat evolution corrected for second-order effects correlates very well with the calculated value of enthalpy change for the catabolism of energy source to the observed products (Belaich, 1963; Grangetto, 1963; Boivinet, 1964; Belaich and Senez, 1967). Details of the procedure of calculation are given in Section IIB. In such experiments the enthalpy of growth is less than the experimental error of the measurements and so cannot be determined (Senez and Belaich, 1965).

When exponential growth takes place under optimal conditions in a nutritionally adequate medium, the energy available from catabolism of the energy source is fully coupled to synthesis of cellular material, except perhaps for a very small amount required for energy of maintenance (Pirt, 1965). The catabolism of sufficient energy source to produce 1 mole of ATP allows the synthesis of approximately 10 g of new cellular material (Bauchop and Elsden, 1960) when complex media provide the monomers for biosynthesis. As the heat of the reactions producing this quantity of ATP is defined by the metabolic pathway, the enthalpy change for the amount of the cata-

TABLE I

ΔH_b values

Organism	Energy source	Medium	Conditions	ΔH_bkcal./g	References
Streptococcus lactis	Glucose	Complex	Anaerobic	$-1 \cdot 51$	Boivinet, 1964
Aerobacter aerogenes	Glucose	Minimal	Aerobic	$-2 \cdot 62$	Grangetto, 1963
A. aerogenes	Succinate	Minimal	Aerobic	$-3 \cdot 82$	Grangetto, 1963

bolic reactions necessary to produce biosynthesis of unit mass of organisms ΔH_b, (Boivinet, 1964) is also defined. Boivinet's tables for these quantities in anaerobic growth of S. lactis show that ΔH_b is a convenient index of metabolic activity. However, ΔH_b varies widely with different media and growth conditions, so that it cannot be regarded as describing any fixed properties of the organisms. Typical values are given in Table I.

2. Growth limited by nutritional factors

In general, the decrease in the rate of cell division at the end of the phase of exponential growth is caused either by limitation of some constituent of the growth medium or by accumulation of toxic products. If an energy source is still present, but growth is restricted by limited availability of constituents of the medium, degradation of the energy source continues, but the catabolic activity of unit mass of organisms may be repressed so that heat evolution is now observed at a lower level. In aerobic organisms, O_2 limitation may be responsible, so that catabolism can change from an oxidative to a fermentative pathway; there are then corresponding very large changes in the products of catabolism and rates of heat production (Stoward, 1962).

The effect of phosphate limitation on catabolism in growing cells of Z. mobilis and E. coli has been studied by Senez and Belaich (1965). Calorimetry was employed to give an elegant demonstration of the change in catabolic activity. In this case, the effect is immediately and completely reversible; Senez and Belaich discuss the limitation in terms of control mechanisms for catabolism.

With a large excess of energy source, the shape of the thermogram is very characteristic. There is an initial period of exponential growth with a concurrent exponential rise in dQ/dt. then the growth rate declines and gradually ceases as the organisms enter the stationary phase. Meanwhile, the rate of heat production gradually declines also. In the case of S. lactis (Fig. 12), the pH of the medium is depressed by the lactic acid, which is the end-product of catabolism, and this pH drop depresses the growth rate.

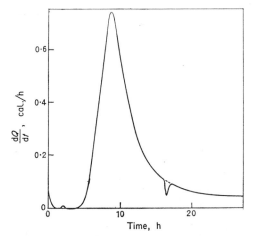

FIG. 12. Rate of heat production from a growing culture of *S. lactis* grown with excess energy source. (From Boivinet, 1964.)

More complex thermograms than those previously described may also be encountered (Prat, 1963); there may be secondary growth or subsequent endogenous metabolism after exogenous energy sources have been catabolized.

3. *Synthesis of storage materials and endogenous metabolism*

The decrease in growth rate at the end of exponential growth means that ATP is no longer required to drive growth at a high rate. Growth may then become partly energetically uncoupled (Senez, 1962) and the pool of ATP in the organisms may increase (Forrest and Walker, 1965a) so that ATP becomes available for syntheses not directly connected with the essential processes of growth; it is found in many organisms, that during this period reserve materials are accumulated (Hungate, 1963; Dawes and Ribbons, 1964). When the exogenous energy sources are finally exhausted after this period of accumulation of reserves, endogenous heat production may subsequently occur from degradation of these reserves. *E. coli*, which may accumulate large quantities of glycogen, can exhibit a substantial endogenous metabolism for long periods after growth has ceased (Fig. 13).

These storage materials are often polysaccharides formed by polymerization of some of the substrates added primarily as energy sources. Thus in arriving at any thermodynamic balance it is essential to carry out accurate assays for the products of catabolism; calculations based purely on postulated pathways may disagree seriously with the observed data. For example, Grangetto (1963) reported that *A. aerogenes*, which also accumulates reserve polysaccharides, gave excellent agreement between the observed and

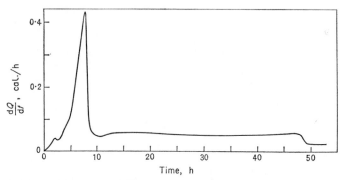

FIG. 13. Rate of heat production during growth with subsequent endogenous metabolism in a culture of *E. coli*. (From Senez and Belaich, 1965.)

calculated enthalpy change with succinate as energy source, but with glucose only about half as much heat was observed as would have been expected from the calculated enthalpy change.

4. *Growth in continuous culture*

With conventional calorimetric apparatus, measurements have been limited to experiments in batch culture. However, with the development of a suitable flow calorimeter (Section III) there seems no reason why growth studies could not be made in continuous culture systems. It should be possible to obtain precise energetic balances under the steady-state conditions for the whole mass of the suspension set up in continuous-culture systems, so that determinations of enthalpy of growth should be practicable. (The term "steady state" is here used in the usual sense, not as in the restricted definition of Section IVA 1.)

The application of microcalorimetry as a method of monitoring the processes taking place in continuous culture systems would also seem straightforward; since the method is capable of high sensitivity, small deviations from the normal conditions could be reliably detected.

B. Non-growing cells in pure culture

1. *Endogenous metabolism and energy of maintenance*

Organisms deprived of exogenous substrates may still exhibit substantial metabolic activity. The processes taking place are often difficult to characterize, particularly in the case of anaerobic organisms, where there may be no readily measurable chemical change. Microcalorimetry can be particularly useful in such a situation, since it is a completely general method of detecting metabolic activity.

S. faecalis in starved suspensions exhibits no detectable respiration, and no pH change occurs in the suspending medium, yet microcalorimetric measurements show that a considerable heat evolution occurs (Forrest and Walker, 1963) (Fig. 14). Environmental factors markedly affect this heat evolution, and the presence of endogenous metabolic activity is correlated with the ability of the organisms to degrade glucose. There is also a constant ATP pool in the organisms during the process, indicating that the energy made available during this endogenous metabolism is coupled to biologically useful functions by ATP (Forrest and Walker, 1965b).

The comparatively large amounts of heat involved indicate that the process supplying energy is unusual; there is no evidence for the type of reserve material often found, polysaccharides or polyhydroxybutyric acid being accumulated by the organisms. The only materials excreted into the

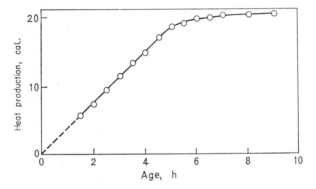

FIG. 14. Endogenous heat production by washed suspension of *S. faecalis* (450 mg of cells): gas phase, nitrogen. (From Forrest and Walker, 1963.)

suspending medium are amino-acids, yet the calorimetric data clearly show that the process occurring cannot be the hydrolysis of peptide bonds, which would account neither for the large amount of heat evolved nor the production of ATP.

Calorimetric measurements also indicated that the previous growth history of the organisms was of importance in allowing the laying down of reserve materials that could later be degraded during endogenous metabolism (Forrest and Walker, 1965a). Cells grown exponentially with adequate nutrition, but with the total cell yield limited by energy source, showed no subsequent endogenous metabolism at a level detectable by microcalorimetry (Figs. 7, 9 and 11). To allow subsequent endogenous heat production, it was necessary to grow the cells on a large excess of energy source.

The existence of endogenous metabolism at a level detectable by microcalorimetry is almost certainly a general property of micro-organisms. Many aerobic organisms exhibit endogenous respiratory activity, and substantial

endogenous heat production has been detected in anaerobic suspensions of
E. coli (Senez and Belaich, 1965) (Fig. 12). Since few endogenous reactions
have been characterized, calorimetry would seem particularly suited to
exploratory studies of endogenous metabolism.

2. *"Heat of dilution"*

This property seems to be analogous to endogenous metabolism, but little
is yet known about it. The effect was first reported by Boivinet and
Grangetto (1963) as a rapid, large heat evolution when a concentrated
suspension of *A. aerogenes* was added to a solution containing an energy
source. It was then considered to be due to the initial interaction between
bacteria and energy source; but more recent work (W. W. Forrest and
R. L. Berger, unpublished results) shows that the effect also occurs when
concentrated suspensions of *S. faecalis* and other bacteria are added to
an excess of the suspending medium in the absence of exogenous substrates.
The effect is thought possibly to be the initial response of the organisms to
adjusting their rate of endogenous metabolism to the changed conditions.
However the rise time for the heat evolution associated with the process is
about 30 sec, which is rather too rapid to be handled accurately by the usual
microcalorimeters, so that detailed characterization of the process has not
yet been attempted.

3. *Catabolism by washed suspensions*

When an exogenous substrate is added to a washed suspension of organisms, the heat production subsequently observed may have components due
to exogenous catabolism and endogenous metabolism. Not all of the added
exogenous material is necessarily catabolized, as there may be assimilation
of exogenous materials into the organisms (Clifton, 1963).

In many organisms, endogenous metabolism is not greatly influenced
by the presence of exogenous substrates (Clifton, 1963); there is some
evidence that endogenous metabolism may instead influence the rate of
exogenous catabolism (Ribbons and Dawes, 1963; Forrest and Walker,
1965b). In *Bacillus subtilis* (Clifton and Cherry, 1966) there is a considerable
degree of interaction between endogenous and exogenous metabolism.
Clifton and Church suggest that this interaction, which is not observed in
many other organisms, is related to the instability of *B. subtilis*. In interpretation of calorimetric data from experiments in washed suspensions, it
is therefore desirable to have an accurate assessment of the contribution
of endogenous metabolism.

Figure 15 shows the course of the heat production from glycolysis in a
washed suspension of *S. faecalis*. The contribution from endogenous
metabolism was determined before substrate was added. The rate of endo-

genous metabolism in this organism is small compared with the rate of exogenous catabolism, and remains constant for some hours, except in very dilute suspension, when it may decrease slightly during exogenous catabolism (Forrest et al., 1961). Having determined the rate of endogenous metabolism, this was subtracted from the total rate of heat production to give the nett rate of heat production from glycolysis.

The rates of glycolysis (Forrest and Walker, 1964) and heat production (Forrest et al., 1961) in this organism both accurately follow zero-order kinetics, so that the trivial initial effects of heat of mixing could be removed by extrapolation of the kinetic record back to the time of mixing (Section IIB 4). This situation of zero-order kinetics seems to apply quite generally, as the Michaelis constants for substrate permeation with many organisms

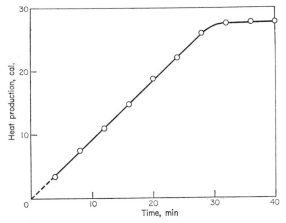

FIG. 15. Heat production from exogenous catabolism of glucose by a washed cell suspension of *Strep. faecalis*. (From Forrest et al., 1961.)

and many substrates are very low (Section IVA), so that the total heat production is related to the amount of substrate added, but the rate of heat production is linearly related to the concentration of bacteria in the suspension (Fig. 16) (Forrest et al., 1961). This relationship between rate of heat production and concentration of organisms holds in the case of *S. faecalis* only with cells grown on a medium containing excess of energy source, so that washed suspensions prepared from such cells possess calorimetrically detectable endogenous metabolism; cells without such endogenous metabolism rapidly lose their ability to catabolize glucose in washed suspension (Forrest and Walker, 1965b). Energy of maintenance then appears to be supplied by the endogenous metabolism that proceeds concurrently with experimental error as acidic products (Forrest et al., 1961); there is essentially no nett incorporation into cellular material. The situation shown in

Figs. 15 and 16 is the extreme case where no coupled reactions need be considered (Senez, 1962) in arriving at a thermodynamic balance for the enthalpy change and heat production during the catabolism of added substrate.

It would appear that a very good correspondence should be obtained in such a simple situation between these observed and calculated values of the enthalpy change, but even here some caution must be exercised. In glycolysis by *S. faecalis* the *observed* products were 95% lactic acid and 5% fatty acids (Forrest *et al.*, 1961). For the usual biochemical purposes this is a "homolactic" fermentation, but if we assume that the homolactic fermentation applies (equation 5), the calculated enthalpy change is $-25 \cdot 8$ kcal./mole. If, however, the other products are taken into account the calculated

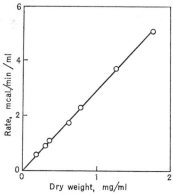

FIG. 16. Rate of fermentation of glucose by washed cell suspensions of *S. faecalis* as a function of bacterial concentration. (From Forrest *et al.*, 1961).

enthalpy change becomes $-29 \cdot 3$ kcal/mole, which gives excellent correspondence with the observed heat of reaction, $-29 \cdot 1$ kcal./mole.

In terms of irreversible thermodynamics, this situation of catabolism by resting cells corresponds to a steady state of metabolism at an intermediate level of activity (Forrest and Walker, 1964).

C. Mixed cultures. Natural systems

The kinetics and energetics of biochemical transformations brought about during the degradation of complex mixtures of natural materials by ill defined mixed populations of microbes such as occur in the rumen, sewage or soils are not easily studied by the techniques applicable to homogenous systems. The end products of degradation are heterogenous and accumulate in considerable quantities and the reactions usually go on slowly for long periods.

The microcalorimetric method is well suited to the study of these systems and has been successfully applied. Van Suchtelen (1931) carried out a series of calorimetric investigations on the microbial energetics of the soil, particularly in regard to the degradation of humus, and the method has more recently been applied to the ruminal fermentation both in the sheep (Walker and Forrest, 1964) and in cattle (Houpt, 1968).

The ruminal fermentation is a good example of these systems; here the natural substrates, mainly carbohydrates, are degraded to give the lower fatty acids (volatile fatty acids, VFA). Its study is important both for the energetic information that can be correlated with the energetic requirements of the whole animal, and for the information obtained about a natural mixed culture. There are difficulties in such studies; the peculiar physical properties of rumen ingesta make it necessary to design specialized apparatus for

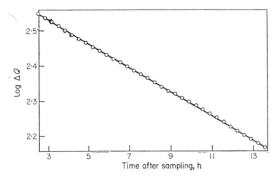

FIG. 17. Rate of heat production by a sample of rumen ingesta from a sheep. The microcalorimetric data were fitted to an exponential function by the method of Guggenheim (1926): Δt, 680 min; k, 0·076 h^{-1}. The total time covered by the plot is 1490 min. (From Walker and Forrest, 1964.)

calorimetric studies (Forrest *et al.*, 1964). Since the samples obtained from the rumen are actively fermenting at the time of introduction to the calorimeter and fermentation continues for a long period, the calorimetric observations must be confined to a small part of the complete degradation. Under these conditions, kinetic analysis becomes awkward (Section 11B 4) and specialized extrapolation procedures are necessary (Walker and Forrest, 1964).

In fact, the calorimetric data turn out to be remarkably simple; despite the very great number of concurrent reactions that must occur, the kinetics of heat production observed *in vitro* from samples of rumen contents are accurately of first order (exponential decay) for long periods (Fig. 17), and the rate of heat production of samples taken from different animals is closely similar; there is a variation between different samples, but this is correlated only with the amount of solid material in the sample and the type of dietary material. The system is strikingly regular in its behaviour, being strongly buffered and poised to maintain anaerobic conditions, though the bio-chemical controls on fermentation are not yet understood.

Because of this regular kinetic behaviour, it is readily possible to study the effect of perturbations of the system caused by additions of inhibitors or substrates. Figure 18 shows the effect on heat production of feeding a sheep and sampling immediately the food was ingested. The wheaten hay chaff fed contained a considerable proportion of readily soluble carbohy-drates, which were rapidly degraded; after this initial period of rapid cata-bolism, the rate declined to a level comparable with that shown in Fig. 17.

Within the limitations imposed by the ill defined nature of the substrates, it is also possible to correlate the observed heat production with thermo-dynamic calculations for ΔH (Forrest, 1967a), in the same way as has been

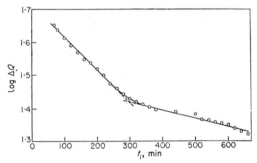

FIG. 18. Kinetic plot of heat production of rumen contents sampled immediately after feeding a sheep. Data plotted as in Fig. 17. (From Walker, 1965.)

done with pure cultures. The calculated enthalpy change for the degradation of 1 mole of glucose residue to 2 moles of VFA is -60.2 kcal., the observed heat evolution for production of 2 moles of VFA was -54 kcal., which is good agreement considering the assumptions necessary in making the calculations.

The exponential decay in the rate of heat production is the type of kinetic behaviour found in microbial degradations in pure culture when the sub-strate concentration is comparable with the Michaelis constants involved. Certainly, the normal pathway for cellulose degradation in the system does not show saturation behaviour, but if cellobiose, which is a normal inter-mediate in cellulose breakdown, is added then it is easily possible to saturate the pathway responsible for cellulose degradation. There is an immediate increase in the rate of heat production, and zero-order kinetics of the addi-tional heat production due to cellobiose degradation is then observed. This additional heat production is superimposed on the normal "endogenous" heat production occurring concurrently (Fig. 8). Detailed procedures for such experiments are set out in Section IIIC. From curves similar to Fig. 8, the Michaelis constant for cellobiose degradation in this system is about 10^{-5}M, suggesting that the overall exponential kinetics are due to low substrate concentrations.

The observed total heat from cellobiose added is however surprisingly low. When 2 mmoles of cellobiose was added to a sample of rumen contents, the total heat from this fermentation was -56 cal., in agreement with the degradation of only 1 mmole of glucose residue to give 2 mmoles of VFA (equation 9). Assay of the reaction mixture confirmed that in fact only 2 mmoles of VFA were formed, and showed a corresponding increase in microbial storage polysaccharides (W. W. Forrest and D. J. Walker, unpublished results); it then becomes obvious that the process occurring was the degradation of 0·5 mmole of cellobiose to yield 2 mmoles of VFA with the concurrent production of 3 mmoles of ATP (Walker, 1965); this ATP was then employed by the organisms to polymerize the remaining 1·5 mmoles of cellobiose. Polysaccharide storage has been demonstrated in pure cultures of rumen organisms (Hungate, 1963).

V. CONCLUSIONS

The factors influencing the microcalorimetric behaviour of micro-organisms are well understood, even in complex systems. Heat production is closely related to catabolic activity; anabolic processes usually make a very small contribution to the overall pattern of heat production, so that there seems little possibility that the techniques currently available will be of general use in the study of anabolic processes.

However, heat production is observed to take place in steady states of catabolism (in terms of thermodynamic fluxes) at widely different levels of activity. These steady states are defined by time-independent parameters, so that the metabolic behaviour of the organisms is predictable and obeys regular kinetic laws. Under these conditions, changes in the behaviour of the system are readily detectable and comparative metabolic studies are most readily performed.

The kinetic definition of rates of heat production is simplest at the lower levels of activity, endogenous metabolism and catabolism by non-proliferating cells, where both the concentration of organisms and the rate of heat production may remain constant for long periods. At the highest level of catabolic activity during exponential growth the situation is more complex, though even here the kinetic expression for growth is simple, and the catabolic activity of unit mass of cells remains constant; however, in addition to the record of heat production, a measure of the increasing mass of microbial cells is necessary to describe the system fully.

In the periods of transition between these steady states, as in the transition from exponential growth to stationary phase, the catabolic activity of the organisms may vary widely as a function of time, so that accurate description of the system is more difficult and more information is necessary to interpret the results.

At any stage of catabolic activity, knowledge of the chemistry of the reactions occurring is not essential for a description of the system, so that the technique is of particular value in the detection and characterization of unknown reactions, or to describe and interpret complex natural systems where the details of the process occurring are unavailable to the usual analytical techniques. With such measurements, the method is essentially comparative and depends on the systematic reproducibility of the system, so that in such cases also interpretation is easier if conditions can be chosen to allow the catabolism to set up a steady state.

If the record of heat production can be interpreted in conjunction with thermodynamic data and chemical information, the method can be used to give quite detailed interpretations of such questions as the correlation of observations with postulated reaction mechanisms, presence of side reactions and accumulation of reserve materials. Particularly in complex systems, the method gives an overall picture of the metabolic activity of the system, with information about which reactions are of importance, and often a clear indication of the direction of further more detailed biochemical study.

Apparatus suitable for these studies is now readily available and well proven in operation, with a great deal of detailed information available about the performance of the apparatus under various experimental conditions, so that all the basic criteria for obtaining and analysing microcalorimetric experimental data are well documented.

REFERENCES

Battley, E. H. (1960). *Physiologia Pl.*, **13**, 628–640, 674–686.
Bauchop, T., and Elsden, S. R. (1960). *J. gen. Microbiol.*, **23**, 457–469.
Bayne-Jones, S., and Rhees, H. S. (1929). *J. Bact.*, **17**, 123–40.
Belaich, J–P. (1963). *C. r. Séanc. Soc. Biol.*, **157**, 316–322.
Belaich, J–P, and Senez, J. C. (1967). *Colloques int. Cent. natn. Rech. scient.*, **156**, 381–394.
Belaich, J–P, Senez, J. C., and Murgier, M. (1968). *J. Bact.*, **95**, 1750–1757.
Benzinger, T. H. (1965). *Fractions*, **2**, 1–10.
Benzinger, T. H., and Kitzinger, C. (1963). *In* "Temperature—its measurement and control in science and industry", Vol. 3, pp. 43–60. Reinhold, New York.
Berger, R. L., Chick, F. Y., and Davids, N. (1968). *Rev. Sci. Instr.*, **39**, 362–367.
Bernhard, S. A. (1956). *J. biol. Chem.*, **218**, 961–969.

Bichowsky, F. R. (1929). *In* "International critical tables", Vol. V, pp. 169–211. McGraw-Hill, New York.

Bichowsky, F. R. and Rossini, F. D. (1936). "The thermochemistry of chemical substances". Reinhold, New York.

Blaxter, K. L. (1962). "The energy metabolism of ruminants". Hutchinson, London.

Boivinet, P. (1964). Ph.D. Thesis, University of Aix, Marseille.

Boivinet, P., and Grangetto, A. (1963). *Cir. hebd. Séanc. Acad. Sci. Paris*, **256**, 2052–2054

Bouffard, A. (1895). *C. r. hebd. Séanc. Acad. Sci. Paris*, **121**, 357–360.

Buzzell, A., and Sturtevant, J. M. (1951). *J. Am. chem. Soc.*, **73**, 2454–2458.

Calvet, E. (1962).*In* "Experimental thermochemistry" (Ed. H. A. Skinner), Vol. 2, pp. 385–410. Wiley, New York.

Calvet, E. (1963). *In* "Recent progress in microcalorimetry" (Ed. H. A. Skinner), pp. 1–110. Pergamon Press, London.

Clifton, C. E. (1963). *Ann. N.Y. Acad. Sci*, **102**, 655–668.

Clifton, C. E., and Cherry, J. (1966). *J. Bact.*, **91**, 546–550.

Dawes, E. A., and Ribbons, D. W. (1954). *Bact. Rev.*, **28**, 126–149.

Dean, A. C. R., and Hinshelwood, Sir Cyril. (1966). "Growth, function and regulation in bacterial cells". Oxford University Press.

Dubrunfaut, M. (1856). *C. r. hebd. Séanc. Acad. Sci. Paris*, **42**, 945–948.

Forrest, W. W. (1961). *J. scient. Instrum.*, **38**, 143–145.

Forrest, W. W. (1967a). *Colloques int. Cent. natn. Rech. scient.*, **156**, 405–416.

Forrest, W. W. (1967b). *J. Bact.*, **94**, 1459–1463.

Forrest, W. W. (1970). *Nature, Lond.*, **225**, 1165–1166.

Forrest, W. W., and Walker, D. J. (1962). *Nature, Lond.*, **196**, 990–991.

Forrest, W. W., and Walker, D. J. (1963). *Biochem. biophys. Res. Comm.*, **13**, 217–222.

Forrest, W. W., and Walker, D. J. (1964). *Nature, Lond.*, **201**, 49–52.

Forrest, W. W., and Walker, D. J. (1965a). *J. Bact.*, **89**, 1448–1452.

Forrest, W. W., and Walker, D. J. (1965b). Nature, *Lond.*, **207**, 46–48.

Forrest, W. W., Walker, D. J., and Hopgood, M. F. (1961). *J. Bact.*, **82**, 648–656.

Forrest, W. W., Stephen, V. A. and Walker, D. J. (1964). *Aust. J. agric. Res.*, **15**, 313–315.

Grangetto, A. (1963). Ph.D. Thesis, University of Aix, Marseille.

Guggenheim, E. A. (1926). *Phil. Mag.*, **2**, 538–542.

Harned, H., and Owen, B. B. (1958). "The physical chemistry of electrolytic solutions". Reinhold, New York.

Horecker, B. L., Thomas, J., and Monod, J. (1960). *J. biol. Chem.*, **235**, 1580–1590.

Houpt, T. R. (1968). *Amer. J. Vet. Res.* **29**, 411–417

Hungate, R. E. (1963). *J. Bact.*, **86**, 848–854.

Knowles, G., Downing, A. L., and Barrett, M. J. (1965). *J. gen. Microbiol.*, **38**, 263–278.

Monk, P. R., and Wadsö, I. (1968). *Acta Chem. Scand.*, **22**, 1842–1848.

Morowitz, H. J. (1960). *Biochem. biophys. Acta*, **40**, 340–345.

Morowitz, H. J. (1968). "Energy flow in biology". Academic Press, New York.

Peterson, W. H., and Wilson, P. W. (1931). *Chem. Rev.*, **8**, 427–480.

Pirt, S. J. (1965). *Proc. R. Soc.*, **B 163**, 224–231.

Prat, H. (1963). *In* "Recent progress in microcalorimetry" (Ed. H. A. Skinner), pp. 111–174. Pergamon Press, London.

Prigogine, I. (1961). "Thermodynamics of irreversible processes". Wiley, New York.

Rahn, O. (1932). "Physiology of bacteria" Blakistons Sons and Co., Philadelphia.

Ribbons, D. W., and Dawes, E. A. (1963). *Ann. N. Y. Acad. Sci.*, **102**, 564–586.

Rossini, F. D., Wagman, D. D., Evans, W. H., Levine, S., and Jaffe, I. (1961). NBS Circular 500, U.S. Govt. Printing Office, Washington.

Roughton, F. J. W. (1941). *J. Am. chem. Soc.* **63**, 2930–2934.

Senez, J. C. (1962). *Bact. Rev.*, **26**, 95–107.

Senez, J. C., and Belaich, J. P. (1965), *Colloques int. Cent. natn. Rech. scient.*, **124**, 357–369.

Skinner, H. A. (1962). *In* "Experimental thermochemistry" (Ed. H. A. Skinner), Vol. 2, pp. 147–155. Wiley, New York.

Skinner, H. A., Sturtevant, J. M., and Sunner, S. (1962). *In* "Experimental thermochemistry" (Ed. H. A. Skinner), Vol. 2, pp. 157–219. Wiley, New York.

Stoward, P. J. (1962). *Nature, Lond.*, **194**, 977–978; **196**, 991–992.

Sturtevant, J. M. (1945). *In* "Technique of organic chemistry" (Ed. A. Weissberger), Vol. 1, pp. 311–434. Wiley, New York.

Sturtevant, J. M. (1962). *In* "Experimental thermochemistry" (Ed. H. A. Skinner), Vol. 2, pp. 427–442. Wiley, New York.

Van Suchtelen, F. H. H. (1931). Archiv *PflBau*, **7**, 519–541.

Walker, D. J. (1965). *In* "Physiology of digestion in the ruminant" (Ed. R. W. Dougherty), pp. 296–310. Butterworth, London and Washington.

Walker, D. J., and Forrest, W. W. (1964). *Aust. J. agric. Res.*, **15**, 299–312.

Wilkie, D. R. (1960). *Prog. Biophys. molec. Biol.*, **10**, 260–298.

CHAPTER XI

Automatic and Continuous Assessment of Fermentation Parameters

JAMES MARTEN

Division of Biomedical Sciences, Damon Corporation, Needham, Mass., U.S A.

The term fermentation has come to be understood to mean decomposition of organic materials brought about by micro-organisms. This process has been used extensively for the manufacture of antibiotics, solvents, steroids and enzymes and other organic materials.

Normally, in an industrial fermentation process, ingredients are batched prior to inoculation, a process which often yields only fair quantities of the desired product. This is because some materials are semi-toxic in high initial concentration while too low a concentration of a particular precursor may fail to give optimum conditions of growth.

In the biosynthesis of streptomycin, for example, phosphate concentration influences the utilization of glucose to the extent that the production of the antibiotic can be reversed by too high a concentration of phosphates. While it is desirable to keep the level of inorganic phosphate as low as possible, an adequate supply of phosphorylated intermediates must, however, be maintained. During the course of the biosynthesis, moreover, the optimum level of phosphate does not remain constant but varies according to the rate of production of the antibiotic. Other parameters may also affect the course and rate of the reaction. Thus, an adequate supply of oxygen and an adequate concentration of glucose and nitrogeneous material should be maintained at all times.

Sampling systems

With automation, the supply of precursors and nutrients can be carefully controlled according to the changing demands of the organism, giving maximum yield of product. While there is no question that continuous control of vital growth parameters is of immense value, monitoring and control systems for the continuous assessment of fermenter contents must meet certain criteria. The system must:

1. Preclude the possibility of contamination of the fermenter contents.
2. Obtain a representative sample of the fermenter contents.
3. Make samples available continuously.

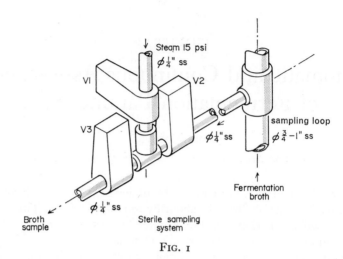

Steam 15 psi
$\phi\frac{1}{4}"$ ss

Vl   V2

V3

sampling loop
$\phi\frac{3}{4}-l"$ ss

$\phi\frac{1}{4}"$ ss

Fermentation
broth

$\phi\frac{1}{4}"$ ss

Broth
sample

Sterile sampling
system

FIG. I

These conditions can be met by combining the classic 3-valve system with continuous dialysis or filtration and continuous addition of a bacterio-stat to the clarified fermenter sample.

The 3-valve system (Fig. 1) consists of a steam valve (V1), a sample valve (V2) and an outlet valve (V3). These valves are controlled by a pro-grammer which allows steam at 15 psi to cleanse each part of the valve system in turn. Each fermenter can be equipped with a large capacity Vanton-type pump for circulation of a representative sample of the tank's contents, through a loop of sufficient diameter to permit rapid circulation of a large volume. It is from this circulating loop that the sample is periodi-cally drawn into the sample cup (Fig. 2). Steam is first used to flush the system while valve V2 is closed and all other valves are open. After a suit-able period V1 is closed and V2 opened allowing material from the fer-menter to flow into the sampling cup. The overflow sample cup obviates the necessity of precise measuring of the sample. After valve V2 is closed and the excess sample has flowed to waste, the contents of the cup is voided to the filtration phase of the analytical system (Fig. 3) which may be a continuous filter module or dialysis system.

Analytical systems

After the prescribed sampling time, valve V1 is opened and the whole sampling system flushed with steam through valve V1 to waste. The pro-grammer then proceeds to repeat the entire operation for the next fer-mentation tank (and for as many tanks as are being monitored). Water

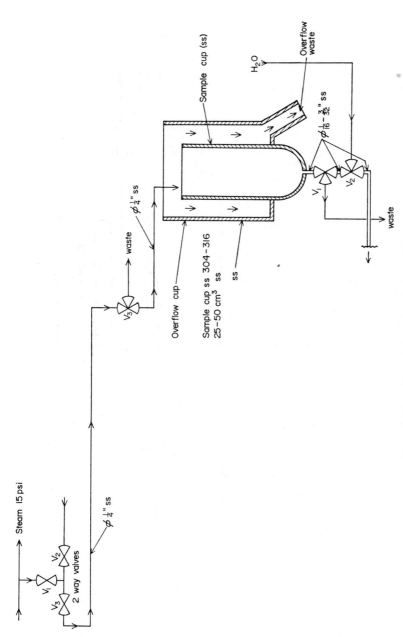

FIG. 2. Sampling system showing overflow cup.

J. MARTEN

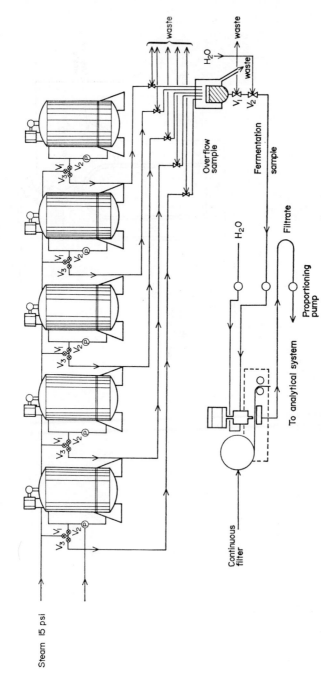

FIG. 3. Sampling and analytical systems for a series of fermenters.

flows through valve V2 into the analytical system during the steam cleaning period. Continuous dialysis is an ideal mechanism for clarifying the sample for analysis for it precludes contamination by virtue of the inability of micro-organisms to transverse the dialyser membrane. The dialyser system is first sterilized and the recipient stream on the opposite side of the dialyser membrane to the sample may be a sterile fluid although this may not be essential. The pores of the dialyser membrane are too small to allow passage of any micro-organism since they are between 40–60 Å across and the smallest cocci measures 2000 Å. Continuous circulation of samples or a sequence of samples through the dialyser (Fig. 4) makes available a diffusate in the recipient stream containing the desired parameter or parameters. For example, glucose, chloride, lactic acid, sodium and potassium may be readily measured in the recipient stream. The intact fermenter sample must be used for total protein or nitrogen determinations and here the use of a positive peristaltic pump prevents back diffusion of fermenter sample.

A simple total control system for one parameter, glucose, is illustrated in Fig. 5. A continuous and sterile sample of the fermenter contents is withdrawn and fed to an analytical system. The analytical technique used is well known and is based upon the reduction of potassium ferricyanide at 95°C and measurement at 420 nm in a continuous flow colorimeter. An acid-hydrolysis step may be included to provide a total sugar assay. The output of the colorimeter is fed to a retransmitting slidewire whose 0–100 MV output voltage is proportional to the measured glucose concentration. A proportional feed pump adds glucose solution to the fermenter in quantities to keep the glucose level at a predetermined optimum value. Other nutrients can be measured simultaneously in additon to those shown in Fig. 4, such as total amino-acids by the ninhydrin reaction; individual amino-acids via their respective decarboxylase enzymes (Cormier and Fornard, 1966); ammonium salts using their reaction with a highly alkaline solution of sodium hypochlorite and phenol (Logsdon, 1960); and phosphate by the vanadomolybdate reaction (Ferretti and Hoffman, 1962).

Steroid analysis

It is often advantageous to continuously monitor the product as well as the precursor and nutrient. A review of steroid assays (Russo-Alesi and Khoury, 1967), although mainly dealing with finished products, provides good source material on automated techniques available. Greely *et al.*, 1965) used the classic Blue Tetrazolium reaction for routine analysis of steroid-containing tablets. They demonstrated that automatic analytical procedures were applicable for dexamethasone in the concentration range 0·5–0·75 mg/ tablet and for prednisone, prednisotone, hydrocortisone and cortisone acetate.

A significant feature of this method is the continuous chloroform extraction to enhance isolation of the steroid before Blue Tetrazolium determination; the earlier normal procedure for cortisone and related α-ketol steroids was tedious.

Beyes (1965) also reported an automated method for determining hydrocortisone, methyl prednisolone and prednisolone in tablets. Cali, Konieczyn and De Marco, (1967) have reported a unique extension of this method to achieve improved sensitivity and specificity. They used enzymatic hydrolysis to follow steroid phosphate stability. Additional specificity results from determining the A ring by UV absorption besides the C-17 side chain by the Blue Tetrazolium reaction.

Russo-Alesi (1967) has described a fully automatic procedure where Δ4, 3-ketosteroids are involved. He used isonicotinic acid hydrazine in the determination of Triamcinolone in tablets. In this reaction, the amount of hydrazone formed measures the steroid present. This method has advantages over the Blue Tetrazolium procedure in that it is simple and avoids difficulties resulting from inadvertent isolation of reducing substances such as lactose accompanying the steroid in extraction. It is frequently not possible to apply direct UV absorption methods because of interferences and degradation products of steroids found in the fermentation media and colorimetric procedures would appear to offer the best approach to monitoring product formation.

Zak et al. (1965) have reported on the automatic determination of 17-ketosteroids and 17-ketogenic steroids using a modified Zimmerman reaction. The Zimmerman procedure is based upon the development of a reddish purple colour when an alkaline solution of m-dinitrobenzene reacts with the steroid ketone at the 17-carbon position. High blanks greatly reduce sensitivity of the method.

Stickler et al. (1966) have reported an automated fluorometric procedure based on the Ittrich method for the determination of estrogens in gravid urine which offers specificity. Steroids are continuously extracted into isopropylether and reacted with Kober reagent. The fluorogen obtained is extracted into p-nitrophenol in alcoholic sym-tetrabromoethane and determined fluorometrically.

Vitamin analysis

Another product group, the vitamins, have been reviewed with regard to automated analytical procedures by Khoury (1966). Again, the techniques described are those essentially for finished product but valuable

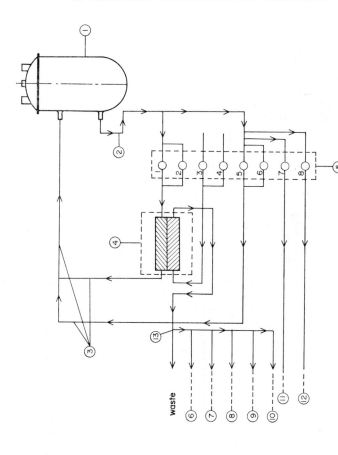

FIG. 4. Multiparameter sampling and dialysis system.

① Chemostat (fermentation vessel)

② Sample loop (input)

③ Sample loop (return)

④ Dialyzer 37 °C

⑤ Sampling pump

⑥ Diffusate – for glucose deter.

⑦ Diffusate – for chloride deter.

⑧ Diffusate – for calcium deter.

⑨ Diffusate – for lactic acid

⑩ Diffusate – for K and Na

⑪ Total sample – for biuret protein

⑫ Total sample – for total nitrogen

J. MARTEN

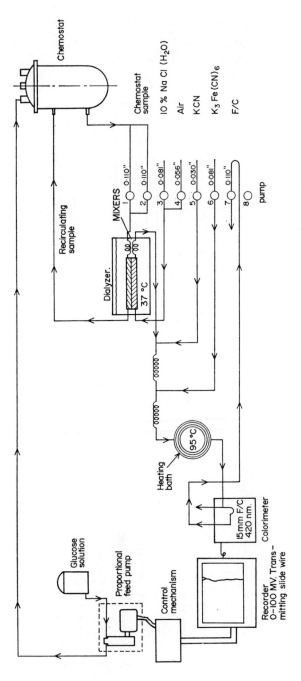

Fig. 5. Analysis and control of nutrient concentration.

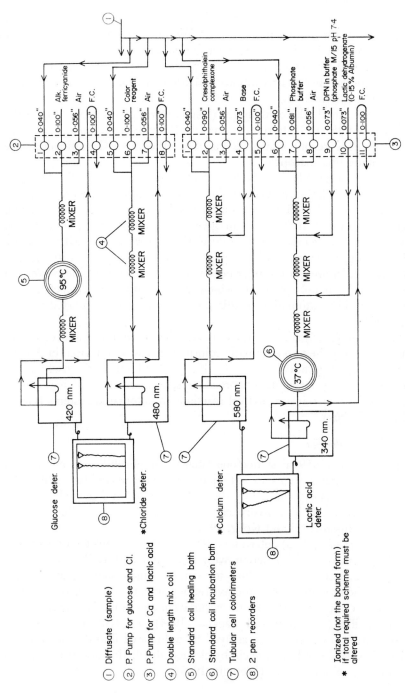

FIG. 6. Multiparameter analytical system.

① Diffusate (sample)

② P. Pump for glucose and Cl.

③ P. Pump for Ca and lactic acid

④ Double length mix coil

⑤ Standard coil healing bath

⑥ Standard coil incubation bath

⑦ Tubular cell colorimeters

⑧ 2 pen recorders

* Ionized (not the bound form)
  if total required scheme must be
  altered

references are given which give good source material for adaptation of these methods for monitoring purposes. The current status of methods for Vitamins B_1, B_2, B_6, B_{12}, C, A, niacinamide and calcium pantothenate is described. The data given includes the necessary equipment and reagents. Flow diagrams, special precautions and problems, and the accuracy and precision of the method.

Automated methods for thiamine (Tsuda *et al.*, 1964) depend upon the oxidation of vitamin B_1 to thiochrome which fluoresces in ultraviolet light. The procedure recommended is based on the method outlined in the United States Pharmacopeia.

Automated methods for riboflavin have been developed (Tsuda *et al.*, 1964). They are all fluorometric and use solvent extraction procedures. The principal chemical methods for niacin involve reactions in which niacin reacts with cyanogen bromide to give a pyridinium compound which undergoes rearrangement yielding derivatives which couple with aromatic amines (Duggan *et al.*, 1957). Pyridoxine can be reacted with diethyl *p*-phenylenediamine, in the presence of potassium ferricyanide, to form a coloured indophenol pigment which is subsequently extracted into chloroform. The automation of this procedure has been reported (Tsuda *et al.*, 1964).

Dowd *et al.* (1965) adapted the only chemical assay for cyanocobalamin to automation while two automatic colorimetric assays for vitamin A have been developed (Anderson *et al.*, 1966). Antibiotics, themselves the products of many fermentation procedures, were recently reviewed with regard to their chemical analytical reactions in automated systems (Gerke and Ferrari, 1967).

Analysis of antibiotics

Ferrari *et al.* (1959) first demonstrated the applicability of continuous flow instrumental systems to automated chemical assays for antibiotics. Streptomycin was determined by the maltol method and penicillin by the iodometric method. The hydroxalamine method for penicillin has also been used (Russo-Alesi and Kelly, 1959).

Grenfeld *et al.*, (1960) determined terramycin by means of the coloured complex formed by its reaction with ferric ion and Kelly and Wilson (1965) have described a method for determining 6-demethylchlortetra-cycline in the presence of 6-demethyl tetracycline. Continuous flow extractions have been used to increase the accuracy of determination for rifamycin and penicillin (Gualandi and Pagano, 1964) and tylosin (Roudebush, 1965). Antimycin A has been assayed by automated fluorescence (Seligal and Vezina, 1967) and lincomycin by clevage, distillation and reaction with a disulphide colour reagent (Prescott, 1965).

Analysis of cellular constituents

Multiple analytical systems can also be adapted for measuring cell constituents as well, thereby giving continuous metabolic information of the cell population. Optimum conditions with regard to the micro-organism itself may thus be maintained and the effect of stimulatory or inhibitory substances studies. Specific automated analyses of DNA and RNA have been recently reported (Van Dyke and Szustbiewica, 1967), which are sensitive, specific and rapid. The nucleic acids, assayed by fluorescence, can be determined in most biological systems in their native state without extensive purification and separation.

There is still much to be done to extend continuous monitoring systems to fermentation control. Existing methods and instrumentation can be simplified and made more reliable. The use of newer techniques such as enzymatic, fluorescent and isotope methods should give researchers encouragement to extend the use of automation to this important application.

REFERENCES

Anderson, R. A., Perrizo, C., and Fusari, S. A. (1966). *Tech. Symp., Auto. in Anal. Chem.*, Vol. 1, 267–273.

Beyes, W. F. (1965). *Tech. Symp., Auto. in Anal. Chem.*, pp. 7–11.

Cali, L. J., Konieczyn, J. M., and De Marco, J. D. (1967). *Tech. Symp., Auto. in Anal. Chem.* Vol. I, 451–456.

Cormier, M., and Fornard, P. (1966). *Tech. Symp., Auto. in Anal. Chem.*, Vol. II, pp. 367–370.

Dowd, N., Killard, A., Pazdera, J., and Ferrari, A. (1965). *Ann. N.Y. Acad. Sci.*, 130, 558–567.

Duggan, D., Bowman, R. L., Brodie, D. B., and Udenfriend, S. (1957). *Arch. Biochem. Biophys.* 68, 1–14.

Ferrari, A., Russo-Alesi, F. M., and Kelly, J. M. (1959). *Anal. Chem.* 31, 1710–1717.

Ferretti, R. J. and Hoffman, W. M. (1962). *J. Ass. Off. Ag. Chem.* 45, 993–996.

Gerke, J. R. and Ferrari, A. (1967). *Tech. Symp., Auto. in Anal. Chem.*, 31, 1710–1717.

Greely, V. J., Holl, W. W., Michaels, T. P., and Sinotte, L. P. (1965). *Ann. N.Y. Acad. Sci.*, 130, 545–549.

Grenfeld, T. C., McLaughlin, D. J., and Kelly, J. M. (1960). *Ann. N.Y. Acad. Sci.*, 87, 857–863.

Gualandi, G., and Pagano, P. (1964). *Intern. Tech. Symp., Auto. in Anal. Chem.*, Technicon GMBH, Frankfurt, pp. 47–57.

Kelly, J. R., and Wilson, L. C. (1965). *Ann. N.Y. Acad. Sci.*, 130, 575–581.

Khoury, A. J. (1966). *Tech. Symp., Auto. in Anal. Chem.*, Vol. I, 286–296.

Logsdon, E. E. (1960). *Ann. N.Y. Acad. Sci.*, 87, 801–807.

Prescott, G. C. (1965). *Tech. Symp., Auto. in Anal. Chem.*, pp. 38–41.

Roudebush, H. E. (1965). *Ann. N.Y. Acad. Sci.*, 130, 582–588.

Russo-Alesi, F. M. (1967). *Ann. N.Y. Acad. Sci.*

Russo-Alesi, F. M., and Kelly, J. M. (1959). *Trans. N.Y. Acad. Sci.*, 21, 497–504.

Russo-Alesi, F. M., and Khoury, A. J. (1967). *Tech. Symp. Auto. in Anal. Chem.*, Vol. I, pp. 491–495.

Seligal, S. N., and Vezina, C. (1967). *Tech. Symp., Auto. in Anal. Chem.*, Vol. I, 497–500.

Stickler, H. S., Holt, S. S., Grauer, R. C., and Gilmore, J. (1966). *Tech. Symp., Auto. in Anal. Chem.*, 70–74.

Tsuda, T., Yamamoto, T., and Yarimizu, S. (1964). *Ann. Sankyo Res. Lab.*, **16**, 109–118.

Van Dyke, K., and Szustbiewica, C. (1967). *Tech. Sym. Auto. in Anal. Chem.*, Vol. I, 543–548.

Zak, B. A., Epstein, E., and Krareshaar, L. A. (1965). *Tech. Symp., Auto. in Anal. Chem.*, 336–340.

CHAPTER XII

Automated Microbiological Assay

ANDRES FERRARI AND JAMES MARTEN

Division of Biomedical Sciences, Damon Corporation, Needham, Mass., U.S.A.

The classical methods for microbiological analysis of antibiotics are tedious and time consuming. They are preferred to chemical assay because some analogs and interfering substances synthesized with the antibiotic affect only the bacteriostatic or bactericidal properties of the antibiotic.

Initial efforts to automate the general procedure were based on the turbidimetric approach, whereby antibiotic and cells were continuously proportioned and mixed together with the nutrient medium, incubated in a coil at 37°C and the extent of growth or specific reaction quantitated by continuous flow turbidimetry (Gerke *et al.*, 1960).

The system consisted of a sampler for programmed distribution of samples and standards; a proportioning pump for propelling samples, standards, nutrient media, inoculum and formaldehyde into the system; a dialyser to permit smooth diffusion of the sample into the recipient nutrient medium and inoculum stream; an incubating system consisting of a coil of polythene tubing; a continuous flow turbidimeter to measure the turbidity of the flowing stream and a recorder. The operational details of the system have been amply described elsewhere (Skeggs, 1957; Ferrari, 1959; Gerke, 1962). The flow diagram shown in Fig. 1 is a simplified schematic of the automated turbidimetric bioassay.

There were, nevertheless, severe problems associated with the automation of the turbidimetric method and it was not until some years later that a technique was finally reported which was fully satisfactory (Platt *et al.*, 1965). This is claimed to be three times more efficient than the original published method. Moreover, antibiotics such as bacitracin, inactive against Gram-negatives such as *Escherichia coli*, can be assayed where no previous system was available.

Because of the initial problems associated with automating the turbidimetric method, it was suggested that a more rapidly occurring phenomenon be employed, such as a physiological parameter. It was reasoned that, while time was needed for sufficient generations of cells to grow to achieve a measurable difference, a physiological parameter would change immediately when the cell was exposed to an adverse medium. The only require-

A. FERRARI AND J. MARTEN

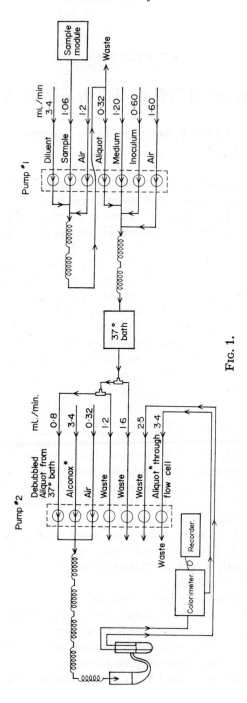

FIG. 1.

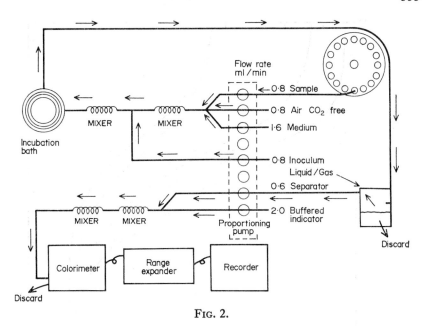

Flow rate
ml/min

←0·8 Sample

0·8 Air CO₂ free

1·6 Medium

0·8 Inoculum

Liquid/Gas

0·6 Separator

2·0 Buffered indicator

MIXER   MIXER

Incubation bath

MIXER   MIXER   Proportioning pump

Colorimeter   Range expander   Recorder

Discard

Discard

FIG. 2.

ments were that the parameter chosen be analysable and that the required sensitivity be adequate. Because one of the more frequently employed micro-organisms, *E. coli*, produces large amounts of carbon dioxide during respiration, this was chosen as the initial physiological parameter to quantitate automatically. The bio-assay consisted of measuring the amount of carbon dioxide respired under uninhibited conditions and the amount respired under inhibited conditions (Fig. 2). The first full report of this new automated concept was made in 1962 (Haney *et al.*). Subsequently, many papers were published employing this physiological parameter (Alegnani and Tylec, 1963; Shaw and Duncombe, 1963; Shaw and Duncombe, 1965).

Carbon dioxide may be detected by means of changing colour intensity of a suitable indicator such as phenolphthalein, combined with a buffer effective in the pH range of the indicator. Mixtures of sodium bicarbonate and sodium carbonate give a choice of buffers that permit the sensitivity of variation to change in carbon dioxide and, hence, the apparent slope of the antibiotic calibration curve to be varied (Fig. 3). High buffer ratios give less sensitive reagents, and hence the antibiotic working range may be extended although some precision may be sacrificed. The characteristics of the reagent is such that the working range covers only the last 25% or so of the total carbon dioxide produced. The high precision of antibiotic

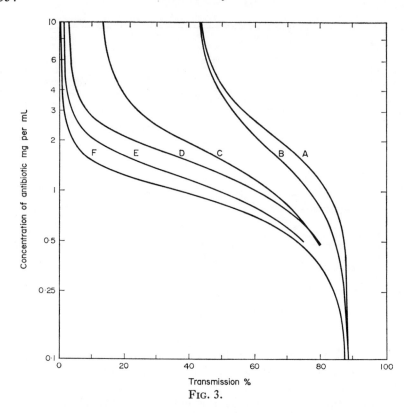

FIG. 3.

assays depends on the delicacy of the system for detecting carbon dioxide obtainable in this way. When high precision is required; for example, in comparing two antibiotic standards whose potencies differ only slightly, a ratio of 1 : 1 of carbonate to bicarbonate is advantageous. Thus, two basis systems are available: (1) using a turbidimetric assay a very precise measurement of the final product is obtained; (2) using the carbon dioxide system, the speed of the assay makes it ideal for fermentation control. The greatest factor which contributes to day-to-day variability is the micro-bial cell-suspension and its preparation. Two solutions to this problem are available. One is to prepare large amounts of the microbial cell suspensions and adjust them to the desired strength, then freeze the prepared suspen-sion at $-20°C$ (Dewart *et al.*, 1965). Cell suspensions prepared in this manner are still satisfactory after 2 months. This method of preparation permits stabilization of the cell preparations and thus achieves a near identical inoculum from day to day.

The other solution to this problem is to employ a continuous culture (Shaw and Duncombe, 1963). Basically, the technique consists of having a

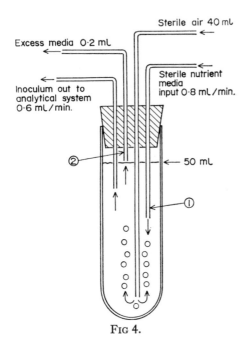

FIG 4.

small, sterile culture vessel of approximately 50 ml capacity. Four tubes are arranged through a top fitting as illustrated (Fig. 4). Sterile nutient media is constantly fed into this vessel at a fixed rate through Tube 1. Tube 2 is adjusted to a given height in order to fix the volume of the culture solution in the vessel. By controlling the volume within the vessel, by adjusting the height of Tube 2, and adjusting the volume input of nutrient medium through 1, the residence time in the vessel may be controlled to provide the desired cell population. The generation time (t_d in min) of a particular organism in a stable, continuous culture, may be calculated from the operating volume of the reservoir (in ml, v) and the input volume of the sterile medium (in ml /min, f) by means of the expression

$$\left(1 + \frac{f}{v}\right)t_d = 2$$

Thus, for a 50 ml reservoir and a throughput of 0·8 ml/min, t equals 44 min. Provided t_d is greater than the minimum generation time of the organism under the particular growth conditions chosen, the culture will be self-maintaining and the generation time will rise to the calculated value as some essential metabolite (for example, available oxygen) becomes growth limiting (for a complete treatment see Tempest, Vol. 2 this series).

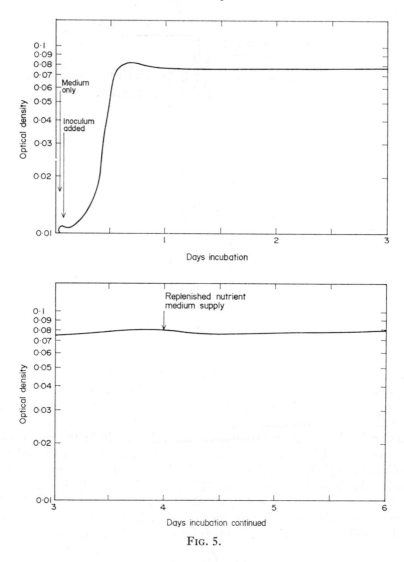

Fig. 5.

The small reservoir volume necessary for the continuous culture for a given input of medium may also be calculated from the same expression if the minimum generation time is known. If, for example, this is assumed to be 20 min for *E. coli*, the minimum volume with an input of 0·8 ml per min is 23 ml. In practice, after seeding the chemostat, it is placed in a 37°C water bath, so that the water level is above that of the contents of the flask. In about 4–6 h the growth and production of the cells has stabilized

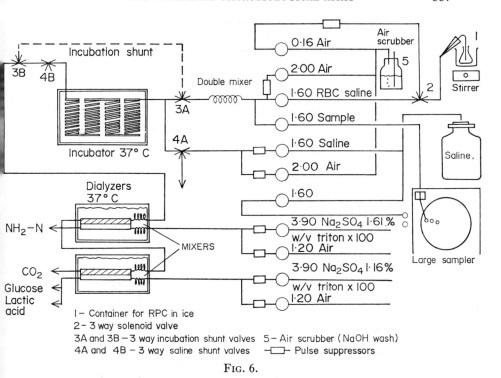

FIG. 6.

itself and can now be used as a constant source of cells for inoculum. Figure 5 illustrates how a constant cell population may be maintained using a system of this kind. Operated in the optimum manner, at a speed of 20 instrumental responses per hour, with a duplicate recording of each sample and assay standards, an overall throughput of six samples an hour is obtainable. The delay within the system is about 45 min. With a stable culture, available results from a group of 12 samples and standards can be obtained within 3 h. A comparison of operating costs with those of conventional routine agar diffusion assay, indicates the advantage of the continuous method, particularly for large numbers of similar samples, but any general conclusion clearly will depend on the nature and variety of work undertaken. Moreover, in certain circumstances, one particular restriction of the continuous assay must be considered. The dose response curves of most antibiotics are characterized by relatively short, approximately rectilinear, working ranges. For this reason, automatic assay is best operated as a one-level method in contrast to the usual two-level method by routine agar diffusion or turbidimetry. The qualitative composition of the samples must, therefore, be known or parallelism of the dose response curve with

TABLE I

Antibiotic and test organisms used in automated bioassays

Antibiotics	Test Organisms* and Reference†			
Tetracycline (s)	Ec : 16, 13, 10		Sf:5(T)	Kp:1(T)
Streptomycin	Ec : 189, 90	Sa:9		Kp:(T)
Neomycin	Ec : 189, 10	Sa:9		Kp:1(T)
Penicillin G	Ec : 89	Sa:9	Sf:5(T)	
Novobiocin	Ec : 89	Sa:9		
Cephalosporin C	Ec : 89	Sa:9		
Bacitracin	Ec : 9	Sa:9	Sf:5(T)	
Penicillin V	Ec : 9	Sa:9		
Thiostrepton			Sf:5(T)	
Vernamycin A			Sf:5(T)	
Vernamycin B			Sf:5(T)	
Dihydrostreptomycin	Ec : 10			
Chloramphenicol	Ec : 10			
Polymyxin	Ec : 10		Sf:5(T)	
Ampicillin			Sf:5(T)	
Pyridinethione			Sf:5(T)	
Virginiamycin		Sa:10		
Nystatin	Ct : 13			
Amphotericin B	Ct : 10, 13	Sc:6		

(T) indicates that a turbidimetric method was used. A respirometric method was used for all others.

Ec = *Escherichia coli*
Sa = *Staphylococcus aureus* (Micrococcus pyogenes var. aureus)
Sf = *Streptococcus faecalis*
Kp = *Klebsiella pneumoniae*
Ct = *Candida tropicalis* (Saccharomyces mellis)
Sc = *Saccharomyces cerevisiae*

that of the standard must be assumed. Further, the estimated potency should lie within about 20% of the true potency. Otherwise, the response will lie outside the working range of the assay so that re-assay at a different dilution may be required. Automated bio-assays have been successfully applied to a broad spectrum of antibiotics. Table I summarizes the antibiotics and test organisms used in automated bio-assays. The development of the methodology in this field has resulted in a remarkable cooperative effort between analysts in a number of pharmaceutical companies throughout the world. Gerke (1960) first demonstrated the applicability of the continuous flow instrumental systems to the automation of turbidimetric and respirometric microbiological assays. Haney et al. (1962) improved the respirometric methods and demonstrated it in routine use with greater

TABLE II

Accuracy of automated bioassays

Antiobiotic	Manual Method*	Ratio of Results Automated/Manual	Ref.
Amphotericin B (fermentations)	T	0·99	6
Amphotericin (formulations)	T	1·03	6
Tetracycline	T	1·03	6
Tetracycline	A	0·97	6
Streptomycin	A	1·00	8
Neomycin	A	1·03	14
Virginiamycin	A	0·99	10
Virginiamycin	T	1·02	10
Polymyxin	A	1·03	10
Tetracycline	A	1·00	10
		AV = 1·01	

A = agar diffusion
T = turbidimetric

efficiency than manual methods. He developed the assay design and method of calculation that enabled correcting of response drift. The potential of continuous dilution for research development applications was also demonstrated. Alegnani and Tylec (1963) demonstrated the utility of the respirometric method in a laboratory required to assay, each day, samples of a number of different antibiotics. A series of short runs, each with a different antibiotic, were programmed in succession without changing the inoculum or medium. Shaw and Duncombe (1963) confirmed the utility of assaying different antibiotics in successive short runs, and they were the first to demonstrate the automated, instrumental system using the continuously grown inoculum. Moreover, they found that young, vigorous *E. coli* grown in this manner, was sensitive to many antibiotics previously thought to be inactive under these circumstances.

Nineteen substances have been assayed by one or more of six micro-organisms as summarized in Table II. Considering the diversity of the 19 substances, it is reasonable to predict that any antibiotic known to act upon one of the six micro-organisms could be assayed. While many more micro-organisms could be employed, it is not unreasonable to predict utility with all the test organisms used in manual methods. While bioassays using microbial cells have been discussed, it must not be concluded that only this type of organism can be employed. Within the last 2 years automated systems have been applied to the study and screening of antiparasitic drugs.

The specific application has been the quest for new and better anti-malarial drugs. The many thousands of drugs which must be screened in order to highlight those with potential anti-malarial properties, would take too long by conventional techniques. Cenedella and Saxe (1966) have described this new application of automated systems.

Basically, the use of the system to automate the bioassay of drugs for anti-malarial properties and for the study of the mechanism by which the drugs exert their action on parasites is similar to the microbiological assay system. Figure 6 illustrates the incubation scheme for this application. Blood of albino rats or mice previously parasitized with *Plasmodium berghie*, is used as the inoculum. After removal of the plasma, a suspension of red cells is made in buffer and maintained uniformly suspended by stirring with a magnetic mixer. The suspension of parasitized erythrocytes is introduced into the system concurrent with the introduction of the sample. A substrate, for example glucose, may also be introduced and the combined streams fed to the incubator.

Incubation is of sufficient duration to enable the drugs to exert any inhibitory action which they may possess on the actively metabolizing parasites. The action of the drug will manifest itself by altering the metabolic activity of the parasite by inhibiting its ability to utilize glucose or whatever other substance is employed and to alter the normal metabolic products of the parasitic activity, which may be lactic acid, pyruvic acid, amino-acids, CO_2 or phosphate.

Upon emergence from the incubator, the stream containing the parasitized blood and sample are sent through one or more dialyser systems. The dialysate is then quantitated by simultaneously analysing the changes which the metabolic activity of the parasite has brought about. Initially, this system is operated without the presence of the drugs as well as with and without incubation in order that the normal metabolic response of the particular parasite inoculum can be established.

In principle, the system will indicate the metabolic effects that the parasites have on a known substrate concentration. Substrate is essential to the metabolic function of the parasite, and in the absence of any inhibitory drug the parasite will act upon the substrate and, thus, a minimum residue of substrate will be found after incubation. On the other hand, if the drug interfers with the utilization of the substrate by the parasite, then higher residual amounts of the substrate will be found. Thus, by selecting appropriate substrates and appropriate analytical parameters, the effects of drugs on parasite metabolism can be assessed as well as providing an indication of the physiological centre associated the mode of action of a particular drug. This represents a major advantage of this mode of drug screening.

Research into drug action has also been extended by the work from the University of Freiburg on correlation of physical and chemical parameters in pharmacology (Haney et al., 1963). This work however, is not limited to intact bodies or even individual organs and has now reached the cellular level where observations of toxicity on cell populations is possible.

The study of cell physiology has been limited in the past because research could not be undertaken without removing the cells from their environment. Moreover, it was almost impossible to process enough samples to gain information concerning the small changes which may be occurring.

A complete study of cell physiology requires that continuous information on the metabolic processes be available and that this knowledge be used to maintain optimum growth conditions. The fulfilment of those requirements can be achieved in the chemostat described previously, a growth vessel where the inoculum can be incubated, agitated, oxgenated and given a constant input of nutritional requirements while aspetic conditions are maintained (for details see Tempest; Evans, Herbert and Tempest; Munson; this Series, Volume 2).

A proportion pump and dialyser present a simple means of withdrawing an intact sample while maintaining this aseptic condition. In such a system, the total cell population can be maintained constant while continuous assessment of a multiple of growth parameters can be used to automatically feed the required amount of nutrients, metabolites, stimulants or inhibitors, toxins or viruses. The effect of these additions on cellular growth can then be measured to produce in effect a cell population having no host variables and no changes in response characteristics unless desired.

Thus far, work has been restricted to microbial cells but application to mammalian cells cannot be far away. An insight into the mechanism of disease processes, pathological conditions and the pharmaco-dynamic action of drugs at the cellular level can be obtained by examining a profile of analyses. In one series of experiments, streptomycin and chloramphenicol inhibition under automation, was compared with the known manual results. The results showed that, within 1 min after the addition of 20 mg of chloramphenicol, turbidity increase abruptly stopped. In the absence of antibiotic, growth would have continued for another 2 h. The orcinol and diphenylamine response curves showed that RNA and DNA also changed abruptly. A slope of the orcinol curve increased sharply for 5 to 10 min after which the slope gradually decreased to zero. The slope of the diphenylamine response curve decreased abruptly and continued without sharp change for the remaining 5 h of the experiment.

The effect of streptomycin differed from that of chloramphenicol. There was no change in any of the responses for 20 min after the addition of

10 mg of antibiotic per ml. Within 40 min, however, all responses established new and much lower slopes.

It can be seen from this review that the possibilities of automated analysis in studying kinetics of bacterial growth are just beginning to be explored. It may be possible in the future to widen the studies in the following areas. (1) the response to addition of external factors, such as drugs, toxins, stimulants and inhibitors; (2) to screen drugs for specific pharmacological qualities; (3) to study pharmacological phenomena for better understanding of animal physiology and metabolism; (4) to correlate physical and chemical parameters, i.e. blood pressure and the rise of glucose level in the circulatory system.

In concluding this review, it is hoped that the growth of the number of researchers skilled in continuous flow methodology will lead to a concentrated attack on these problems. Automated bio-assays contribute to an increased output, but also reveal information on mode of action of drugs on the cellular level which unquestionably will lead to the development and discovery of new drugs against disease processes.

REFERENCES

Alegnani, W. C., and Tylec, F. W. (1963). Presented at the meeting of the American Society for Microbiology, Cleveland, Ohio, May, 1963.

Cenedella, R. J., and Saxe, L. H. (1966). Technicon Symposium, *Auto. in Anal. Chem.* **1**, 281.

Dewart, R., Naudits, F., and Lhoest, W. (1965). *Ann. N.Y. Acad. Sci.*, **130**, 686.

Ferrari, A. (1959). *Anal. Chem.*, **31**, 1710.

Gerke, J. R. (1962). *Ann. N.Y. Acad. Sci.*, **93**, 625.

Gerke, J. R., Haney, T. A., Pagano, J. F., and Ferrari, A. (1960). *Ann. N.Y. Acad. Sci.*, **87**, 782.

Haney, T. A., Gerke, J. R., Madigan, M. E., Pagano, J. F., Ferrari, A. (1962). *Ann. N.Y. Acad. Sci.*, **93**, 627.

Haney, T. A., Gerke, J. R., and Pagano, J. F. (1963). Automation in Microbiological Assays, "Analytical Microbiology", p. 219, Academic Press, N.Y.

Platt, T. B., Gentile, J., and George, M. J. (1965). *Ann. N.Y. Acad. Sci.*, **130**, 6646.

Shaw, W. H. C., and Duncombe, R. E. (1963). *Analyst*, **88**, 694.

Shaw, W. H. C., and Duncombe, R. E. (1965). *Ann. N.Y. Acad. Sci.*, **130**, 647.

Skeggs, L. T. (1957). *Amer. J. Clin. Path.*, **28**, 114.

Greely, V. J., Hall, W. W., Michaels, T. P., Sinotte, L. P., (1965). *Ann. N.Y. Acad. Sci.*, **130**, 657.

CHAPTER XIII

The Acetylene Reduction Test for Nitrogen Fixation

J. R. POSTGATE

A.R.C. Unit of Nitrogen Fixation, University of Sussex, Falmer, Sussex

I. PRINCIPLE

The acetylene-reduction test for the presence of nitrogenase, the enzyme complex responsible for biological nitrogen fixation, has become widely used in laboratories all over the world because of its ease and sensitivity. It is based on the observations of Dilworth (1966) and Schöllhorn and Burris (1967) that preparations of the enzyme nitrogenase reduce acetylene specifically to ethylene. Numerous other alternative substrates for nitrogenase exist, such as cyanides and isocyanides (see Postgate, 1970, for a summary of the properties of nitrogenase and for further references) and these have occasionally been used as tests for nitrogenase activity. But because of its relative lack of toxicity and ease of preparation, acetylene is now the substrate of choice. In using this test the experimenter should remember that plant material such as ripening fruit may produce ethylene, but not from acetylene; so may certain moulds (Ilag and Curtis, 1968). No interference from such sources has been reported to the writer's knowledge; nevertheless, when testing a new microbial culture with acetylene it is wise to include a control without acetylene and also a control culture grown in a medium containing an ammonium salt at about 0.2% w/v, giving an ammonium ion concentration sufficient to inhibit nitrogenase synthesis. Acetylene reduction repressed by growth with ammonium ions is *prima faciae* evidence for nitrogenase.

When the acetylene test is applied to enzyme preparations and extracts of microbes, the normal components necessary for the assay of nitrogenase must be supplied. These are Mg^{2+} and ATP. The latter is usually supplied as part of an ATP-generating system, the most common example of which is the mixture of creatine phosphate and creatine kinase described below. In extracts, the reaction requires a reductant unless, as in certain anaerobic bacteria, a substrate such as pyruvate can be used which acts both as a reductant and as a source of ATP. Tests with extracts must normally be in anaerobic conditions; with both extracts and live bacteria the acetylene must form a sufficiently large proportion of the atmosphere to exceed its Michaelis constant.

Since the reduction of acetylene to ethylene requires the net transport of two electrons to the substrate, and the reduction of N_2 to ammonia requires the net transport of six electrons, it is possible to get an estimate of actual N_2-fixing activities of systems simply by dividing the acetylene reduction rate by three. This estimate can be useful provided the experimenter remembers that it is only valid if electron transport or access of substrate are not rate-determining factor in the system being assayed. Membrane-bound nitrogenase preparations may be limited by electron supply; bulky systems such as soil cores may show large differences in rates of C_2H_2 and N_2 diffusion.

II. ASSAY

In the earliest experiments ethylene was detected by its infrared absorption or by conventional mass spectrometry. Gas–liquid chromatography was soon recognized in many laboratories as a far more convenient and sensitive method of assaying ethylene. Stewart *et al.* (1967) and Hardy *et al.* (1968) described, in considerable experimental detail, the application of the acetylene reduction test to samples from natural environments making use of gas–liquid chromatography to detect the ethylene. The following account differs in only minor details from their methods and describes the procedures now used routinely in the writer's laboratory.

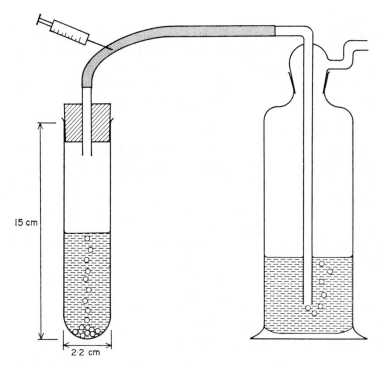

FIG. 1. A simple apparatus for generating acetylene. Calcium carbide (about 1 g) is dropped into 15 ml H_2O in the left-hand tube. After all the air between the tube and Dreschel bottle has been displaced, but while C_2H_2 is still being formed, samples are removed from the rubber connecting tube with syringe and needle.

A. Source of acetylene

Acetylene is available commercially, in cylinders, either diluted by other gases such as argon or nitrogen, or under pressure in solution in acetone. The pure gas is explosive under pressure and is not commercially available. Commercial acetylene usually contains traces of methane and ethylene (1 to 10 parts/10^8 v/v) which must be allowed for in a "blank" test. Acetylene is more conveniently prepared as needed from calcium carbide and water: a "lump" (about 1 g) of calcium carbide is dropped into about 15 ml distilled water in the test-tube of the simple apparatus illustrated in Fig. 1. The stopper is replaced at once; acetylene is evolved rapidly and soon displaces all air in the rubber tube. Samples of acetylene are withdrawn as needed by piercing the rubber tube with a syringe and needle; they are then injected into the test system. Samples should be taken while the gas is being evolved, so that they emerge at a marginally hyperbaric pressure, otherwise air may be introduced into the syringe and may affect assays of oxygen-sensitive enzyme preparations. Acetylene so prepared is not pure: traces of phosphine can be detected by smell and small but variable amounts of methane (1 to 10 parts/10^8 v/v) and ethylene (0·1 to 1 parts/10^8 v/v) are present. The phosphine does not interfere with the tests and the contaminant hydrocarbons are, in the writer's experience, present in lower concentrations than in commercial "pure" acetylene.

B. Choice of gas chromatograph

An instrument with a flame-ionization detector is usually chosen because it is highly sensitive and its responses are not complicated by non-combustible gases. If the Pye 104 gas–liquid chromatograph is used, a 5 ft (152 cm) "Porapak R" column held constant at between 45°C and 70°C is satisfactory. The carrier gas is nitrogen, flowing at 50 ml/min, and hydrocarbons emerge in the order indicated in Fig. 2. Methane emerges very soon; the peak due to ethylene emerges somewhat before the peak due to the acetylene added but is clearly distinguishable. Ethane would normally be masked by the acetylene in such a system but its formation is not normally relevant to the acetylene test. The initial attenuation setting should be "10" (that in Fig. 2 is 10^3-fold greater because it was a calibration run). Depending on temperature and flow rate of carrier gas, assays take from 3 to 6 min each; use of shorter columns can speed up the handling of samples.

C. Calibration of detector

In theory a small volume of ethylene (available commercially at over 99% purity in "lecture demonstration" cylinders) could be injected into the chromatograph and the area under the appropriate trace on the instrument's recorder could be used as referent. In practice, biologists work with acetylene so much diluted with inert gas that peak heights, rather than areas beneath peaks, are adequate quantitative measures of ethylene, and calibration with a sample diluted in carrier gas is preferable. A simple dilution procedure follows:

> Determine the true volume of a nominally 500 ml conical flask by completely filling it with water, sealing it with a "Suba-seal" (W. Freeman & Co. Ltd, Barnsley, Yorkshire) rubber closure so as to trap as little air as possible (less than 0·5 ml) and pouring the contents into a measuring cylinder. Flush the flask out with N_2 and close it with the same seal; inject 1 ml of commercial ethylene of over 99% purity. After 5 min at room temperature to allow complete mixing, inject replicate samples into the gas chromatograph. Deduce standard from the peak height, the dilution, and amplification (or attenuation) setting of the instrument.

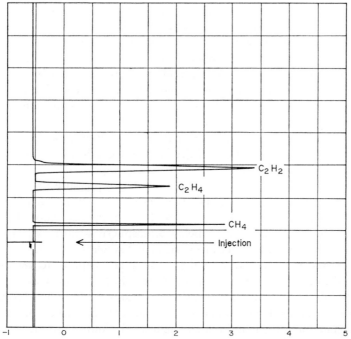

FIG. 2. Traces obtained from the Pye 104 gas chromatograph injected with 1 ml of an artificial mixture of CH_4, C_2H_4 and C_2H_2 (0·325% v/v of each) in N_2. Recorder speed 12·5 in./h; attenuation 10^4; other details as in text.

D. Preparation and injection of sample

Details of the systems appropriate to different classes of sample will be given later. In all of them, acetylene mixed with other gases is exposed to the material under test in a vessel closed with a rubber seal and gas samples are removed at intervals with syringe and needle. Progressive conversion of acetylene to ethylene is usually obvious in a short time: the "blank" ethylene content of acetylene prepared from calcium carbide rarely exceeds 0·1 nl/ml and an active culture or enzyme preparation (of an azotobacter for example) should produce about 2 ml ethylene/mg protein/h at 30°C. Cultures of slow-growing populations which give low yields of organisms/g carbon substrate utilized (e.g. *Desulfovibrio*) may nevertheless take up to 24 h to give unequivocally positive results. Four important sources of error should be mentioned.

(i) Carry over of gases in the syringes. Plastic syringes, and syringes made of glass if they contain grease or are damp on their internal surfaces, retain traces of acetylene, ethylene or methane tenaciously. Therefore, if a certain syringe is used for a test that gave a strongly positive result and is then used immediately for one that is really negative, considerable carry-over usually occurs and a false result may be obtained. It is advisable to assign one syringe for each test set up and to use plastic, disposable syringes. These are usually marketed sterile, in plastic or paper envelopes; the sterilization procedure has usually generated detectable traces of lower hydrocarbons within the syringe. These should be removed by pumping out two or three times.

Syringes containing gas samples may be stuck into an inverted rubber bung and kept for 2 to 4 h before injection into a gas–liquid chromatograph without serious losses of ethylene.

(ii) A second error may arise from the relative pressure inside the test system after it has been sampled. If a vessel of approximately 8 ml, for example, set up at atmospheric pressure, has 1 ml of gas removed from it, the pressure in the vessel will be below atmospheric so air may leak into it. It is therefore advisable to set up experimental systems with an excess of gas corresponding approximately to the amount one expects to remove for assay and to accept a small consequent error in gas content of samples.

(iii) Solubility of lower hydrocarbons in rubber. Natural rubber, synthetic rubber and silicone rubber all absorb lower hydrocarbons from atmospheres containing them and release them slowly into atmospheres free of them. It follows that rubber closures for test systems can rarely be used twice. The experimenter should reconcile himself to the expense of throwing them away when they have been used once because, if a closure has been used in a test which gave a strongly positive result, it will have absorbed some of the ethylene and, if it is next used with a negative test, ethylene will diffuse out of the closure and simulate very convincingly the formation of ethylene by a nitrogenase preparation. This phenomenon was illustrated by Kavanagh and Postgate (1970) who failed to devise a method of "cleaning" contaminated rubber closures.

(iv) Chemical catalysis must be avoided. For example, hydrogen, if purified by passage through a catalytic deoxygenator, may entrain particles of Pd which can catalyse a purely chemical reduction of C_2H_2 to C_2H_4 by H_2 in water.

III. TESTS WITH PURE CULTURES OF MICROBES

This Section will include no discussion of media for nitrogen-fixing bacteria or algae. The techniques described apply to all the usual formulations for media deficient in or free of fixed nitrogen, which are discussed elsewhere in this Compendium (Lapage *et al.*, this Series, Vol. 2a).

A. Agar slants

Aerobic nitrogen-fixing bacteria often show low or even zero acetylene-reducing activity at the atmospheric partial pressure of oxygen. Certain facultatively anaerobic bacteria only fix nitrogen (or reduce acetylene) in the absence of air. A culture of bacteria on a nitrogen-deficient agar medium as a conventional slant, provided a reasonable amount of growth has taken place, provides micro-environments in which the pO_2 ranges from approximately zero (in the centre of the bacterial mass) to atmospheric (on the outer surface of the bacterial mass). A simple qualitative test of an agar slant culture in a test-tube may be made if the cotton wool plug is pushed in, an unsterilized rubber seal is put over the mouth of the tube and sufficient acetylene is injected to occupy about 1% of the gas volume. About 5 ml air should be injected immediately afterwards, to give an excess pressure to allow for sampling, and gas samples should be removed at 2, 7 and 24 h intervals for gas–liquid chromatography. Progressive formation of ethylene during this period is evidence that the population includes nitrogen-fixing micro-organisms but gives no information on their type or activity.

B. Aerobic microbes

Even very active nitrogen-fixing bacteria, such as species of *Azotobacter*, can have their nitrogen-fixing capacity lowered to zero by vigorous shaking in air or exposure to high oxygen tensions (Drozd and Postgate, 1970). It is therefore necessary to handle such aerobes gently and to use gentle shaking speeds during assay. A typical experimental procedure would be to inoculate 5 ml of a nitrogen-deficient medium (in a 25 ml conical flask) with the organism under test. Sometimes it is desirable to add a small, growth-limiting amount of fixed nitrogen to permit initiation of growth and give a reasonable population for assay: 80 to 100 μg yeast extract/litre will give faintly turbid growth of most non-nitrogen-fixing bacteria and is not known to interfere with acetylene reduction by true nitrogen-fixing bacteria. When the culture has grown, the cotton wool plug is either replaced by a sterile rubber closure or is pushed in sufficiently to allow an unsterilized rubber seal to be inserted in the neck of the flask. One ml acetylene is injected and the flask incubated with gentle shaking for 24 h. Samples are taken at 2, 7 and 24 h intervals for gas chromatography. If contamination is to be avoided, the plug should remain in the flask because the acetylene is not sterile. With many tests, asepsis is unnecessary because the result is unequivocally positive after 1 or 2 h, long before any conceivable contaminant could show detectable activity.

Acetylene reduction rates may be obtained by more frequent sampling but can not be converted to nitrogen fixation rates because nitrogen is present and will compete with acetylene for the nitrogenase. To obtain data in principle convertible to nitrogen fixation rates, the cultures should be flushed out with a mixture or argon (or helium)+20% v/v oxygen before testing.

Many aerobic nitrogen-fixing bacteria are micro-aerophilic in that they fix very slowly if at all at atmospheric pO_2 values. When checking a new strain it is wise to include tests at low pO_2 values such as 0·1 and 0·05 atm. This principle also applies to blue-green algae.

C. Facultative anaerobes

The tubes designed by Pankhurst (1967) for culture of the anaerobic sulphate-reducing bacteria are ideal for this test. Their volume is 44 ml and they are marketed by Astell Laboratory Service Co. Ltd., 172 Brownhill Road, London, S.E.6. Their use in this context was described by Campbell and Evans (1969). In their description a procedure was given for blowing sterilized nitrogen through the vessel to ensure anaerobic conditions. Further experience in the writer's laboratory has shown that this precaution is unnecessary: the oxygen absorbed by the pyrogallol can be replaced by injecting an equivalent volume of nitrogen and anaerobic conditions are obtained in about 2 to 3 h after setting up the tubes. The average volume of a Pankhurst tube is 40 ml, so 12 ml nitrogen injected is usually sufficient to replace the oxygen absorbed and to allow an excess of gas for sampling.

Pankhurst tubes are set up as illustrated in Fig. 3 and sterilized, preferably containing 5 or 10 ml medium. The culture is inoculated and the plug of the main tube is replaced by a sterile rubber closure ("Suba-seal", size 33). A little absorbent cotton wool is placed in the side arm and, after adding 0·5 ml of saturated aqueous pyrogallol and 0·5 ml of an alkali solution containing 10% w/v $NaOH + 15\%$ w/v K_2CO_3, the side arm is rapidly closed with a non-sterile Suba-seal. About 1 h later, 12 ml N_2 from a cylinder is injected via the side arm. When the culture has grown, 1 ml acetylene is injected through the side arm and, after 2 h to allow for diffusion through the tube linking the side arm to the centre tube, the centre tube is sampled aseptically (see below) and the gas analysed. Progressive formation of ethylene is evidence for presence of nitrogenase.

To take a sample of gas aseptically, sterilized needles and syringes are needed; the top of the rubber closure should be swabbed with ethanol to avoid contamination of the contents during the sampling operation.

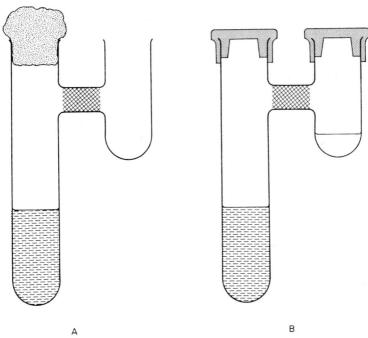

A   B

FIG. 3. Pankhurst tubes set up for acetylene reduction test. A: Tube as sterilized, ready for inoculation. B. Tube as set up after inoculation. The main plug has been replaced by a sterile size 33 "Suba-seal" closure; the side vessel contains alkali and pyrogallol (see text) supported on absorbent cotton wool. N_2 will be injected into this side vessel to replace O_2 absorbed by pyrogallol; C_2H_2 will be introduced during or after growth (see text).

D. Obligate anaerobes

The Pankhurst tube procedure applies equally to obligate anaerobes. In the reaction between pyrogallol and the alkali mixture given above, carbon dioxide is evolved and may alter the pH value of a weakly buffered medium. The proportions of carbonate to hydroxide in the mixture prescribed have been chosen to lower this effect to a minimum; nevertheless, after three or four days' incubation the pH of the test medium may have changed to a value unsuitable for growth of the organisms—this has happened in the writer's experience with sulphate-reducing bacteria—in which case the test must be discarded and a new one set up.

The reaction between pyrogallol and alkali yields small amounts of carbon monoxide. In theory this could interfere by inhibiting growth and/ or acetylene reduction; in practice interference of this kind has not been observed.

E. Photosynthetic microbes

Tests with pure cultures of photosynthetic bacteria, which are all anaerobes when growing photosynthetically, can be made as described in Pankhurst tubes provided these are illuminated appropriately. The alkali in the alkali+pyrogallol mixture will absorb a certain amount of H_2S from a sulphide-containing medium, so tests involving coloured sulphur bacteria should include thiosulphate as well as sulphide. Some Thiorhodaceae do not metabolize thiosulphate; it may then be necessary to add extra sulphide after a day's incubation.

For aerobic photosynthetic microbes (such as blue-green algae) the method outlined in B above may be adopted with appropriate illumination.

IV. TESTS OF SAMPLES OF NATURAL ORIGIN

A. Detection of nitrogen fixation

Stewart, Fitzgerald and Burris (1967) described a procedure for use with water samples, soil samples and root nodules; Hardy et al. (1968) described related procedures for enzymes, cultures and field samples. The basic principle which emerges from both of these procedures is the desirability of disturbing the eco-system being studied as little as possible. Hardy et al. obtained soil cores and replaced the atmosphere by a mixture of argon, oxygen and acetylene; the fact that the soil would contain various micro-environments of lower pO_2 than ambient meant that the assay method would give a fair representation of the capacity of that particular soil core to fix nitrogen. It would not necessarily give any measure of the numbers of nitrogen-fixing bacteria nor of their potential activity, since many of them, whether aerobic, facultative or anaerobic, might be inactivated by the pO_2 prevailing.

It is obvious that any of the tests described in the previous Section for pure cultures can be adapted for detection of nitrogenase activity in samples of natural waters or soils, so it is unnecessary to repeat them with full experimental details. To the warning of Hardy et al., that the eco-system should be disturbed as little as possible, should be added the warning that, if it is so disturbed and the disturbance results in increased aeration, then even aerobic bacteria such as *Azotobacter* may become apparently inactive (Drozd and Postgate, 1970).

B. Enumeration of nitrogen-fixing bacteria

Campbell and Evans (1969) pointed out that the Pankhurst tube test could be adapted very easily to give estimates of the numbers of anaerobic and facultatively anaerobic nitrogen-fixing bacteria in natural materials.

Unfortunately the nature of the test precludes its use with enumeration procedures more precise than the Most Probable Number (MPN) count (Postgate, This Series, Vol. I). In principle the procedure is very simple:

Decimal dilutions of water samples are prepared using a suitable diluent. The culture medium devoid of carbon source is preferable to physiological saline or water as diluent because there is a risk that anaerobes may be sensitive to dilution shock as are Azotobacteraceae (Billson, Williams and Postgate, 1970). Decimal dilutions from soil are made by the procedure of Pochon (1956). These dilutions are sub-cultured into quintuplicate Pankhurst tubes; up to 100 μg yeast extract/l may be present to permit marginal growth of non-nitrogen-fixing organisms. After incubation at 30°C for 2 to 4 days the tubes are scored for growth, thus giving estimates of the non-specific anaerobes present in the sample. Acetylene, generally 1 ml, is injected and samples of gas (1 ml) are removed for gas–liquid chromatography after 2, 7 and 24 h. Progressive formation of ethylene indicates nitrogen-fixing bacteria among the populations; those showing positive results are scored and Most Probable Numbers of non-specific anaerobes and anaerobic nitrogen-fixing bacteria are obtained from tables in the usual manner. Modification of this assay to include photosynthetic anaerobes, by illuminating the test cultures, is self-evident.

The acetylene reduction test is not easily adapted for counting aerobic nitrogen-fixing bacteria in natural samples. It might at first seem true that the procedure described in III B above, using shallow layers of cultures in conical flasks, would be quantitatively effective but there are two reasons why it will fail:

(i) If any significant growth of non-specific aerobes occurs at all, the concentration of *dissolved* oxygen may become lowered to values at which facultative, or even obligate, anaerobes can fix nitrogen and reduce acetylene. False positives will be scored.

(ii) Attempts to allow for this error by adopting high aeration or shaking rates are likely to inhibit growth of aerobes such as *Azotobacter*, *Derxia* or *Mycobacterium flavum* from high dilutions because none of these readily initiates growth from very small inocula unless the ambient pO_2 is low.

Obligately aerobic nitrogen-fixing bacteria are the most inconvenient organisms to enumerate quantitatively and the acetylene test is only useful in this context when a reasonable mass of suspected nitrogen-fixing aerobes —such as a colony on a plate—has been obtained. Though it falls outside the strict scope of this contribution, it is pertinent to recall that colony size on a Petri dish culture of a nitrogen-deficient agar medium can be very misleading (Hill and Postgate, 1969).

V. TESTS WITH MICROBIAL EXTRACTS AND
PURIFIED ENZYMES

The low molecular weight, non-haem iron component of nitrogenase, usually called "fraction 2", is extremely sensitive to oxygen. Though partially purified preparations from aerobic bacteria may not be very oxygen-sensitive, as soon as such preparations become at all highly resolved, anaerobic handling is mandatory. For experiments of this kind the amounts of material available are usually small and the procedure for the acetylene reduction test is scaled down as much as possible. Enzyme preparations require a reductant (usually sodium dithionite), a source of ATP (usually as an ATP-generating system) or a substrate which combines both functions such as the sodium pyruvate used with crude extracts of *Clostridium pasteurianum* (Carnahan *et al.*, 1960). The following procedure has been well tested in the writer's laboratory:

Small vials of approximately 8 ml capacity, such as those used for marketing antibiotics for injection, are set up with 1 to 2·5 ml of a medium for assay of nitrogenase activity. Table I gives two typical recipes. The non-enzymic components are introduced into the vessel first, then the vessel is flushed out with argon (or helium) and stoppered with a rubber closure. Acetylene (0·4 ml) is introduced into the vessel by injection through the rubber closure and the reaction is initiated by injecting creatine kinase (if this is being used) followed at once by the microbial extract. Two or 3 ml of argon (or helium) are then injected to give an excess pressure for sampling; gas samples (0·5 ml) are taken at intervals during shaking at 30°C for gas–liquid chromatography. With normal preparations, 5 min samples between zero and 20 min should be adequate.

The amounts of dithionite and buffer prescribed should not be exceeded since either may become inhibitory at higher concentrations; Smith and Evans (1970) stated that double the dithionite prescribed here inhibited extracts of a nitrogen-fixing blue-green alga. The creatine phosphate and the creatine kinase in the prescription in Table I provide, with the relatively small amount of ATP added, a system for continuously regenerating ATP as it is utilized in the acetylene reduction process. During this reaction ATP is converted to ADP which, if allowed to accumulate, inhibits nitrogen fixation and therefore acetylene reduction. The ATP-generating system converts the ADP back to ATP. Moustafa and Mortenson (1967) dispensed with the ATP-generating system on the grounds that the actylene reduction method is so sensitive that many hundreds of nanomoles of ethylene can be formed before sufficient ADP accumulates to inhibit the reaction. The procedure used is essentially similar to that

TABLE I

Conditions for assay of nitrogenase in microbial extracts using acetylene

(Vf = 1 to 2·5 ml: atmosphere A or He + C_2H_2)

(i) With dithionite:	
"tris" buffer, pH 7·4	25 mM
$MgCl_2$	5 μ mole ⎫ ATP-
ATP	5 μ mole ⎬ generating
Creatine phosphate	10 mg ⎪ system
Creatine kinase	0·5 mg ⎭
$Na_2S_2O_4$	about 3 mg*
Extract	3 to 20 mg protein.
(ii) With pyruvate:	
"tris" buffer, pH 7·4	25 mM
$MgCl_2$	5 μ mole
Sodium pyruvate	200 mg
Extract	3 to 20 mg protein

* Smith and Evans (1970) recommended about 0·6 mg (2·5 μmole/1·5 ml) for *Anabena* extracts.

described in the last paragraph except that creatine phosphate and creatine kinase are omitted. The magnesium is not omitted because it is needed for acetylene reduction as well as for the action of creatine kinase. Gas samples are taken as usual and a time course for ethylene production is plotted; the nitrogenase activity is derived from the initial rate of ethylene production.

VI. CONCLUSION

The acetylene reduction test provides strong evidence for nitrogenase and is of considerable value both at the ecological level and in enzymology. With a good gas–liquid chromatograph its sensitivity is about 1000 times that of traditional Kjeldahl analyses, measurements of NH_3 production or isotopic tests with $^{15}N_2$. This fact must be borne in mind when activities assessed by other methods are being compared with acetylene reduction; it is possible to obtain extracts or organisms with apparently high acetylene-reducing activity but undetectable N_2 fixation or $^{15}N_2$ incorporation. Usually a simple calculation of specific rates shows that these are experimental artefacts, but it is still theoretically possible that ATP-activated reduction of acetylene to ethylene might occur by mechanisms unrelated to nitrogen fixation. Critical experiments should therefore be checked by tests involving actual reaction with nitrogen and, where possible, tests involving repression of the system by amonium ions.

REFERENCES

Billson, S., Williams, K., and Postgate, J. R. (1970). *J. applied Bact.*, **33**, 270.

Campbell, N. E. R., and Evans, H. J. (1969). *Can. J. microbiol.*, **15**, 1342.

Carnahan, J. E., Mortenson, L. E., Mower, H. F., and Castle, J. E. (1960). *Biochim. biophys. Acta*, **44**, 520.

Dilworth, M. J. (1966). *Biochem. biophys. Acta*, **127**, 285.

Drozd, J. W., and Postgate, J. R. (1970). *J. gen. Microbiol.*, **60**, 427.

Hardy, R. W. F., Holsten, R. D., Jackson, E. K., and Burns, R. C. (1968). *Plant Physiol.*, **43**, 1185.

Hill, S., and Postgate, J. R. (1969). *J. gen. Microbiol.*, **58**, 277.

Ilag, L., and Curtis, R. W. (1968). *Science*, **159**, 1357.

Kavanagh, E. P., and Postgate, J. R., (1970). *Laboratory Practice*, **19**, 159.

Moustafa, E., and Mortenson, L. E. (1967). *Nature, Lond.*, **216**, 1241.

Pankhurst, E. S. (1967). *Laboratory Practice*, **16**, 58.

Pochon, J. (1956). *Annls Inst. Pasteur, Paris*, **89**, 464.

Postgate, J. R. (1970). *Nature, Lond.*, **226**, 25.

Schöllhorn, R., and Burris, R. H. (1967). *Proc. Nat. Acad. Sci., U.S.A.*, **57**, 213.

Smith, R. V., and Evans, M. C. W. (1970). *Nature, Lond.*, **225**, 1253.

Stewart, W. D. P., Fitzgerald, G. P., and Burris, R. H. (1967). *Proc. Nat. Acad. Sci., U.S.A.*, **58**, 2071.

Author Index

Numbers in *italics* refer to the pages on which references are listed at the end of each chapter.

A

Abelson, P. H., 102, 103, 104, 106, *106*, *107*, 232, *246*
Abood, L. G., 278, *282*
Abraham, S., 127, 133, *151*, *153*
Ackerman, E., 41, *53*
Ackerman, M. E., 112, *153*
Aikman, D. P., 148, *151*
Alegnani, W. C., 333, 339, *342*
Allen, M. J., 264, 267, 268, 269, 274, 275, 276, 278, 279, 282, *282*, *283*
Alvarez, J., 133, 134, 144, 149, *153*
Andersen, J., 13, *23*
Anderson, A. W., 227, *229*
Anderson, R. A., 328, *329*
Anliker, R., 121, 123, *154*
Armstrong, J. McD., 19, *23*
Arnoff, S., 140, *155*, 179, *181*
Arnon, D. I., 11, *24*
Aronoff, S., 66, *106*
Aronson, A. T., 242, *246*
Axelrod, B., 177, *181*

B

Bach, S. J., 13, *23*
Baddiley, J., 177, *181*
Baer, R. F., 55, 56, *63*
Baggiolini, M., 139, *151*
Baille, L. A., 143, *151*
Barker, H. A., 5, *24*
Baker, N., 133, *153*
Bandvrski, R. S., 177, *181*
Barrett, M. J., 305, *317*
Bartley, J. C., 127, *151*
Bartley, W., 4, *23*
Bassham, J. A., 158, 160, 164, 168, 172, 173, 174, 175, *181*, *182*, *183*
Battley, E. H., 286, 290, *316*
Bauchop, T., 289, 298, 305, *316*
Baxter, C. F., 136, 137, *151*
Bayne-Jones, S., 286, *316*
Belaich, J.-P., 286, 289, 290, 291, 296, 302, 303, 304, 305, 306, 308, 310, *316*, *318*
Bell, C. G., 114, *151*
Bellamy, D., 4, *23*
Benson, A. A., 173, 174, *182*
Benzinger, T. H., 295, *316*
Berger, R. L., 41, *53*, 297, *316*
Bergmann, F. M., 158, *182*
Berlin, N. J., 133, *154*
Bernhard, S. A., 290, *316*
Beyes, W. F., 324, *329*
Bezman, A., 144, *154*
Baily, J. J., 227, *230*, 267, 268, *283*
Bichowsky, F. R., 289, *317*
Bickel, 139
Bieleski, R. L., 177, *182*
Bilson, S., 353, *356*
Birks, J. B., 112, 114, *151*
Bjerre, S. H., 227, *230*
Blaxter, K. L., 286, 288, *317*
Bock, R. M., 243, *246*
Boivinet, P., 286, 289, 290, 299, 302, 305, 306, 307, 310, *317*
Bolton, E. T., 102, 103, 104, 106, *106*, *107*, 232, 241, *246*
Bonnichsen, R., 12, *23*
Bosquet, W. F., 130, *151*
Bouffard, A., 285, *317*
Bourne, E. J., 177, *182*
Boursnell, J. C., 66, *106*
Bowen, R. J., 267, *283*
Bowman, R. L., 132, *153*, 328, *329*
Bradley, A. F., 55, 56, 57, 61, 62, *63*
Brattgard, S. O., 134, *154*
Bray, G. A., 124, 126, *151*
Brierley, G. P., 27, *53*
Brink, F., Jr. 27, 31, *53*
Britten, R., 102, *106*
Britten, R. J., 102, 103, 104, 106, *106*, *107*, 232, 241, 243, *246*
Brodie, A. F., 20, *23*
Brodie, D. B., 328, *329*
Brown, D. A., 144, *152*
Brown, D. E., 26, *53*
Brown, F. H., 120, 121, *152*

Subject Index